INTRODUCTORY COMPUTER METHODS AND NUMERICAL ANALYSIS

RALPH H. PENNINGTON, Ph.D.

Chief, Mathematics Branch
Air Force Weapons Laboratory
Albuquerque, New Mexico

The Macmillan Company
Collier-Macmillan Limited, London

To Anne

Sixth Printing, 1969

Library of Congress catalog card number : 65–10730

THE MACMILLAN COMPANY
COLLIER-MACMILLAN CANADA, LTD.,
TORONTO, ONTARIO

PRINTED IN THE UNITED STATES OF AMERICA

PREFACE

Perhaps no field of science has changed so rapidly in the past few years as has the field of applied mathematics. The most important factor in this change has been the development of the high-speed digital computer. Indeed, it is not too much to claim that the development of the computer has revolutionized some parts of mathematics. So complete has been the change that those of us who received our formal education prior to the advent of the computer have been given a perspective toward many mathematical problems which is no longer valid. While we have learned methods for solving many mathematical problems, we have not been taught which of these problems are difficult to solve and which are easy in terms of modern technology. (Unfortunately, these last few statements seem to be true for many who are even now receiving their formal education in science and engineering.)

This text attempts to do two things in relation to the situation just described —to give usable computer methods for solving the more elementary problems in applied mathematics and to give some perspective as to how easy or how difficult these problems are to solve on a computer.

It is assumed that the reader has an understanding of mathematics through integral calculus, but little or no acquaintance with the digital computer. The organization of the text reflects this assumption as to audience: the first several chapters give a very elementary introduction to digital computers and computer programming; the remaining chapters give a somewhat more advanced discussion of the standard topics of numerical analysis, from a computer-oriented point of view. The reader will find the same topics here as in most standard introductory works in numerical analysis: error analysis, evaluation of functions, integration, solution of algebraic and transcendental equations, systems of linear equations, matrices, curve-fitting, interpolation, numerical differentiation, and solution of ordinary differential equations. But he will find the discussions of these topics to have a considerably different orientation from that found in classical numerical analysis texts. Some of the most cherished hand calculation methods are treated lightly or omitted, and other methods relegated to slight mention in the standard texts have been covered in detail. The effort has been to stress methods which are of proven

v

value in the computer solution of present-day problems in science and engineering. In line with the assumption that the reader has not necessarily been exposed to mathematics beyond calculus, the discussions of matrices and ordinary differential equations have been made quite elementary, paralleling to a certain extent the material frequently covered in a college curriculum as a course in "Engineering Mathematics," or "Mathematics for Engineer and Physicists." Indeed, the author would suggest that this text provides material for a first course in this area which is more suitable and useful for scientists and engineers than many current courses.

Much effort has been made to bring to light some of the insidious accuracy problems all too often ignored in computer work. Hamming* has said: "The purpose of computing is insight, not numbers." While the author is in agreement with the sentiment expressed by this statement, he believes that a more accurate statement of the situation is the following: "The purpose of computing is numbers. If these numbers are accurate, they can be used to gain insight." Many examples appear in the text in which the computer will blithely offer wrong answers to a problem while giving every superficial indication of having solved the problem correctly. The heavy emphasis placed on accuracy throughout the text is felt to be completely warranted.

It is clearly difficult to describe how things are done on a computer without making reference to a specific computer. On the other hand, reference to a specific computer could tend to make a volume of this sort too specialized. The author has taken the approach, occasionally used by others in the field, of describing a hypothetical computer having features characteristic of computers in general, but not defined in such detail as to require the reader to become deeply engrossed in its subtleties and peculiarities. This hypothetical computer serves as a vehicle for explaining machine language programming in an explicit fashion. After some feeling for the process of machine language programming has been developed, flow charts and the FORTRAN-type compiler are introduced. Most of the numerical analysis portion of the text then makes parallel use of the more nearly universal language of flow charts and FORTRAN in describing computer calculations.

In constructing the FORTRAN programs given throughout the text it was necessary to reach compromises among several competing factors. The main factors considered in the construction of each program or subroutine were the following:

1. Ease of understanding for the student.

2. General applicability of the program.

3. Protection against undiscovered accuracy loss.

4. Efficient use of machine time.

---

* Hamming, R. W., *Numerical Methods for Scientists and Engineers*, New York: McGraw-Hill Book Company, Inc., 1962.

Generally speaking, the factors near the top of this list were given heaviest weight in making the required compromises. Since this particular weighting is not necessarily the proper one for any individual user of the text, it is best to consider the programs and subroutines not as a "library" to be removed from the text and used as is, but rather as a set of reference standards, to be modified to fit individual needs before use.

This volume was developed as text material for a computer-oriented course in numerical analysis, taught by the author for the College of General Studies of The George Washington University. The material in Chapters I to VII, and a few selected topics from the later chapters, was covered in one semester. The volume has also been used as text material for a training course for young scientists at the Air Force Weapons Laboratory; in this course, the students had some modest previous exposure to computers and a more advanced educational level, and the entire text was covered in a survey fashion in one semester. Both were conducted as classroom courses, but the text is also suitable for a laboratory course, using almost any standard computer, preferably with a FORTRAN-type compiler. In this latter situation, the author strongly recommends a brief introduction to machine language programming near the beginning of the course. For this purpose, Chapters II and IV of the text can be followed closely, using a properly constructed interpretive routine and the "machine language" given in those chapters; or the text could be followed more loosely, substituting a direct indoctrination on the machine for Chapters II and IV. As suggested earlier, the author believes that the best use of the text is for a one-year laboratory course for scientists and engineers immediately following integral calculus.

The author is grateful to Professor Nels David Nelson, Department of Mathematics, and to Dean Grover LaMarr Angel, College of General Studies, The George Washington University, for their cooperation in authorizing the experimental course which led to this volume, to Mrs. Mullins and the staff of the College of General Studies for their valuable assistance in the reproduction of materials, and to Mrs. James Young for the many tedious hours of typing the manuscript.

RALPH H. PENNINGTON

ALBUQUERQUE, N. M.

CONTENTS

CHAPTER I *Number Systems*

1.1 INTRODUCTION

In this book we intend to explain the use of the digital computer as a tool for
mathematics through calculus.   Specifically we are going to address ourselves
to that part of mathematics having to do with calculating, that is to say,
performing operations with numbers.   If we wish to start at the beginning,
then, we must first talk about numbers and number systems.   This might
sound like an altogether too elementary approach.   After all, we learned
about numbers and counting in grade school.   Why rake over a subject so
thoroughly learned so long ago?   Surprising as it may seem to readers not
already acquainted with digital computers, there is indeed a compelling
reason for reviewing such basic topics as numbers, counting, and the basic
arithmetic operations of addition, subtraction, multiplication, and division.
The reason is this: in school we learned to count by tens, and we ordinarily
do all our arithmetic in a number sytem based on ten.   There are other ways
of counting, other ways of doing arithmetic.   While the tens system seems
the simplest to us, because of our long acquaintance with it, there are certain
disadvantages to it.   For reasons which will appear as the reader proceeds,
digital computers can often be made to perform more rapidly and more
simply if they are designed to use number systems other than our familiar
tens system.   Thus there is a real profit to be gained by starting with a review
of number systems, provided we do so from a broadened viewpoint and free
ourselves from the habits of thought about numbers and counting that have
developed from long association with one particular system, the tens system.
In this chapter we shall attempt to develop such a broadened viewpoint.
We shall reach into the earliest days of civilized man to examine the origin of
number systems, and into the earliest days of our own education to review and
examine our understanding of the basic laws of arithmetic.   In these we find
the key to understanding the uses, and the advantages and shortcomings,
of one of the newest tools of mankind, the digital computer.

1

1.2 ORIGIN OF NUMBER SYSTEMS

Throughout recorded history, the development of civilized societies has been accompanied by the development of systems of counting. These number systems appear to have been the product of gradual growth and evolution, rather than the product of a single discovery.

In each primitive society, although such events cannot be documented by recorded historical evidence, there must have been a series of minor discoveries or developments in the use of numbers. The earliest stage was probably a process of comparison. One can easily visualize primitive man, prior even to the development of more than a rudimentary language, comparing two piles of rocks by matching the rocks pair by pair, and thus ascertaining that there are more rocks in one pile than in the other. Such a one-to-one system of comparison must have been essential to even the most elementary type of barter. A next logical development is comparison of objects with the fingers, and for numbers less than ten, at least, the representation of the number of objects in a group by holding up an equal number of fingers. This representation of numbers by fingers is in all probability by far the oldest means used by man. From primitive beginnings, the representation of numbers on the fingers was gradually extended to include numbers in the thousands, by the introduction of special finger combinations for units, tens, hundreds, and thousands. At some early stage, names and symbols for these numbers developed. Egyptian hieroglyphic numerals as early as 3300 B.C. were based on symbols for 1, 10, 100, 1000, and 10,000.

Although the usefulness of the fingers in number representation has led to widespread development of number systems based on multiples of ten, the number ten is by no means the only base used for number systems. The Babylonian system made combined use of ten and sixty as bases. Traces of number systems based on three, four, five, six, eight, and twenty are found among the Indians of North America. Some suggestion of a number system based on twelve is contained in our twelve-inch foot, and the British twelve pence in a shilling. In modern societies, however, the number system based on ten seems to have won out; not because of any intrinsic advantage, but rather, it would appear, because of the presence of ten fingers on the hands. The science of computing has introduced a requirement for number systems based on practical considerations of a different sort. In particular, the binary system (base 2), the octal system (base 8), and the hexadecimal system (base 16) have been found to offer certain advantages for use with computers. We will need to develop some degree of familiarity with these number systems before proceeding toward an understanding of digital computers.

1.3 THE DECIMAL SYSTEM

Our present decimal system is a development of the Hindu-Arabic system which originated in India, probably in the third century B.C. A major step was the invention, sometime between the second century B.C. and the ninth century A.D., possibly by an unknown priest or scholar, of a symbol for zero. Simple as it sounds to us now, this was a real stepping stone in the development of our number system: with the use of a symbol for zero, a so-called "place value" system became feasible. It became possible to write any integer, however large, by the use of the proper combination of characters chosen from ten basic ones. The advantage of this development becomes clear when one reflects on the difficulties encountered in trying to write very large numbers in the Roman numeral system. The next development of consequence, which probably occurred in about the sixteenth century, was the introduction of the decimal point and generalization of the symbolism to include decimal fractions. Since that time, it has been possible to represent all positive whole numbers and fractions in the decimal system by the use of the zero and nine other characters. The use of the minus sign allows extension of the notation to include negative numbers. In modern notation, the basic characters of the decimal system are:

$$0, \quad 1, \quad 2, \quad 3, \quad 4, \quad 5, \quad 6, \quad 7, \quad 8, \quad 9$$

The number next after 9 is represented by re-using the character 1 followed by the character 0. In general, for any number the digit first to the left of the decimal point stands for the number of units, the digit next to the left stands for the number of tens, the digit next to the left stands for the number of hundreds (ten times ten), and so forth. Likewise, the digit to the right of the decimal point stands for the number of tenths, the next, the number of hundredths, and so forth. For example, the number 963.05 stands for 9 hundreds plus 6 tens plus 3 units plus 0 tenths plus 5 hundredths. These values are indicated by the following diagram:

$$
\begin{array}{ccccc}
9 & 6 & 3 & .\quad 0 & 5 \\
\downarrow & \downarrow & \downarrow & \downarrow & \downarrow \\
9 \times 10^2 & 6 \times 10^1 & 3 \times 10^0 & 0 \times 10^{-1} & 5 \times 10^{-2}
\end{array}
$$

We will review the operations of arithmetic in this well-known system before venturing into the less familiar systems used with digital computers.

1.31 Decimal Addition

Addition of decimal numbers is accomplished by repeated application of a set of rules for addition for the nine characters and zero. The grade school student learns the sums of all pairs of characters zero plus zero through nine plus nine, e.g., $1 + 1 = 2$, $1 + 2 = 3$, $1 + 3 = 4$, etc., and the rules for carry from one column of digits to the next, and with these few tools can eventually add any finite collection of decimal numbers. Ordinarily, the student learns these basic sums so thoroughly that he can perform them with great rapidity. For most individuals, however, speed in addition of large numbers is limited by the fact that the mind has difficulty in retaining all the digits involved so that the result of the operation must be written on paper as the addition is performed.   Inadequate memory, rather than slowness in performing the basic additions, is the limitation in speed of addition by humans.

Example 1.   Find the sum of 1754 and 6483.

Let us proceed stepwise through the addition in painstaking detail, assuming that all we know how to do is add any two of the basic characters.   We write the problem as

$$1754$$
$$6483$$
$$\overline{}$$

The first step is $4 + 3 = 7$.   We record the 7, then perform the addition $5 + 8 = 13$.   We record 3, and carry the 1.   The next required sum is $1 + 7 + 4$, but we do not know how to add numbers three at a time.   We must add by pairs, i.e., $1 + 7 = 8$, $8 + 4 = 12$.   Then we record the 2 and carry the 1.   The final sum is $1 + 1 + 6$, which we do as $1 + 1 = 2, 2 + 6 = 8$. Then we record the 8 and our answer is complete, 8237.   When we list all these steps which our minds go through in performing an addition such as this one, it seems to be quite a laborious process.   It would seem that when we perform such an addition rapidly we might make use of a few mental shortcuts.   For most of us, however, the mind performs separately each of the steps given above.

Each of the additions in Example 1 can be performed mentally in a fraction of a second, so that the total time for calculation in the above problem is probably somewhat less than a second.   The total time for the problem, however, includes the time to write the two numbers and their sums, a matter of perhaps 5 to 10 seconds.   We shall see later that computers can perform this same operation in a very small fraction of a second, as little as a few millionths of a second for some machines, and therein will be found their value in mathematical problems.

1.32   Decimal Subtraction

Subtraction is ordinarily first learned by relearning the addition rules for the basic characters backwards.   For example, the addition rule $9 + 7 = 16$ has as its corresponding subtraction rule $16 - 9 = 7$.   Once a set of rules of this sort is learned, together with some rules for borrowing from the adjacent column, the subtraction process can be performed for any two numbers.

When subtraction is first learned, it is ordinarily learned in terms of subtracting a smaller number from the larger one.   At a later stage the concept of signed numbers is learned, and the concept of subtraction is generalized to encompass "algebraic addition." If two numbers having different signs are to be added, the one which is the smaller in absolute value is subtracted from the larger one, and the sign of the larger affixed. With this concept, a number consists not only of the digits and decimal point, but also includes the plus or minus sign. The plus sign is frequently left unwritten. The mental processes involved in algebraic addition will be reviewed in an example.

Example 1. Add algebraically 1562 and −3539.

Since the second number is numerically greater than the first, we subtract the first from the second and affix the sign of the second. Thus we first perform

$$3539$$
$$-1562$$

The first operation is $9 - 2 = 7$. For the next step, since we cannot perform $3 - 6$, we borrow one from the 5, leaving $5 - 1 = 4$, and then perform $13 - 6 = 7$. Then, since we cannot perform $4 - 5$, we borrow one from the 3, leaving $3 - 1 = 2$, and thus perform $14 - 5 = 9$. Then we perform $2 - 1 = 1$. Our answer at this point is 1977, to which we must affix a minus sign, since the negative number was the larger of the two. Our final answer, then, is −1977.

It is possible to simplify the rules for algebraic addition by using a different way of representing a negative number. The method is to represent the negative number by its so-called "nines complement." If, as in the example above, we are dealing with four digit whole numbers, we could replace negative numbers by the value obtained by subtracting from 99999, e.g., the nines complement representation of −3539 would be 96460. Then the "algebraic" addition of 1562 and −3539 is done by performing the ordinary addition:

$$1562$$
$$96460$$
$$\overline{98022}$$

The answer is 98022, and the leading 9 tells us that this number is a nines complement. It is just the nines complement representation of −1977, our previous answer. We see that if nines complements were always used for negative numbers we would not need separate rules for subtraction but could get by with just the addition rules. Some digital computers use such a scheme in order to reduce the amount of circuitry required. Since we shall not make use of the nines complement in this text, we shall not pursue this matter further. It is only fair to warn the reader, however, that there are some subleties in using the nines complement which did not appear in the above problem. For example, when two negative numbers are added, or when a positive and negative number combine to give a positive result, the answer is not in an immediately recognizable form. The reader interested in pursuing this matter can quickly ascertain for himself by working a few problems in algebraic addition what complications do arise in using the nines complement.

The time required for subtraction is about the same as that for simple addition, both for hand computation and for electronic computers.

1.33   Decimal Multiplication

There are several ways of regarding the process of multiplication. One is to regard it simply as repeated addition. For integers, the concept is directly applicable. For example, by the product 965×158 we mean, "add 965 to itself, then add 965 to that sum, and so forth, until the number 965 has been used 158 times." Multiplication of two decimal fractions requires an additional step. We perform the multiplication as if the two numbers were integers and then locate the decimal point according to the rule learned in elementary arithmetic. In practice, of course, we would not attempt to perform the product 965×158 by repeated additions. We would rely instead on the fact that multiplication of any two numbers may be accomplished by repeated application of the rules of multiplication for the ten basic characters, zero times zero through nine times nine. As for addition, the grade school student learns these rules quite thoroughly, $1 \times 1 = 1$, $1 \times 2 = 2$, etc., and then learns how to use them repeatedly to multiply large numbers.

Example 1.   Find the product of 965 and 158.

The operation is normally written as follows:

$$
\begin{array}{r}
965 \\
158 \\
\hline
7720 \\
4825 \\
965 \\
\hline
152470
\end{array}
$$

The calculation consists of the following chain of steps: $8 \times 5 = 40$, $8 \times 6 = 48$, $48 + 4 = 52$, $8 \times 9 = 72$, $72 + 5 = 77$, $5 \times 5 = 25$, $5 \times 6 = 30$, $30 + 2 = 32$, $5 \times 9 = 45$, $45 + 3 = 48$, $1 \times 5 = 5$, $1 \times 6 = 6$, $1 \times 9 = 9$, $0 = 0$, $2 + 5 = 7$, $7 + 2 = 9$, $9 + 5 = 14$, $1 + 7 = 8$, $8 + 8 = 16$, $16 + 6 = 22$, $2 + 4 = 6$, $6 + 9 = 15$.

Clearly, multiplication is a much longer process than addition. The problem given above required about 20 individual multiplications and additions to find the product of the two three-digit numbers, whereas addition of this same pair of numbers would have required only five operations.

1.34   Decimal Division

Division is the inverse of multiplication, and, like multiplication, can be performed in different ways. Just as multiplication can be performed by repeated additions, division can be performed by repeated subtractions. For example, we may divide 13 into 156 by subtracting 13 from 156, then subtracting 13 from the result, etc. After twelve subtractions the result is zero, so 13 goes into 156 twelve times. This process can be generalized to allow for decimal fractions, but it is quite awkward for hand computation and very seldom used. The more common procedure is a sort of trial and error process, in which each digit of the answer is first guessed and then verified by multiplication.

Example 1.   Divide 532 by 19.

We first attempt to guess how many times 19 will go into 53. If we guess 3, then we perform $19 \times 3 = 57$. Our trial value was too high, so we next guess 2. We perform $19 \times 2 = 38$, so 2 is the first digit of the quotient. We next perform $53 - 38 = 15$, and now try to guess how many times 19 will go into 152. If we guess 8, we then perform $19 \times 8 = 152$, so the second digit of the quotient is 8, and there is no remainder, so the complete quotient is 28. The information required to perform this operation was: first, the rules for multiplication of the basic characters; second, the rules for subtraction of the basic characters; and third, a system for guessing each trial digit. This latter aspect is one which presents real difficulties for a digital computer. It can be avoided by using some variation on the scheme for division just described or by using the binary number system, as will be demonstrated later.

1.35   Notation for Decimal Arithmetic

The operations of decimal arithmetic have just been described using the standard notation for numbers ordinarily used in hand computation. This notation has developed over the years as a practical one for that process. It certainly is not the only one possible, nor is it necessarily the most convenient one for use with digital computers. We will next investigate this problem of notation, and become acquainted with one which, while more cumbersome for hand computation than our customary one, is more adaptable for use on a digital computer.

Any notation which symbolizes a number completely must include three parts:

(*1*)   The sign.

(*2*)   The digits arranged in their proper order.

(*3*)   The location of the decimal point.

There is no universal notation used in connection with all digital computers. However, it is worth while to become familiar with one special type of notation that is frequently used, the floating point notation.   While this notation will seem awkward in the hand computations required for familiarization, it is quite valuable when used for its intended purpose.

1.36   Floating Point Notation

In the ordinary notation, the location of the decimal point is indicated by putting a period in the appropriate location among the digits.   In floating point notation, the number is written without a decimal point and is followed by a second number which specifies how many places to the right or to the left of the first digit the decimal point should be placed.   For example, in this notation the number 1463.54 might be written as:

$$146354 \qquad +4$$

The number 146354 is known as the mantissa and $+4$ is known as the exponent.   The basic position of the decimal point is considered to be immediately to the left of the first digit of the mantissa.   The exponent of $+4$ is interpreted to mean "move the decimal point four places to the right of its basic position." Since shifting the decimal point one place to the right is equivalent to multiplying by ten, the number is the same as:

$$.146354 \times 10^4$$

In this same floating point notation, the number .00962 would be represented by

$$962 \qquad -2$$

In a more common form of the floating point notation, the use of plus or minus signs on the exponent is avoided by a simple subterfuge.   Since exponents larger than 49 or less than -49 are seldom required to express the size of a number in any practical problem, the arbitrary addition of 50 to the exponent will produce some integer from 1 to 99 as the exponent part of the number.   With this convention, an exponent of 50 would indicate no shift of the decimal point, an exponent of 51 a shift one place to the right, an exponent of 49 a shift one place to the left, and so forth.   In this notation, then, the first of the illustrative numbers above would be written:

146354   54

and the second:

962   48

A negative number, such as -43.7 would be written as -437 52. Notice that a zero as the lead digit of a mantissa cannot be ignored. A mantissa of 0418 is not the same as a mantissa of 418, since the first stands for .0418 and the second for .418. The exponent of a floating point number can be changed by adding or removing leading zeros. Thus the numbers:

-00437 54, -0437 53, -437 52

are all the same. While it is always possible to increase the exponent by adding leading zeros, it is not possible to reduce the exponent if the leading digit of the mantissa is nonzero, since by its definition the mantissa must be less than one. The process of adding or removing lead zeros is known as shifting. The addition of a zero is a shift to the right of one place and the removal of a zero is a shift to the left of one place. The normal form for a floating point number is that in which the leading digit is nonzero.

1.37 Floating Point Arithmetic

The basic arithmetic operations may be carried out in floating point notation by remembering that the exponent really represents multiplication by some power of ten. For the second type of floating point notation introduced above, the processes will be stated as theorems.

Theorem I. *The sum of two floating point numbers is obtained by the following steps:*

1. Shift the number having the smaller exponent to the right a sufficient number of places to make the exponents equal.

2. Place a decimal point to the left of the lead digit of each mantissa and add the mantissas.

3. If the sum of the mantissas is less than one, then that sum is the mantissa of the result and the common exponent is the exponent of the result.

4. If the sum of the mantissas is greater than or equal to one, then that sum with decimal point moved one place to the left is the mantissa of the result and the common exponent increased by one is the exponent of the result.

PROOF: Let the numbers have mantissas M_1 and M_2 and exponents N_1 and N_2, respectively. M_1 and M_2 are understood to be decimal fractions with the decimal points in front of the leading digits. Assume $N_1 > N_2$. Then the numbers are:

$$M_1 \times 10^{N_1-50} \quad \text{and} \quad M_2 \times 10^{N_2-50}$$

The sum is:

$$M_1 \times 10^{N_1-50} + M_2 \times 10^{N_2-50}$$

or

$$(M_1 + M_2 \times 10^{N_2-N_1})10^{N_1-50}$$

Since $N_1 > N_2$, and $M_2 < 1$, then $M_2 \times 10^{N_2-N_1} < 1$.

If $M_1 + M_2 \times 10^{N_2-N_1} < 1$, then the sum has that number for a mantissa and N_1 as exponent and the theorem is proved. If $M_1 + M_2 \times 10^{N_2-N_1} \geqslant 1$, since $M_1 < 1$ and $M_2 \times 10^{N_2-N_1} < 1$, then surely $M_1 + M_2 \times 10^{N_2-N_1} < 10$ and $(M_1 + M_2 \times 10^{N_2-N_1})10^{-1} < 1$. But the sum can be written $(M_1 + M_2 \times 10^{N_2-N_1})10^{-1} \times 10^{N_1-49}$, which is a number having mantissa $(M_1 + M_2 \times 10^{N_2-N_1})10^{-1}$, or the sum with decimal point shifted one place to the left and exponent $N_1 + 1$.

Example 1. Find the sum of 142   53 and -262 51.

The second number must be written -00262 53. Then:

$$\begin{array}{r} .142 \\ -.00262 \\ \hline .13938 \end{array}$$

So the sum is 13938   53.

Example 2. Find the sum of 642   47 and 5416   47.

The exponents are equal, so the mantissas are added directly:

$$\begin{array}{r} .642 \\ .5416 \\ \hline 1.1836 \end{array}$$

Since the sum of the mantissas is greater than one, the decimal point must be moved one to the left to obtain the mantissa of the sum, and the common exponent increased by one to obtain the exponent of the sum. The result is 11836   48.

Theorem II. *The product of two floating point numbers is obtained by the following steps:*

1. Place a decimal point to the left of the lead digit of each mantissa and multiply the two mantissas as ordinary decimal numbers to obtain the mantissa of the product.

2. Add the two exponents and subtract 50 from the sum, to obtain the exponent of the sum.

3. Affix the sign according to the ordinary rules of algebra.

The proof is left to the student.

Example 3. Find the product of 123   51 and −214   48.

The product of the mantissas is:

$$
\begin{array}{r}
.123 \\
- .214 \\
\hline
492 \\
123 \\
246 \\
\hline
- .026322
\end{array}
$$

The characteristic of the product is $51 + 48 - 50 = 49$.   Hence the product is:

$$-026322 \qquad 49$$

or, shifting the number to its normal form:

$$-26322 \qquad 48$$

Note that, since the decimal points of the mantissas precede the first digit, the mantissas obtained for the product will have a number of digits equal to the sum of the numbers of digits for the two given numbers.   As in the above example, a leading zero may be introduced.   In this case a shift will reduce by one the number of digits in the mantissa.

Theorem III. *The quotient in floating point division is obtained by the following steps:*

1. Shift the dividend until its mantissa is smaller in absolute value than the mantissa of the divisor (again considering the mantissa to have a decimal point in front of its lead digit).

2. Divide the mantissa of the dividend by the mantissa of the divisor to obtain the mantissa of the quotient.

   3.   *Subtract the exponent of the divisor from the exponent of the dividend and add* 50 *to the result to obtain the exponent of the quotient.*
   4.   *Affix the sign according to the ordinary rules of algebra.*

The proof is left to the student.

Example 4.   Divide 144   53 by 120   52.

Since .144 is greater than .120, the dividend must first be written as 0144   54. Then the division gives:

$$
\begin{array}{r}
.12 \\
\hline
.120\ )\overline{.0144} \\
120 \\
\hline
240 \\
240
\end{array}
$$

so that the mantissa of the result is 12.   The exponent is $54 - 52 + 50 = 52$. Thus the result is 12   52. We might write this number as 120   52. The question of the significance of the added zero and of significant figures in general will be discussed later.

EXERCISE I

1.   Express the following numbers in floating decimal form:

a.	41.92	f.	98740
b.	328.1	g.	1.82×10^3
c.	.0483	h.	4.71×10^{-6}
d.	.918	i.	6.64×10^{21}
e.	.007845	j.	3.87×10^{-19}

2.   Express the following numbers in ordinary decimal form:

a.	371	52	e.	8671	56
b.	465	49	f.	−3986	53
c.	−383	50	g.	00478	49
d.	472	47	h.	−00081	55

3.   Add algebraically the following pairs of floating decimal numbers:

a.	1386	52	d.	4392	51
	4501	52		−3913	52
b.	1641	53	e.	−3417	49
	7621	49		−7284	49
c.	6131	52	f.	7736	49
	−4721	52		−7749	49

4. Multiply the following pairs of floating decimal numbers:

a.	120	52	d.	220	65
	110	52		−120	68
b.	130	51	e.	310	64
	−440	48		400	36
c.	256	52	f.	−960	51
	100	51		−960	51

5. Divide the first number by the second in each of the following pairs of floating decimal numbers:

a.	160	53	d.	100	51
	400	52		300	51
b.	1728	49	e.	333	47
	1200	53		−111	52
c.	−400	47	f.	796	58
	200	45		317	44

1.4 THE DOZEN SYSTEM

We are so accustomed to counting by tens that when we try to utilize a different number system there are many habits of thinking which are quite difficult to discard. In order to point out some of these pitfalls, we shall next discuss the dozen, or duodecimal, system. In this system let us use the symbols

0,   1,   2,   3,   4,   5,   6,   7,   8,   9,   D,   E

as the basic characters. The letter D is for the decimal number ten and the letter E for decimal eleven. Let us call them dec and el to keep from confusing them with the decimal names. The number next after el is one dozen, which in this notation would be written 10. The next number, which is the decimal number thirteen, is one dozen and one, which would be written 11. In some ways it would have been better to discard the symbols 1 through 9 and use entirely new ones for our basic characters, because the use of the decimal symbols suggests decimal rules which are not true in the duodecimal system. For example, the decimal addition rule six plus five equals eleven is to be replaced by six plus five equals el:

$$6 + 5 = E$$

The decimal rule six plus seven equals thirteen is to be replaced by six plus seven equals one dozen and one, or:

$$6 + 7 = 11$$

Thus care must be used not to slip back into thinking by decimal rules. A new table of addition must be learned for the basic characters of duodecimal arithmetic, and likewise a new table of multiplication. For example, five times eight equals a decimal forty, or duodecimal three dozen and four, or:

$$5 \times 8 = 34$$

To write duodecimal numbers of any size, we employ the place value system, using a digit location with respect to a duodecimal point (*not* decimal point) to determine its value. Each place to the right or left of the duodecimal point differs in value from its neighbouring one by a factor of a dozen. The diagram shows the decimal value of each of the digits in the duodecimal number 4E7.2D9.

4	E	7	.	2	D	9
↓	↓	↓		↓	↓	↓
4×12^2	11×12^1	7×12^0		2×12^{-1}	10×12^{-2}	9×12^{-3}

The dozen system is in some respects more convenient than the decimal system. This convenience results primarily from the fact that twelve has many more divisors than ten. Twelve is divisible by one, two, three, four, six, and twelve. Thus many hand calculations are somewhat simpler in duodecimal than in decimal notation. Several of the common fractions which are repeating in decimal form are not in duodecimal form. For instance, the fraction one-third is the same as four-twelfths, or in duodecimal form .4. Some of the simple fractions in duodecimal form are:

$$1/6 = \text{decimal } 2/12 = \text{duodecimal } .2$$
$$1/4 = \text{decimal } 3/12 = \text{duodecimal } .3$$
$$1/3 = \text{decimal } 4/12 = \text{duodecimal } .4$$
$$1/2 = \text{decimal } 6/12 = \text{duodecimal } .6$$

Despite its convenience, the duodecimal system will in all probability never be adopted for hand calculations. It is not particularly advantageous for computer applications so we leave it without further discussion and turn to the systems that are most useful for digital computer applications.

1.5 THE BINARY SYSTEM

A very useful system for digital computer work is the binary system, or the number system with base two. The only basic characters of this system are:

$$0, \quad 1$$

The number next after one, or the decimal number two, is written as 10.

The next number, or decimal three, is written as 11. As in any other system, we use the place value method, where the location of a digit with respect to the binary point determines its value. Each place to the right or left of the binary point differs in value from its neighbor by a factor of two. The diagram shows the decimal value of each of the digits in the binary number 101.101:

1	0	1	.	1	0	1
↓	↓	↓		↓	↓	↓
1×2^2	0×2^1	1×2^0		1×2^{-1}	0×2^{-2}	1×2^{-3}

A major advantage of binary notation is the fact that only two digits, 0 and 1, are required in the representation of any number. These digits, or bits, as they are frequently called, can readily be represented by any of many physical systems capable of being in either of two different states. For example, on a paper tape or card, a 1 can be represented by a hole and a 0 by the absence of a hole; on magnetic tape or other magnetizable material, a 1 can be represented by a magnetized spot and a 0 by no magnetization or by magnetization of opposite polarity; in an electric circuit, a 1 can be represented by a voltage pulse and a 0 by no pulse or by a pulse of opposite polarity.

Another advantage of binary notation is that, with only two characters, very few laws are required to cover the possible combinations of these in addition and multiplication. For example, the basic multiplication tables consist of $0 \times 0 = 0$, $0 \times 1 = 1 \times 0 = 0$, $1 \times 1 = 1$. This will be pursued further in later sections.

A major disadvantage of the binary system is the large number of bits required to express numbers of very moderate size. For example:

$$\text{binary } 1000000000000 = \text{decimal } 2^{12} = \text{decimal } 4096$$

Thus a thirteen digit binary number may be required to represent a four digit decimal number. In general, since:

$$\log_{10}2 = .30103$$

then:

$$2^N = 10^{N \log_{10}2} = 10^{.3N}$$

so that an N-bit binary number is roughly equivalent to a $.3N$ digit decimal number. While computers frequently use binary numbers internally to exploit the advantages mentioned above, the numbers are frequently read into and out of the machine in some other form to avoid the tedious process of handling numbers having very large numbers of digits.

1.51 Binary to Decimal Conversion

A number given in binary form is easily converted to decimal form, since each bit simply represents some power of two. The process will be illustrated.

Example 1. Convert the binary number 11001101.1011 to decimal form.

This number is equivalent to $2^7 + 2^6 + 2^3 + 2^2 + 2^0 + 2^{-1} + 2^{-3} + 2^{-4}$:

$$
\begin{array}{rcl}
2^7 & = & 128 \\
2^6 & = & 64 \\
2^3 & = & 8 \\
2^2 & = & 4 \\
2^0 & = & 1 \\
2^{-1} = (1/2) & = & .5 \\
2^{-3} = (1/8) & = & .125 \\
2^{-4} = (1/16) & = & .0625 \\
\hline
& & 205.6875
\end{array}
$$

1.52 Decimal to Binary Conversion

The conversion of a decimal to binary form is somewhat more difficult than the reverse process. It is perfomed most easily with a table of the powers of two available. Table I gives all powers from 2^{15} to 2^{-15}.

A decimal number is converted to binary by subtracting out the largest power of two contained, then the largest contained in the remainder, etc. The binary number is constructed by writing a one in each bit position corresponding to a power successfully subtracted out.

TABLE I

$2^0 = 1$	$2^{-1} = .5$
$2^1 = 2$	$2^{-2} = .25$
$2^2 = 4$	$2^{-3} = .125$
$2^3 = 8$	$2^{-4} = .0625$
$2^4 = 16$	$2^{-5} = .03125$
$2^5 = 32$	$2^{-6} = .015625$
$2^6 = 64$	$2^{-7} = .0078125$
$2^7 = 128$	$2^{-8} = .00390625$
$2^8 = 256$	$2^{-9} = .001953125$
$2^9 = 512$	$2^{-10} = .0009765625$
$2^{10} = 1024$	$2^{-11} = .00048828125$
$2^{11} = 2048$	$2^{-12} = .000244140625$
$2^{12} = 4096$	$2^{-13} = .0001220703125$
$2^{13} = 8192$	$2^{-14} = .00006103515625$
$2^{14} = 16384$	$2^{-15} = .000030517578125$
$2^{15} = 32768$	

An example will serve to clarify the process.

Example 1. Convert the decimal number 2168.33 to binary form.

$$
\begin{array}{rrl}
& & 2168.33 \\
\text{Subtracting out } 2^{11} & = & 2048 \\
\hline
& & 120.33 \\
\text{Subtracting out } 2^6 & = & 64 \\
\hline
& & 56.33 \\
\text{Subtracting out } 2^5 & = & 32 \\
\hline
& & 24.33 \\
\text{Subtracting out } 2^4 & = & 16 \\
\hline
& & 8.33 \\
\text{Subtracting out } 2^3 & = & 8 \\
\hline
& & .33 \\
\text{Subtracting out } 2^{-2} & = & .25 \\
\hline
& & .08 \\
\text{Subtracting out } 2^{-4} & = & .0625 \\
\hline
& & .0175 \\
\text{Subtracting out } 2^{-6} & = & .015625 \\
\hline
& & .001875
\end{array}
$$

The process can be continued if a smaller remainder is desired. To the accuracy so far attained, our binary number has ones in the 12th, 7th, 6th, 5th, and 4th places left of the decimal point (one higher in each case than the power of 2 removed) and in the 2nd, 4th, and 6th places to the right of the decimal point. Thus the number is:

$$100001111000.010101$$

Note that the conversion from decimal to binary was not exact. The fractional part of the decimal number terminated after two digits, whereas the complete binary representation would have a nonterminating fractional part.

1.53   Binary Addition

The basic laws of binary addition are: $0 + 0 = 0$; $0 + 1 = 1 + 0 = 1$; $1 + 1 = 10$. With these laws, and handling carry just as for decimal addition, we can add any two binary numbers.

Example 1. Find the sum of 11010.1 and 10110.0

The sum is:

$$11010.1$$
$$10110.0$$
$$\overline{110000.1}$$

The steps are, starting at the right hand end: $1 + 0 = 1$; $0 + 0 = 0$; $1 + 1 = 10$; $1 + 0 + 1 = 10$; $1 + 1 + 0 = 10$; $1 + 1 + 1 = 11$.

The basic rules of binary addition are so simple that it is worth while to compile a summary of slightly more elaborate addition rules which include the carry digit directly. Note that, with the carry digit, for some digit positions in the above problem the combination of three bits is involved— the two binary bits of the summands and the carry from the next lower digit position. Two quantities result from this operation—the sum bit to be recorded and the carry to be taken to the next digit position. The complete process of addition for a single digit position consists of combining the summand digits and the incoming carry to obtain a sum bit and an outgoing carry. The possible combinations are given in Table II.

TABLE II

BINARY ADDITION RULES

Digit Values								
First Summand	0	0	0	0	1	1	1	1
Second Summand	0	0	1	1	0	0	1	1
Incoming Carry	0	1	0	1	0	1	0	1
Result								
Sum digit	0	1	1	0	1	0	0	1
Outgoing Carry	0	0	0	1	0	1	1	1

Binary addition is simply the process of applying the rules of Table II to each digit position, starting at the right and moving to the left. The incoming carry for the right hand digit position is automatically zero. Addition of a large column of binary numbers is most readily accomplished by adding the first two, then the third to the sum, and so forth.

1.54   *Binary Subtraction*

As in decimal arithmetic, binary subtraction may be accomplished by applying the rules for binary addition in reverse.

Example 1.   Add algebraically 11011 and -10110.

The operation is:

$$
\begin{array}{r}
11011 \\
-10110 \\
\hline
101
\end{array}
$$

The steps are: $1 - 0 = 1$; $1 - 1 = 0$; $10 - 1 = 1$; $0 - 0 = 0$; $1 - 1 = 0$.

Also as in decimal arithmetic, it is possible to avoid the additional complication of rules for subtraction by using complements for negative numbers. Since the number base is now two instead of ten, we are interested in a "ones complement" rather than a "nines complement."

For purposes of illustration, in order to avoid some of those subtleties of the use of complements noted in section 1.32, let us consider:

Example 2.   Add algebraically -11011 and 10110.

Without using complements, we would subtract the second number from the first, since the second has the small numerical value, thus:

$$
\begin{array}{r}
11011 \\
-10110 \\
\hline
101
\end{array}
$$

Then because the numerically larger number was negative, we would affix a minus sign, obtaining -101 as our final answer.

Let us now use the ones complement for this problem.   Since we are using five digit numbers, we would form the ones complement of 11011 by subtracting it from 111111, giving 100100.   It is interesting to note that this number differs from the original by having a one in the place of the minus sign and in each digit position having each "one" replaced by "zero" and each "zero" replaced by "one."   Thus, it is quite easy to form the ones complement of a binary number.   With this notation, the above example becomes:

$$
\begin{array}{r}
100100 \\
10110 \\
\hline
111010
\end{array}
$$

The answer is just the ones complement representation of -101.

1.55   Binary Multiplication

Binary multiplication can be performed in a manner analogous to decimal multiplication by use of the simple multiplication rules: $0 \times 0 = 0$; $0 \times 1 = 1 \times 0 = 0$; $1 \times 1 = 1$.

Example 1.   Find the product of 1101.1 and 1.0111.

Starting this operation as in decimal arithmetic we have:

$$
\begin{array}{r}
1101.1 \\
1.0111 \\
\hline
11011 \\
11011 \\
11011 \\
11011 \\
\hline
\end{array}
$$

At this point we arrive at the problem of adding several binary numbers together.   As mentioned earlier, this is most readily accomplished by adding only two numbers at a time.   In the following rearrangement, this is done, the addition being carried out after each step of the multiplication:

$$
\begin{array}{r}
1101.1 \\
1.0111 \\
\hline
11011 \\
11011 \\
\hline
1010001 \\
11011 \\
\hline
10111101 \\
11011 \\
\hline
10011.01101 \\
\end{array}
$$

first intermediate sum

second intermediate sum

final answer

The rule for placement of the binary point in the product is the same as for decimal arithmetic.

In ordinary decimal multiplication the practice is to start multiplying at the right hand digit of both multiplicand and multiplier.   There is some advantage to this, since one has the problem of carry from one column to the next one on the left.   For example, in the decimal product:

$$
\begin{array}{r}
16 \\
\times\, 27 \\
\hline
\end{array}
$$

the first step is to take 7 times 6, obtaining 42, and record the 2 and carry the 4 until the next product, 7 times 1, is formed.   In binary multiplication, this problem never arises, since the only products are: $0 \times 0 = 0$; $0 \times 1 = 0$; $1 \times 0 = 0$; and $1 \times 1 = 1$.   In no case does one of these operations give a two digit result. Since no carry is involved in binary multiplication, the operation is just as easily performed from the right as from the left. In the binary product:

$$1011.01$$
$$\times\ 1110.10$$

the first step can be taken by multiplying the multiplicand by the *left* hand bit of the multiplier, and recording the answer beginning with the *left* bit under the left bit of the multiplier. Then the second bit of the multiplier can be used, and that product recorded starting under the second bit of the multiplier. At this stage, the work will appear as follows:

$$1011.01$$
$$1110.10$$
$$101101$$
$$101101$$

In accordance with our practice of adding binary numbers only two at a time, the next step is addition of the two numbers so far obtained. Since binary addition *does* sometimes give a carry, it is necessary to perform the addition starting at the right hand end of the numbers. After this is done, the calculation appears as:

$$1011.01$$
$$1110.10$$
$$101101$$
$$101101$$
$$10000111$$

The next step is another multiplication, this time by the third digit of the multiplier. This operation, recorded in the proper location, gives:

$$1011.01$$
$$1110.10$$
$$101101$$
$$101101$$
$$10000111$$
$$101101$$

Continuing this process of multiplications and additions, we finally obtain:

$$
\begin{array}{r}
1011.01 \\
1110.10 \\
\hline
101101 \\
101101 \\
\hline
10000111 \\
101101 \\
\hline
100111011 \\
101101 \\
\hline
10100011.001
\end{array}
$$

This procedure has the advantage that the most significant part of the answer is developed first, and the less significant parts later.   If it is known that only a certain number of significant digits are required in the answer, it is possible to carry the problem far enough to obtain that many significant digits and then quit.

1.56   Binary Division

Binary division is somewhat more direct than decimal division in that the trial and error nature of the process is removed.   Each digit in the quotient will be either 1 or 0, indicating that the divisor will divide into a group of digits of the dividend either once or not at all.   An example will serve to make the process clear.

Example 1.   Divide 1011 into 110.110100.

$$
\begin{array}{r}
.100111 \\
1011\,\overline{)\,110.110100} \\
101\ \ 1 \\
\hline
1\ \ 0101 \\
1011 \\
\hline
10100 \\
1011 \\
\hline
10010 \\
1011 \\
\hline
111
\end{array}
$$

1.57   Binary Floating Point

As in the decimal notation, the location of the binary point of binary notation can be designated by a separate number rather than by placing a period between two digits of the number. The number is written as a mantissa, assumed to be a quantity less than one, having the binary point in front of the first digit, and an exponent, which tells how many places the binary point must be moved from its assumed position at the left of the mantissa to give the true value of the number. Since a one place shift of the binary point corresponds to a multiplication or division by two, the exponent in this case indicates the power of two which is to be multiplied by the mantissa. Negative exponents are ordinarily avoided by adding some arbitrary number to the exponent. Frequently the decimal number 128, or binary 10000000, is used. This allows representation of numbers as small as 2^{-128}, or about 10^{-38}, without using negative exponents. Since the exponent in floating binary notation represents a power of two and that in floating decimal represents a power of ten, it is not possible to convert from binary to decimal and vice versa by converting mantissa and exponent separately.   Instead it is necessary to change to ordinary binary or decimal notations to perform the conversion.   Binary floating point notation is so cumbersome for use outside a computer that it will not even be demonstrated here.   Experience in operations with binary floating point is not needed for the material that follows. We merely point out that binary floating point arithmetic is analogous to floating decimal in all important respects: addition is accomplished by shifting until the exponents are equal and then adding mantissas; multiplication by multiplying mantissas and adding exponents, correcting the final exponent for the arbitrarily added part used to avoid negative exponents.

1.58   Multiplication of Mantissas

The process of binary multiplication can be simplified somewhat in form if we concern ourselves only with mantissas.

Consider the product:

$$
\begin{array}{r}
.101101 \\
\times\,.110101 \\
\hline
101101 \\
101101 \\
\hline
10000111 \\
101101 \\
\hline
1001001001 \\
101101 \\
\hline
.100101010001 \\
\end{array}
$$

performed according to the system learned previously for binary multiplication starting at the left. The first step was to multiply .101101 by .1. If we do only this operation as a separate problem, we obtain:

$$.101101$$
$$\times .1$$
$$\overline{ .0101101}$$

The result is precisely the same as the multiplicand, except that it is shifted to the right by one position with respect to the binary point. The second step in the original problem is to multiply .101101 by .01. If we do this operation as a separate problem, we obtain:

$$.101101$$
$$\times .01$$
$$\overline{ .00101101}$$

This result is also precisely the same as the multiplicand, except that it is shifted to the right by two positions with respect to the binary point. It now becomes clear that the operation of multiplying a multiplicand by a 1 in the nth digit position of the multiplier is equivalent to shifting the multiplicand n places to the right with respect to its binary point. The original problem can be rewritten, keeping track of the binary point in each step, and then the work appears as follows:

$$.101101$$
$$\times .110101$$

.0101101	(1)
.00101101	(2)
.10000111	(3)
.0000101101	(4)
.1001001001	(5)
.000000101101	(6)
.100101010001	(7)

The numbered steps can be described in words as follows:

Because there is a 1 in the first bit position of the multiplier, the multiplicand is shifted one place to the right, giving (1) as a first partial result.

Because there is a 1 in the second bit position of the multiplier, the multiplicand is shifted two places to the right, giving (2), which is then added to (1) to give (3), a new partial result.

Because there is a 1 in the fourth bit position of the multiplier, the multiplicand is shifted four places to the right, giving (4), which is then added to (3) to give a new partial result (5).

Because there is a 1 in the sixth bit position of the multiplier, the multiplicand is shifted six places to the right, giving (6) which is then added to (5) to give the final result (7).

It is seen, then, that multiplication of two mantissas can be described as a process of repeatedly shifting the multiplicand to the right and adding.

EXERCISE II

1. Write the first 64 decimal integers as binary integers.

2. Write the following binary numbers in decimal form:

    a.   101.11
    b.   100111.011
    c.   111.1111

    d.   −100000.0001
    e.   .101010101
    f.   −11000000001

3. Write the following decimal numbers in binary form:

    a.   128.375
    b.   4.5
    c.   63.875

    d.   5460.7
    e.   .931842
    f.   764893.9

4. Perform the following binary addition and subtractions:

    a.   1.11011
         1.00100

    d.   .111001
         −.101001

    b.   .110010
         .000111

    e.   .11110
         −.10101

    c.   11.0111
         10.1101

    f.   .10001
         −.01111

5. Perform the following binary multiplications:

    a.   .110101
         × .011011

    d.   .1111
         × .1111

    b.   .011
         × .011

    e.   .10111001
         × .11100111

    c.   .1001
         × .1111

    f.   .11001100101
         × .10111101111

6. Perform the following binary divisions:

    a.   .01 ÷ .1
    b.   .01101 ÷ .101
    c.   .1011101 ÷ .11001
    d.   .11001101 ÷ .111

1.6 OTHER NUMBER SYSTEMS

We have seen that the laws of arithmetic take on an especially simple form in the binary number system, a fact which makes the binary system a natural one for digital computers to use for their internal operation. On the other hand, it should be clear from the example problems in binary arithmetic given above that the binary notation is cumbersome and long, and that a requirement to convert all numbers to binary before using them in a computer would impose quite an inconvenience. Actually, the problems given above as examples used very short binary numbers. In computers it is quite frequently desirable to use numbers that, in decimal form, would require nine decimal digits. In binary form such numbers require roughly thirty digits, an unmanageable size for hand calculations. Consequently, while the binary system is frequently used for operation within a computer, circuits are frequently provided to allow the machine to accept or put out numbers in some other system. The decimal system is sometimes used for this purpose. However, the decimal to binary conversion is a rather difficult one, and some machines are constructed to use number systems which stand in a simpler relation to the binary system. In particular the octal system, based on 8, and hexadecimal system, based on 16, are frequently used. We will discuss each of these systems briefly.

1.61 The Octal System

The number system based on 8 has as its basic characters:

$$0, \quad 1, \quad 2, \quad 3, \quad 4, \quad 5, \quad 6, \quad 7$$

The next number after 7, or decimal 8, is formed by writing 10. The next number, decimal 9, is octal 11. If arithmetic were to be performed in octal notation, new addition and multiplication rules would have to be learned. For example, five plus six is equal to the decimal number eleven, which is eight and three, or octal 13. Thus, in octal, $5 + 6 = 13$. Since we are not particularly interested in the octal system for arithmetic purposes, we shall not pursue this point.

In an octal number, the value of a digit is determined by its position in relation to an octal point. Moving a digit to the left by a place increases its value by a factor of octal 10 (or decimal 8) and moving it to the right reduces its value by the same factor. The diagram shows an octal number, and below each digit the decimal value of that particular digit is given:

7	6	3	4	.	1	5	2
↓	↓	↓	↓		↓	↓	↓
7×8^3	6×8^2	3×8^1	4×8^0		1×8^{-1}	5×8^{-2}	2×8^{-3}

It is somewhat unfortunate that the symbols 1 through 7 are used in octal notation because through long usage we have learned to associate the decimal meanings and laws of decimal arithmetic with such numbers. There is nothing in the appearance of the above number to indicate that it is not an ordinary decimal number. When there is the possibility of confusion, as in this case, we shall indicate the number system being used by a subscript after the number which gives the decimal value of the base being used. Thus the above number would be written:

$$7634.152_8$$

1.62 Octal-Decimal Conversion

Octal to decimal and decimal to octal conversion can be accomplished in a manner completely analogous to binary-decimal conversion. A detailed discussion of the process will not be given here. A different and somewhat simpler way of converting between octal and decimal is to convert first to binary and then to the other system. As will be seen shortly, octal-binary conversion is so simple as to be trivial, so that this double conversion is not at all difficult.

1.63 Octal-Binary Conversion

A clue to the process of octal-binary conversion can be obtained by writing the first several octal and corresponding binary numbers, as in Table III (decimal values have also been listed for reference):

TABLE III

Decimal	Octal	Binary
1	1	1 (or 001)
2	2	10 (or 010)
3	3	11 (or 011)
4	4	100
5	5	101
6	6	110
7	7	111
8	10	1000
9	11	1001
10	12	1010
11	13	1011
12	14	1100
13	15	1101
14	16	1110
15	17	1111
16	20	10000

If we study this table we see that it takes at most three binary bits to represent one octal digit. If we look more closely, we see that the same three binary bits always represent the same octal digit. For example, the octal number 5 is binary 101. The octal number 15 is 1101, the first 1 is the binary number standing for octal 1 and the binary 101 again stands for 5. This condition arises from the fact that eight is two cubed. In the binary system, a shift to the right of one position of the binary point corresponds to a multiplication of the number by two. A shift of three positions corresponds to a multiplication by two cubed, or eight. For an octal number, a shift of one position of the octal point is equivalent to multiplication by eight also; thus three binary positions are precisely equivalent to one octal position. This means that transformation from octal to binary can be accomplished merely by replacing each octal digit by its three-bit binary equivalent. Conversely, transformation from binary to octal can be accomplished by grouping the binary bits in threes starting from the binary point and working in both directions, and then replacing each three-bit group by its octal equivalent.

Example 1. Convert 764.301_8 to binary.

The binary groups are used to replace individual digits, as indicated:

$$
\begin{array}{cccccc}
7 & 6 & 4 & . & 3 & 0 & 1 \\
\downarrow & \downarrow & \downarrow & & \downarrow & \downarrow & \downarrow \\
111 & 110 & 100 & . & 011 & 000 & 001
\end{array}
$$

The resulting number is the required binary number. Some additional insight into the process can be obtained from the following diagram, which illustrates for the integral part the values of the numbers in decimal form:

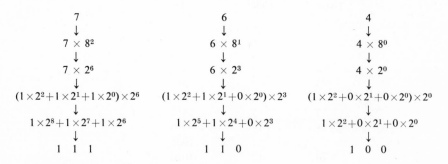

Example 2. Convert 11011.10111 to octal.

Grouping the digits by threes, starting from the binary point, we have:

$$11 \quad 011 \quad . \quad 101 \quad 110$$

It is necessary to introduce an additional zero in the first group and last group in order to have three binary bits in each group, thus:

011   011   .   101   110

Each of these groups is now replaced by its octal equivalent, giving:

33.56_8

1.64 The Hexadecimal System

The hexadecimal system, or number system based on sixteen, requires a zero and 15 other symbols for its basic characters. We shall use:

0,   1,   2,   3,   4,   5,   6,   7,   8,   9,   F,   G,   J,   K,   Q,   W

The number next after W (or decimal 15) is 10, which stands for the decimal number 16. The decimal number 17 is represented by hexadecimal 11. As with the other number bases we have discussed, the value of a digit is determined by its location with respect to a point, in this case a hexadecimal point. Moving a digit to the left by one place increases its value by a factor of hexadecimal 10, or decimal 16, and moving it to the right reduces its value by the same factor. The diagram shows a hexadecimal number, and below each digit the decimal value of that digit:

6   F   J   .   Q   9

↓   ↓   ↓   ↓   ↓

6×16^2 10×16^1 12×16^0 14×16^{-1} 9×16^{-2}

As with octal, this system offers great ease in conversion to binary. Since decimal sixteen is the fourth power of decimal two, precisely four binary bits are required to represent each hexadecimal digit. These binary representations of the hexadecimal digits are given in Table IV.

A hexadecimal number is converted to binary by replacing each hexadecimal digit by its four-bit binary equivalent, and a binary number is converted to hexadecimal by grouping the bits into four-bit groups, working to the right and left from the binary point, and then replacing each group by the equivalent hexadecimal digit.

Example 1. Convert $76QF.0K_{16}$ to binary.

Using the relations from Table IV:

7   6   Q   F   .   0   K

↓   ↓   ↓   ↓   ↓   ↓

0111   0110   1110   1010   .   0000   1101

TABLE IV

Decimal	Hexadecimal	Binary
0	0	0000
1	1	0001
2	2	0010
3	3	0011
4	4	0100
5	5	0101
6	6	0110
7	7	0111
8	8	1000
9	9	1001
10	F	1010
11	G	1011
12	J	1100
13	K	1101
14	Q	1110
15	W	1111
16	10	10000

Example 2.   Convert 101111.0110111 to hexadecimal.

Grouping the digits by fours, starting from the binary point, we have:

$$10 \quad 1111 \quad . \quad 0110 \quad 111$$

Completing the first and last groups with zeros and using Table IV, we have:

$$\begin{array}{cccc} 0010 & 1111 & . & 0110 & 1110 \\ \downarrow & \downarrow & & \downarrow & \downarrow \\ 2 & W & & 6 & Q_{16} \end{array}$$

1.7   BINARY REPRESENTATIONS OF QUANTITIES

It has been seen that, for the octal and hexadecimal systems, the digits can be represented quite easily in binary form.   Thus it is extremely simple to construct devices which will automatically convert octal or hexadecimal numbers to their binary equivalent.   For example, a typewriter keyboard can be wired to a tape punching unit so that pressing the key on the typewriter will cause holes to be punched in paper tape. A hole in the tape can be read as a binary digit one, and a space without a hole as a binary digit zero.   If then the typewriter keys are so wired that pressing the "5" key punches two holes separated by a blank space, and so forth, numbers in octal form can be typed on the keyboard and the same numbers in binary form will appear on the tape.

Likewise, if four binary positions are used for each key instead of three, then the typing of a hexadecimal number on the keyboard can be made automatically to produce a binary number on the tape. There are numerous other ways in which octal or hexadecimal numbers can be automatically converted to binary. It would carry us too far from the subject of this book to attempt to enumerate in detail the various electrical or mechanical systems that can be used for this purpose. The above illustrations should serve to show that such devices are indeed feasible.

1.71 Binary Coded Decimal

Suppose a typewriter has been connected to a paper tape system in such a way that hexadecimal digits typed on the keyboard automatically produce the four-bit binary equivalents listed in Table IV on the tape. Suppose now instead of a hexadecimal number, a decimal number is typed on the keyboard. The result is an arrangement of holes and spaces, or binary zeros and ones, four for each decimal digit typed. For example, the decimal number 93645 would produce the combination:

$$
\begin{array}{ccccc}
9 & 3 & 6 & 4 & 5 \\
\downarrow & \downarrow & \downarrow & \downarrow & \downarrow \\
1001 & 0011 & 0110 & 0100 & 0101
\end{array}
$$

Conversely, given the binary digits shown, we can reconstruct the decimal number intended. Thus the arrangement of binary digits can be used to represent the decimal number. Note carefully, however, that the array of binary digits *is not* the binary number having the same *value* as the original decimal number. In fact, considered as a number, it has no simple relation to the decimal number. For example, the decimal number 96 would appear as follows if each digit were replaced by its four-bit binary representation:

$$
\begin{array}{cc}
9 & 6 \\
\downarrow & \downarrow \\
1001 & 0110
\end{array}
$$

On the other hand, since $96 = 2^6 + 2^5$, the binary notation for 96 is:

$$96_{10} = 1100000_2$$

The latter number, 1100000, is a true binary number, having the same value as the decimal number 96. The former number, 10010110, which happens to be the binary number equal to the decimal number 150, can be considered as a *code symbol* for the number 96. It can be used if we are interested only in having the number 96 coded as a combination of ones and zeros, and do not intend to attempt binary arithmetic with the coded symbols. The representation of a decimal number by symbolizing each decimal digit as a group of ones and zeros is referred to as binary coded decimal.

1.72 Binary Coding of Other Characters

Just as the decimal or digits can be assigned a binary coding for purposes of representation on punched paper tape or in other systems in which only zeros and ones can be used, so also can any other symbol or character used on a typewriter keyboard or in printing be assigned a binary coding. Most computers make use of such a coding for all of the letters of the alphabet and some of the other standard pointing symbols found on typewriter keyboards. From four to six bits are used for this purpose. With four bits, 2^4 or 16 different quantities can be represented. With five bits, 2^5 or 32 different quantities can be represented. This still is not sufficient to allow a different coding or representation for the 10 decimal characters plus the 26 letters of the alphabet. With six bits, 2^6 or 64 different quantities can be represented, so that a different representation is available for each numeral, each alphabetic character, and each of the more common other printing symbols. An example of a binary coding system using six bit positions is shown in Table V.

TABLE V

A TYPICAL SIX-BIT BINARY CODING SYSTEM

Character	Binary Code	Character	Binary Code	Character	Binary Code
0	000000	I	101001	.	010001
1	000001	J	101010	,	010010
2	000010	K	101011	:	010011
3	000011	L	101100	;	010100
4	000100	M	101101	-	010101
5	000101	N	101110	/	010110
6	000110	O	101111	'	010111
7	000111	P	110000	"	011000
8	001000	Q	110001	&	011001
9	001001	R	110010	+	011010
A	100001	S	110011	$\neq$	011011
B	100010	T	110100	$	011100
C	100011	U	110101	*	011101
D	100100	V	110110	=	011110
E	100101	W	110111	(	001010
F	100110	X	111000	)	001011
G	100111	Y	111001		
H	101000	Z	111010		

Not all possible six-bit combinations have been assigned meanings in the table. Some of the spares might be used to control typewriter space or back space or carriage return keys.

Example 1. Using the binary code given in Table V, write $31.27 in binary coded form.

The solution is:

01110000001100000101000100001000111

EXERCISE III

1. Write the complete addition table for the basic characters of:

    a. The octal system.
    b. The hexadecimal system.

2. Write the complete multiplication table for the basic characters of:

    a. The octal system.
    b. The hexadecimal system.

3. Write the following numbers in binary form:

    a. 721.3_8 e. $.00613_8$
    b. -46.25_8 f. $.0FQJ_{16}$
    c 100_{16} g. $-WW.WW_{16}$
    d. $QW.7F_{16}$ h. 10100_8

4. Write the following binary numbers in octal form:

    a. 101.011   d. .0000111
    b. 1110.000101   e. 1011.1101
    c. 10000.   f. 10111.11101

5. Write the numbers of Problem 4 in hexadecimal form.

6. Write the following decimal numbers in binary, and also in a binary-coded decimal, using six-bit positions for each character as in Table V:

    a. 8   d. 17.125
    b. 24   e. 4.5
    c. 36.375   f. 91.2

7. Give a general proof of the validity of the octal to binary conversion method given in Section 1.63.

8. Prove that a fraction which has a terminating fractional part in binary form also has a terminating fractional part in decimal form.

9. The decimal integer 153 can be converted to octal as follows:

$$
\begin{array}{r}
8 \,)\, 153 \\
\hline
19 \quad \text{remainder } 1 \\
8 \,)\, 19 \\
\hline
2 \quad \text{remainder } 3 \quad = 231_8 \\
8 \,)\, 2 \\
\hline
0 \quad \text{remainder } 2 \\
\end{array}
$$

read up

In words, the conversion can be accomplished by performing successive divisions by 8 and forming an octal number by listing the remainder in reverse order. Show that this method can be used to convert any decimal integer to octal.

10. The decimal fraction .172 can be converted to octal as follows:

$$
\begin{array}{r}
.172 \\
\times\; 8 \\
\hline
\end{array}
$$

read   1 .376
down $\times\;$ 8
          ─────
          3 .008
          $\times\;$ 8
          ─────
          0 .064
          $\times\;$ 8
          ─────
          0 .512
        $=$ .1300 $+$

In words, the conversion is accomplished by repeated multiplications by 8, taking after each multiplication the integral part of the product as the next digit of the octal number. Show that this process can be used to convert any decimal proper fraction to octal.

CHAPTER II *The Digital Computer*

2.1 INTRODUCTION

Now that we have seen that our normal manner of using numbers and performing arithmetic operations is not the only one possible, and have gained some acquaintance with other number systems and methods of arithmetic, we are prepared to learn how to use a digital computer. We are faced with another problem, however. There is not just one kind of digital computer but instead there are dozens of kinds and models, constructed by different groups and companies. Further, each passing year sees the introduction of new developments and the growing obsolescence of older models. Which computer should we study? How can we be sure that the computer we select will not be obsolete in a very few years? This quandary is not as hopeless as it seems at first. Despite the fact that digital computers differ from one another, there are some basic similarities. If we understand the basic features common to nearly all digital computers, then we will be in a position to learn how a computer performs mathematical calculations. The approach we will take, then, is *not* to describe any actual present-day computer, but instead to discuss the features characteristic of digital computers in general, and then to describe a hypothetical machine which possesses such features in as simple a form as possible. Once the fundamentals of operation are understood, the way is clear for understanding the methods for solution of mathematical problems given later in the text. The reader who studies these methods carefully will find himself in the possession of certain principles he should then be able to apply easily to any actual computer. Further, and perhaps more important, he should have some feel for the general capabilities and limitations of computers for performing calculations.

2.2 MAJOR COMPONENTS

Certain major components are required in a computer if it is to perform arithmetic operations. It must be able to add, subtract, multiply, and divide numbers given to it. Early computers contained circuitry to perform these

35

operations and little else. This circuitry formed what might be termed an "arithmetic unit." As the value of speed in performing calculations became recognized it was found that an arithmetic unit alone was inadequate. In order that numbers could be made available quickly to the arithmetic unit, a memory unit capable of storing many numbers and transferring them automatically to and from the arithmetic unit was required. In order that the arithmetic unit could quickly receive the proper numbers from the memory unit and perform the desired arithmetic operations, an automatic control unit was required. In order that the proper numbers could be placed in the memory unit to begin a problem and the answers be obtained after completion of the problem, input and output units were required. There are then five major components in the typical digital computer: arithmetic unit, memory unit, control unit, input unit, and output unit. Each will be discussed in sufficient detail to give an idea of the various systems used, and then a fictitious unit described which will be a part of a hypothetical computer used in the later portions of the book.

2.3 MEMORY

When calculations are done by hand, or with a desk-type calculator, the person performing the calculation must frequently record the results of individual additions, subtractions, multiplications, or divisions on a worksheet and then re-use these results at a later stage in the calculation. One of the major contributions to the speed of modern digital computers is the elimination of this cumbersome process by the use of memory units in which intermediate results are recorded, stored, and fed back into the circuits of the machine as needed, automatically and quickly. The term "memory" is usually employed to designate these functions, as well as the machine unit performing them, because they are somewhat analogous to the human mental process of remembering. The alternative term "storage" is sometimes used.

2.31 *Memory Cells*

A number is usually stored in memory in the form of electrical or mechanical representations of binary bits. The memory is subdivided into cells, each cell being able to store all the bits of a single number. In the ordinary computer all the memory cells, or registers as they are frequently called, are capable of storing some fixed number of binary bits. About 30 is the usual number, although some machines use as few as 12 bits or as many as 64. As was indicated in the preceding chapter, 30 binary bits are equivalent to roughly $30 \times 3 = 9$ decimal digits. It might seem that four or five decimal digits would be adequate. However, the problems described in later chapters will show that rounding errors involved in calculations can easily cause the loss of several significant figures. Occasions will be found, not too infre-quently, when 30 binary bits are insufficient. Because the binary bits con-tained in a memory cell need not actually represent a binary number, but may instead be a binary coding for some combination of letters, numbers, or other characters, the contents of a memory cell are ordinarily referred to as a "word." A "word" may be a true binary number, or binary coding for a true word in the linguistic sense, or merely some combination of letters, numbers, or other symbols in a binary coded form.

2.32 Some Types of Memories

Although it is not the purpose of this text to describe computer hardware and although advances in technique will in all probability lead to drastic changes in hardware with little or no change in logical design of the system, a cursory description of a few of the simpler memory devices will be given.

In some of the magnetic-type memories, a small spot on a ferromagnetic surface is magnetized by being moved under a coil through which an electric pulse is passed at the right moment. It remains magnetized as long as de-sired, thus storing the information that the pulse recorded. Whenever the information is needed, the spot is moved under another coil, in which it induces an electric current. The ferromagnetic surface may be on a tape, a disc, or a drum, or may have any of several other configurations. The par-ticular section of the surface where the binary bits of a single word are stored constitutes a single cell of the memory.

In an acoustic-type memory, a glass tube filled with mercury is closed off at each end by a quartz crystal. An electric pulse, received by one of the crystals, is translated into mechanical motion by the piezoelectric effect. This motion is imparted to the mercury, travels down the mercury column as a sound pulse, is received by the other crystal and reconverted into an electric pulse. This pulse is conducted back to the first crystal and is thus kept cir-culating. Because of the relatively slow speed of sound (as compared with and electric pulse in a wire, which travels with almost the speed of light) all the binary bits of several words can follow each other around through the mercury and circuit. A single memory cell is simply a section in this moving train. A word may be stored by introducing the set of electrical pulses at the proper time, and may be read out by allowing the pulses to be admitted to the external circuitry at the proper time. The acoustic-type memory is rather cumbersome, and is no longer in general use.

In cathode-ray tube memories, a binary digit is represented by the presence or absence of an electric charge on a specified spot on the screen of a cathode-ray tube. An electric beam is swept across the surface depositing the charge either in a sharp dot (for a binary 1) or a blurred dot (for a binary 0). The number is read by directing another beam at the spot. This second beam will develop a different voltage depending on the shape of the pre-existing charge. A single memory cell consists of a sequence of locations on the scope face.

The newer core storage systems rely on ferromagnetic, ferroelectric, or superconductive elements as storage elements. In a magnetic core storage, for example, each element may consist of a tiny ferrite ring, less than one tenthousandth of an inch in diameter. A single binary bit can be stored in the ring by running a current pulse through a wire which passes through the hole in the ring. Transistors are used to control the current flow in the wire. Even a relatively small memory may require thousands of such rings and transistors.

There are many other types of memory devices. However, those mentioned should serve to give some idea of general nature of memory units.

2.33   Cell Identification, Capacity, and Access

The examples of memories have indicated that a single memory cell may consist of some particular physical item, such as a section of the surface of a ferromagnetic surface, or some particular sector of a moving train of signals, as in an acoustic memory. For arithmetic purposes it matters not how the number is stored, but only that there is some means of identifying each individual cell, so that a number stored in a particular cell is not lost but can be read out when desired. Perhaps the simplest way is to assign to each cell an identifying number (we shall use a decimal numbering system for this purpose). For an idealized machine for later use, we will assume a memory consisting of 10,000 memory cells, numbered from 0000 to 9999. Each cell will be assumed to have space for 36 binary bits, thus allowing for a 35-bit binary number plus a sign bit. We will not specify the particular electro-mechanical nature of this memory.

2.34   Capacity

We have assumed a memory of 10,000 words for the idealized machine to be used in later considerations. This would seem to afford storage facility for far more words than would ever be required. Indeed many computers have much less storage facility. On the other hand, there are many with even greater storage facility, and there are reasons for desiring much larger memories. A 10,000 word memory will be sufficient for all the calculations we will care to describe in this text.

2.4   ARITHMETIC UNIT

The heart of the computer is the arithmetic unit, that part of the machine which performs addition, subtraction, multiplication, or division of two numbers. In the discussion of number systems, we found that arithmetic is particularly simple when performed with binary numbers, so we shall describe a machine which does arithmetic in this manner. In Sections 1.53 to 1.58, we described in some detail the steps involved in performing binary arithmetic. The purpose of those discussions was to give some feel for the types of operations which the electrical circuits in the arithmetic unit must be able to accomplish. For the material in the remainder of the book it is not necessary to understand just how the circuitry does perform these operations. For readers interested in pursuing this matter further, some further discussion is given in the next section. It may be omitted without loss of continuity.

2.41 Logic of Arithmetic Circuitry

The ability to design electrical circuits capable of performing arithmetic operations stems from the fact that all arithmetic operations can be reduced to just two logical operations, termed "negation" and "conjunction." These are operations which form part of the subject matter of the field of mathematical logic. In terms of binary bits, the operation of negation consists of replacing one by zero or zero by one. The operation of conjunction consists of considering two binary bits, and if both are one the result is one; otherwise the result is zero. These logical operations are easily realized by electrical circuits.

For example, consider a system that uses a positive voltage pulse to represent a digit "one" and a negative pulse to represent a digit "zero." Then a negation circuit has one input and one output, so connected that a positive pulse at the input produces a negative pulse at the output and a negative pulse at the input causes a positive pulse at the output. Similarly, a conjunction circuit has two inputs and one output, so connected that the presence of positive pulses at both inputs causes a positive pulse at the output, but any other combination of input pulses gives a negative output pulse. Rather than become involved in the field of electronics, let us now take for granted that negation and conjunction circuits can indeed be built, and then demonstrate how these can be used as building blocks to make a binary adder. To do this we will talk both in terms of statements from mathematical logic and in terms of the equivalent electrical circuits. Statements using the logical operations of negation and conjunction can be written in a simple symbolic form. Let us use $'$ to indicate negation, $\&$ to indicate conjunction, and p, q, r, etc. to indicate binary digits either zero or one. Then the relation:

$$p = q'$$

would mean p is zero if q is one, and p is one if q is zero. An electrical circuit which will produce p as an output if q is provided as an input can be represented symbolically as in Figure 2-1. The left hand line represents the input and the right hand line represents the output. The box itself represents the particular combination of vacuum tubes, or relays, or transistors used to do the operation.   A similar representation can be given for the operation of conjunction.   The relation:

$$p = q \ \& \ r$$

means that p is 1 if both q and r are 1, and otherwise p is zero.   An electrical circuit which will produce p as an output if q and r are provided as inputs can be represented symbolically as in Figure 2-2.   Any number of logical

Figure 2–1   **Figure 2–2**

statements can be constructed using the operations of negation and conjunction.   One of the more interesting ones is:

$$p' = q' \ \& \ r'$$

which says, from the definition of conjunction, that p' is one if and only if q' and r' are one; or, stated another way, p' is zero if and only if either q' or r',

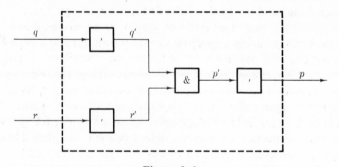

Figure 2–3

or both, is zero; or, stated yet another way, p is one if and only if either q or r, or both, is one.   The statement can also be written:

$$p = (q' \ \& \ r')'$$

This operation can be represented by the circuitry shown in Figure 2-3. The entire part of the circuit inside the dotted line has q and r as inputs and p as an output.   It demonstrates that the above relation can be considered as an operation on q and r to obtain p.   This operation has the name "disjunction," and is sometimes represented by the symbol V.   With this symbol, the above relation can be represented by:

$$p = q \lor r$$

and the corresponding circuit by the single box shown in Figure 2-4. The conjunction operation is sometimes called the "and" operation, and disjunction the "or" operation.

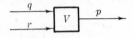

Figure 2–4

By means of a combination of "and," "or", and negation circuits, it is possible to make circuits that will obey all the rules of binary addition as given in Table II of Section 1.53. Let p and q represent the first and second summand bits, and r the incoming carry bit. Let s be the sum bit. From Table II we see that there are four conditions that will make $s = 1$. They are:

(*1*) p, q, and r all $= 1$.
(*2*) $p = 1, q$ and r both $= 0$.
(*3*) $q = 1, p$ and r both $= 0$.
(*4*) $r = 1, p$ and q both $= 0$.
We can restate these as:
(*1*) p, q, and r all $= 1$.
(*2*) p, q' and r' all $= 1$.
(*3*) p', q, and r' all $= 1$.
(*4*) p', q' and r all $= 1$.
Finally, we can state that $s = 1$ if any of the four conditions hold and $s = 0$ otherwise by writing:

$$s = (p \ \& \ q \ \& \ r) \ V \ (p \ \& \ q' \ \& \ r') \ V \ (p' \ \& \ q \ \& \ r') \ V \ (p' \ \& \ q' \ \& \ r)$$

The circuit representation of the above statement is quite involved, but can be drawn by straightforward application of the simple negation, "and," and "or" circuits. It is drawn in Figure 2-5. The above expression for s is not the only possible one which will properly define s. Another is:

$$s = \{p \ \& \ [(q \ \& \ r) \ V \ (q' \ \& \ r')]\} \ V \ \{p' \ \& \ [(q' \ \& \ r) \ V \ (q \ \& \ r')]\}$$

The circuit to represent this expression would differ from that above. Methods are available in the field of mathematical logic to find the representation which requires the least number of circuit elements.

Just as we have developed an expression for the sum, an expression for the outgoing carry can be developed. If the symbol t is used for the outgoing carry bit, an expression which contains all the rules for outgoing carry contained in Table II of Section 1.53 is:

$$t = (p \,\&\, q \,\&\, r) \, V \, (p' \,\&\, q \,\&\, r) \, V \, (p \,\&\, q' \,\&\, r) \, V \, (p \,\&\, q \,\&\, r')$$

A circuit representation can be drawn for this statement. If it is combined with that of Figure 2-5, a unit is obtained which receives three inputs, p, q, and r, and yields two outputs, s and t, obeying all the rules of Table II.

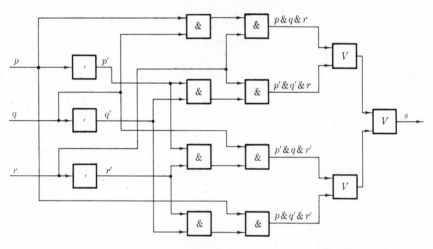

Figure 2–5

Such a circuit is a binary adder. It can be represented diagrammatically as a single unit, as in Figure 2-6. This unit represents essentially all the equipment required to perform binary addition. If the lowest order bits of two binary numbers are fed into the p and q inputs and a zero in the r input, the lowest order bit of the sum will appear on the s output, and the carry bit, if any, will appear on the t output. If then the next to lowest order bits of

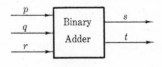

Figure 2–6

the summands are fed into p and q, and the t output fed into r, the next lowest order bit of the sum will appear on s, and the next carry, if any, will appear on the t output. By repetition of this process (which, incidentally, requires quite careful timing of the signals), all of the digits of the sum can be generated sequentially on the s output. The process can be accelerated by use of a separate binary adder for each bit position in the numbers, connecting the "*t*" output of one stage directly to the "*r*" input of the next stage.

In the description of binary subtraction, multiplication, and division, it was pointed out that these operations involved little more than minor variations of the rules for binary addition. The statement of these operations in terms of negation and conjunction will not be given here. Suffice it to say that the circuitry for these operations is quite analogous to that for addition.

2.42 *The Accumulator and Multiplier—Quotient Registers*

In the arithmetic unit of a computer it is convenient to use two special memory cells, ordinarily separate from the memory unit of the machine and assigned names rather than numbers for identification. They are used to hold the numbers actually being worked on by the arithmetic circuits of the machine, and are somewhat analogous to the registers present in a desk calculator. The first of these is the accumulator register, used ordinarily to receive the sum in addition problems or the difference in subtraction problems. For multiplication or division, a single register is not sufficient for temporary storage of the numbers involved. The multiplier-quotient register (MQ register) is ordinarily used to contain the multiplier in a multiplication problem while the product is being built up by repeated additions in the accumulator. It is also generally used in division to contain the quotient as it is built up, while the accumulator contains the dividend as altered by the repeated subtractions involved in a division problem.

2.5 CONTROL UNIT

It has been seen that there are various electrical and mechanical means of storing numbers and that it is possible to design circuits to perform arithmetic with these numbers. These operations can be done with great speed. However, unless the correct numbers from the memory can be made automatically available to the arithmetic unit and that unit made to perform automatically the correct arithmetic operation, this speed may be of little value. Thus an automatic control system which will route numbers from memory to arithmetic unit and cause the arithmetic unit to perform the correct operation on these numbers is an essential part of any high-speed digital computer.

2.51 *Gating Circuits*

The basis of the operation of a control unit is the repeated application of gating circuits, or gates. There are electrical connections from each of the memory cells to the accumulator and MQ register, and from these to the arithmetic circuits. These connections are interrupted by "gates." As long as these gates are closed, there is no way for information to flow from one part of a computer to another. The process of control consists of opening the proper gates, at the proper times, to connect the desired combination of memory cells and arithmetic circuits. In actual fact, the gates are electrical circuits, which are opened or closed by voltage pulses. Each gate can be designed so that only the correct combination of pulses will cause it to open. For example, for our machine having memory cells 0000 to 9999, each cell can have a gate which will be opened only by the combination of voltage pulses that corresponds to the binary coding of the gate number. Then binary bits corresponding, for example, to the decimal number 8452, when sent to all memory cell gates, would open only that corresponding to memory cell 8452, so that information could flow into or out of that cell but no other. In like manner, just as memory cell gates can be controlled by chosen combinations of binary bits (or, more accurately, the equivalent voltage pulses), so also can gates for the various arithmetic circuits be controlled by combinations of binary bits. For example, if the arithmetic unit of our machine has separate sets of "add" circuits, "subtract" circuits, "multiply" circuits, and "divide" circuits, we could have it so connected that the gate for the "add" circuits is opened by the pulses which represent the letter "A," the gate for the subtractor circuits is opened by the pulses which represent the letter "S," and so forth. With such an arrangement, the series of binary bits for the letter "A," followed by those of, say, the number 4635, can cause the gates of memory cell 4635, the adder circuits, and the accumulator to open, allowing the adder circuits to add the number stored in 4635 to the number which was residing in the accumulator. In this general fashion, the proper combinations of binary bits, introduced into the control unit of the computer, can cause the computer to perform arithmetic calculations with numbers stored in the memory. The next section shows how the control process can be regarded as a process in mathematical logic; it can be omitted without loss of continuity.

2.52 *Mathematical Logic of Control*

Section 2.41 described the relation between electrical circuits, some statements from mathematical logic, and the operations of arithmetic. The same considerations can be applied directly to the gating circuits used in the control unit. Conceptually, a conjunction circuit such as described in Section 2.41 can be regarded as a simple gate. The relation:

$$p = q \ \& \ r$$

can be read "$p = 0$ if $r = 0$, but $p = q$ if $r = 1$." In other words, the value of r determines whether or not p is allowed to be determined by q. The value of r closes or opens the gate. If $r = 0$ the gate is closed, and whether q be zero or one, p is zero.   If $r = 1$, the gate is open and p takes on the value of q. The circuit diagram in Figure 2-7 indicates r as the gate control, q as the input,

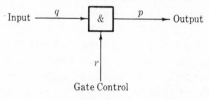

Gate Control

Figure 2–7

and p as the output.   Gates with more complicated controls are easy to construct.   For example the relation:

$$p = q \ \& \ (r \ \& \ s' \ \& \ t \ \& \ u \ \& \ v')$$

can be considered as a gate between q and p which is open only when $r = 1$, $s = 0$, $t = 1$, $u = 1$, $v = 0$.   The circuitry can be drawn as in Figure 2-8. If the proper combination of ones and zeros is fed into r, s, t, u, and v, the gate opens.   Otherwise it remains closed.   Gates of this sort can be used to

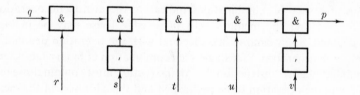

Figure 2–8

control the connections between memory cells and the arithmetic unit.   To demonstrate this fact, let us assume we have a computer with only a three cell memory, cells numbered 1, 2, and 3.   For cell number 1 we will use a gate of the form:

$$p = q \ \& \ (r' \ \& \ s)$$

for cell number 2 a gate of the form:

$$p = q \ \& \ (r \ \& \ s')$$

and for cell number 3 a gate of the form:

$$p = q \ \& \ (r \ \& \ s)$$

Then the gate for cell 1 will be opened by $r = 0$, $s = 1$, cell 2 by $r = 1$, $s = 0$, and cell 3 by $r = 1$, $s = 1$.   Considering the combinations r, s as a two digit binary number, the number 01 sent to all gates will connect cell 1 only, the number 10 sent to all gates will connect cell 2 only, and the number 11 sent to all gates will connect cell 3 only.   In like manner, for our machine having 10,000 memory cells, gates can be designated that will be opened only by the bit combination corresponding to the binary coding of the decimal identification number of the cell.   Then the binary bits corresponding, for example, to the decimal number 8452, when sent to all memory cell gates, would open only that corresponding to memory cell 8452.   Just as memory cell gates can be controlled by chosen combinations of binary bits, so can the gates for the various arithmetic circuits be controlled by combinations of binary bits.   It is convenient, for example, to have the gates connecting the adder circuits respond to the binary pulses which represent the letter A, the subtractor circuits respond to the binary pulses representing the letter S, and so forth.

2.53   Machine Instructions

As has been stated before, it is not our purpose to become involved in details of computer design.   Enough has been said to indicate how control can be accomplished through the presentation to the gating circuits throughout the machine of binary bit combinations indicating the arithmetic operation to be performed and the memory cells involved.   These may be in binary-coded decimal, or in octal or hexadecimal with the operation denoted by a number, or in other form.   A single such combination of binary bits is termed a "command" or an "instruction."   An instruction must contain those binary bits defining the operation to be performed and the addresses of the memory cells involved.   The actual nature of the instruction will depend on the circuitry used in the control unit.   By the use of complicated circuitry, machines capable of executing very complicated instructions can be constructed. If simpler, more economical circuitry is desired, a machine capable of less complex operations must be accepted.   We will assume that our hypothetical machine has a rather simple control unit, capable of executing only very simple instructions, which are placed in the control unit in binary-coded decimal.   We will not even ask how the control unit works, for all we need to know is what instructions it is capable of executing.   Each instruction for our machine will involve only one operation and one memory location.   Such an instruction is known as a "single address" instruction.

The basic instructions to which our machine will be considered to be able to respond are given below.   The symbol XXXX is considered to be some four digit number from 0000 to 9999.   The commands are

B XXXX: Bring the contents of memory location XXXX into the accumulator. (The contents of location XXXX are not destroyed, but remain unchanged.   The previous contents of the accumulator are destroyed.)

A XXXX: Add the contents of memory location XXXX to the contents of the accumulator, and store the result in the accumulator. (The contents of location XXXX are unaltered, but the previous contents of the accumulator are destroyed.)

S XXXX: Subtract the contents of memory location XXXX from the contents accumulator, and store the result in the accumulator. (The contents of XXXX are unaltered, but the previous contents of the accumulator are destroyed.)

M XXXX: Multiply the contents of the accumulator by the contents of memory location XXXX, and store the result in the accumulator. (The contents of XXXX are unaltered, but the previous contents of the accumulator are destroyed.)

D XXXX: Divide the contents of the accumulator by the contents of memory location XXXX, and store the result in the accumulator. (The contents of XXXX are unaltered, but the previous contents of the accumulator are destroyed.)

C XXXX: Clear the contents of the accumulator into memory location XXXX. (The previous contents of XXXX are destroyed, and the contents of the accumulator are replaced by zeros.)

The above commands will serve as a starting point for the use of the computer. At a later stage it will be found necessary to use some additional ones. They will be defined when needed.

2.54 *Introduction to Programming*

It can be seen that the process of performing calculations with a digital computer is essentially reduced to placing the proper numbers in the memory, having the machine execute the proper sequence of commands, and then extracting the result from the machine. The heart of the problem is the process of writing down the sequence of commands which the machine is to execute. This sequence of commands is known as the "program," and the process of preparing the program is called "programming" or "coding." A few examples of a program will be given. In these examples, it will be assumed that the number a is already stored in memory location 8001, b is in 8002, c is in 8003, and d is in 8004.

Example 1. Find $a + b + c + d$ and store the result in 8005.

SOLUTION: The program is:

B 8001 (brings a into the accumulator)
A 8002 (adds b, giving $a + b$ in the accumulator)
A 8003 (adds c, giving $a + b + c$ in the accumulator)
A 8004 (adds d, giving $a + b + c + d$ in the accumulator)
C 8005 (clears $a + b + c + d$ to 8005)

Example 2. Find $(ac - b)/d$ and store the result in 8156.

SOLUTION: The program is:

   B 8001   (brings a into the accumulator)
   M 8003   (multiplies by c, giving ac in the accumulator)
   S 8002   (subtracts b, giving $ac - b$ in the accumulator)
   D 8004   (divides by d, giving $(ac - b)/d$ in the accumulator)
   C 8156   (clears $(ac - b)/d$ into 8156)

Example 3. Find $ad + bc$ and store the result in 8005.

SOLUTION: The program can begin:

   B 8001   (brings a into the accumulator)
   M 8004   (multiplies by d, giving ad in the accumulator)

At this point we are faced with a problem, since the product bc is not yet available, nor can we multiply b by c without destroying the contents of the accumulator.   In order to preserve the product ad while we compute bc, we must temporarily move ad to some memory cell.   Almost any cell will do. Let us choose 8005.   Then the remaining commands are:

   C 8005   (clears ad into 8005)
   B 8002   (brings b into the accumulator)
   M 8003   (multiplies by c, giving bc in the accumulator)
   A 8005   (adds ad, giving $ad + bc$ in the accumulator)
   C 8005   (clears $ad + bc$ to 8005)

In this problem we used location 8005 for temporary storage of an intermediate result, the product ad.   This product was later destroyed by clearing the final answer into 8005, but this was of no particular concern to us because the quantity was no longer needed.   A memory register was thus used as "working storage."   Notice that, if we had stored ad in location 8002, this would have caused trouble; for it would have destroyed the number b, which was needed later in the problem.   This is a type of programming error that must be scrupulously avoided.

2.55   *Internal Storage of the Program*

We have seen how to prepare a program which can be used to control the machine and cause it to perform the desired calculation.   For the simple problems discussed so far, the programs consisted of only a few instructions. For more complex problems, programs often contain hundreds or even thousands of instructions.   The machine can execute each single instruction in thousandths or even millionths of a second. It would be ridiculous to require the machine to wait for a second or so after each instruction for a human operator to insert a new instruction. This would be time enough for the machine to execute from a thousand to a million more instructions if they were readily available. One of the major strides of computer development was the idea, developed in about 1945, of using memory cells for storage of instructions as well as of numbers. The machine can be wired to begin at memory cell 0000 and read out the contents of that cell into the control unit and execute the instruction, then to read out the contents of 0001 and execute that instruction, and to proceed sequentially through the memory in a similar fashion until ordered to stop.

EXERCISE IV

In the following problems, assume the numbers a, b, c, etc. are already stored in memory cells as indicated:

3150 a	3155 f
3151 b	3156 g
3152 c	3157 h
3153 d	3158 i
3154 e	3159 j

1. Write programs to compute the following quantities and store the result in memory cell 3160.

   a. $bd + f + h$

   b. $cdg - a$

   c. $ae + f/j$

   d. $bf - dh$

   e. $b/j - af + d/h$

   f. $a + ab + abc + abcd + abcde$

   g. $a + b(c + d(e + f(g + h)))$

   h. $(ac - fj)/(bd + gh)$

   i. $\begin{vmatrix} a & b & c \\ d & e & f \\ g & h & i \end{vmatrix}$

2. Write the algebraic expression for the quantity last stored in location 3160 by each of the following programs:

   a.
   ```
   B  3151
   D  3152
   A  3156
   C  3160
   ```

   b.
   ```
   B  3156
   A  3151
   S  3157
   C  3160
   ```

   c.
   ```
   B  3153
   C  3160
   A  3154
   C  3160
   ```

   d.
   ```
   B  3155
   D  3152
   C  3160
   B  3151
   M  3153
   M  3154
   C  3161
   ```

e.	B 3151	f.	B 3154
	C 3152		M 3156
	B 3154		C 3160
	D 3152		C 3160
	C 3160		

g.	B 3153	h.	B 3159
	M 3153		D 3157
	C 3160		C 3160
	S 3155		A 3154
	M 3155		M 3158
	A 3160		D 3157
	C 3160		A 3160
			C 3160

2.56   Handling of Positive and Negative Numbers

In describing the arithmetic instructions in Section 2.53, the descriptions were given as if all numbers involved would always be positive numbers. This, of course, is not the case.   It would be desirable, in fact almost necessary, to have the "add" command capable of adding any two numbers, regardless of sign.   There are several ways in which this can be done.   For example, complements can be used for negative numbers.   For our machine, however, we will assume that the first bit position in each memory cell and in the accumulator and MQ registers is reserved for a sign bit, which will be zero for a positive number and one for a negative number.   When the "add" command is given, the machine gates these sign bits through separate circuits and compares them.   If the sign bits are the same, the machine uses the adder circuits and adds the numbers.   If the sign bits are opposite, the machine uses the subtractor circuits and subtracts the numbers and then affixes the sign of the larger.   The signs for S, M, and D commands are handled in a similar fashion.   In short, we will assume that for our machine all numbers are signed and the commands will automatically take care of the signs during any calculation, so we need no longer concern ourselves with this matter.

2.57   Location of the Binary Point

Also ignored in describing the arithmetic instructions is the problem of location of the binary point during the calculation.   Since the point is not represented by a symbol within the machine, some simple way of keeping track of the proper location of the binary point must be devised.   A simple way to cope with this problem, and a way used in many computers, is to require that the numbers be stored and used in mantissa form, that is, with binary point in front of the first bit position.   This means that all calculations would have to be done utilizing numbers less than one.   This is an inconvenience, but not necessarily an extremely serious one, at least for the simpler types of calculations. The internal operations of the machine are very straightforward. For example, a machine might have room for 36 bits in each memory cell, the accumulator, and the MQ register. The first position would be the sign position and the remaining 35 bits would represent the number itself, with binary point assumed to be in front of these 35 positions. For addition or subtraction, the binary points are always properly aligned, and the corresponding pairs of bits to be added are always in corresponding bit positions in the two numbers involved. For multiplication, the operation is done from the right as in Section 1.55 of Chapter I. For division the process is as illustrated in Section 1.56 of Chapter I. Since the binary point is in front of all 35 bits in both dividend and divisor, the binary point will automatically belong in front of the first bit position in the MQ register as the quotient is built up there. These operations are illustrated in the next section.

2.58 Fixed Point Operations

Arithmetic operations of the type described above, where the binary point is considered to be in a certain fixed position in all registers, are termed "fixed point" operations. The steps the machine goes through in the performance of fixed point arithmetic will be illustrated by examples. For simplicity it will be assumed in the examples that the memory cells have room for only 6 bits, a sign plus five binary positions. These examples are to be taken as typical of the logic involved in fixed point operations, and not as closely resembling actual machine functioning. Many variations of the methods shown here are possible. Positive numbers will be used in these examples. The extra manipulation required to handle the sign will not be shown.

Example 1. Find $a + b$, where $a = .10101$ is stored in 2450, and $b = .01001$ is stored in 2451.

A program which performs this operation is:

    B 2450
    A 2451

The principal parts of the machine involved in this operation are memory cells 2450 and 2451, the accumulator, and the binary adders. The contents of these registers will be followed through the logical steps of the operation.

BEGINNING CONDITION (FIGURE 2–9): a is in 2450, b is in 2451, and the contents of the accumulator are unknown.

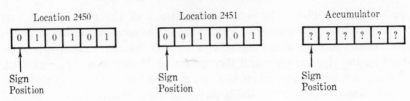

Figure 2–9

STEP 1 (FIGURE 2–10): The command B 2450 moves the contents of *a* to the accumulator, destroying its previous contents.

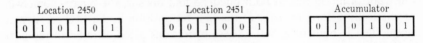

Figure 2–10

STEP 2 (FIGURE 2–11): The command A 2451 starts the binary addition. At this point memory cell 2451, the adder, and the accumulator are the only parts of interest. The low order digits go into the adder, which combines them according to the rules of Table II, Section 1.53, giving a sum digit zero and a carry of 1.

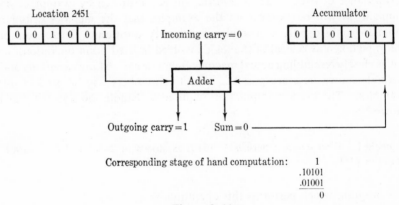

Corresponding stage of hand computation:
```
         1
      .10101
      .01001
      _____
         0
```

Figure 2–11

STEP 3 (FIGURE: 2–12): The low order sum digit zero having been stored back in the accumulator, the next order bits enter a binary adder, with the preceding outgoing carry as the new incoming carry.

STEP 4 (FIGURE 2–13): The sum bit having been stored back in the accumulator, the next order bits enter the adder.

STEP 5 (FIGURE 2–14): The sum bit having been stored back in the accumulator, the next order bits enter the adder.

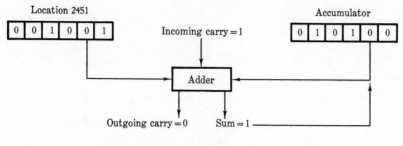

Corresponding stage of hand computation: .10101
            .01001
              10

Figure 2–12

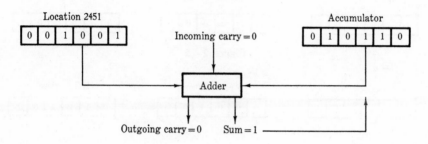

Corresponding stage of hand computation: .10101
            .01001
            110

Figure 2–13

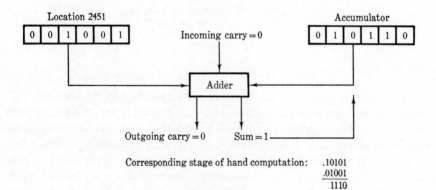

Corresponding stage of hand computation: .10101
            .01001
          1110

Figure 2–14

STEP 6 (FIGURE 2–15): The sum bit having been stored back in the accumulator, the highest order bits enter the adder.

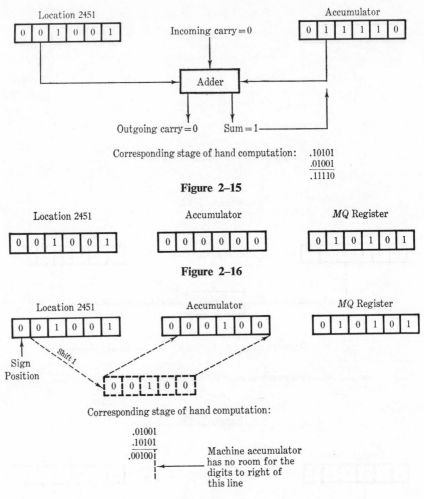

Figure 2–15

Figure 2–16

Figure 2–17

After this last sum is stored, the complete sum is now in the accumulator. Note that there should be no outgoing carry. If there is one, this means that the sum of the numbers being added is greater than one, and such a number cannot be stored in a memory cell in this type of machine. An outgoing carry from the high order addition is called an overflow. The machine can be wired to respond to an overflow pulse in a variety of ways. It can simply stop and flash a light on the control panel, or automatically look in a new memory location for its next instruction.

Example 2. Find ab, where $a = .10101$ is stored in 2450 and $b = .01001$ is stored in 2451.

A suitable program is:

B 2450
M 2451

The beginning condition and the first step, performing B 2450, are as in the previous example. The rest of the procedure will be represented in less detailed steps than were used in the previous example.

STEP 2 (FIGURE 2–16—p. 54): At the command M 2451, the machine first transfers *a* from the accumulator to the MQ register and sets the accumulator register to zero.

STEP 3 (FIGURE 2–17—p. 54): Since there is a one in the high order place of the MQ register, the number in 2451 is brought from memory, shifted to the right one place, and added into the accumulator.

STEP 4 (FIGURE 2–18): Since there is a one in the third order place of the MQ register, the number in 2451 is brought from memory, shifted to the right three places, and added into the accumulator.

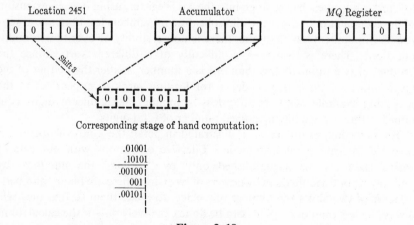

Corresponding stage of hand computation:

$$
\begin{array}{r}
.01001 \\
.10101 \\
\hline
.00100 \\
001 \\
\hline
.00101 \\
\end{array}
$$

Figure 2–18

STEP 5 (FIGURE 2–19): Since there is a one in the fifth order place of the MQ register, the number in 2451 is brought from memory, shifted to the right five places, and added into the accumulator.

The answer in the accumulator is .00101. Step 5 contributed nothing, since the shifting made all of the digits of too low an order to affect the result. When two numbers, each having five binary places, are multiplied, the result

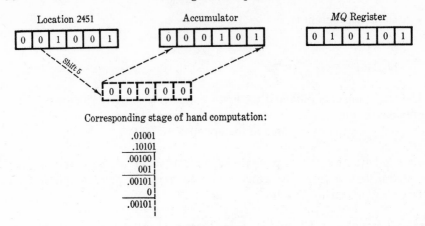

Corresponding stage of hand computation:

```
 .01001
 .10101
 .00100
  001
 .00101
   0
 .00101
```

Figure 2–19

should have ten binary places. Since there is room for only five digits in the accumulator, the five lowest order digits have been lost in the above operation. Most machines allow all ten digits to be kept (and reduce roundoff error) by storing the five lower order bits in the MQ register. To illustrate this procedure, steps 3, 4, and 5, above are repeated in Figure 2–20, allowing the low order bits in each case to go into the MQ register, using it as an extension of the accumulator. Since the multiplication of numbers less than one always results in numbers less than one, there is no possibility of overflow in multiplication. There is, however, a difficulty of a different sort. Since the product of two numbers less than one is a number smaller than either of the given numbers, there is a tendency for leading zeros to appear, as in the preceding example, with resulting loss in number of significant digits contained within a word having a fixed number of total digits.

The preceding examples have illustrated in detail the kinds of operations involved in fixed point arithmetic. Effective operations with numbers of varied sizes can be accomplished only by "scaling" the numbers, by multiplying or dividing them by powers of two (since these are binary numbers, a factor of two shifts the number one place) to make them so that they will always be less than one. This can be done effectively only if the calculations are relatively simple and the numbers to be encountered are rather well known in advance. Otherwise numbers obtained during the calculation may become too large and cause overflow on addition or division, or become too small and contain too few significant figures for sufficient accuracy. While such operations are possible, a great deal of versatility is gained by utilizing floating point rather than fixed point arithmetic. We shall introduce the use of floating point arithmetic on computers in the next section and then henceforth assume all our machine calculations to be performed in that manner.

Step 3:

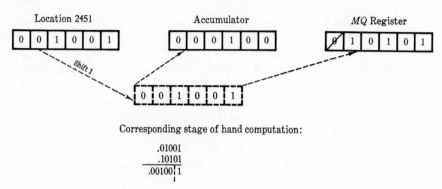

Corresponding stage of hand computation:

.01001
.10101
.00100|1

Step 4:

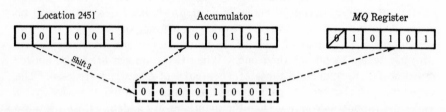

Corresponding stage of hand computation:

.01001
.10101
.00100|1
01|001
.00101|101

Step 5

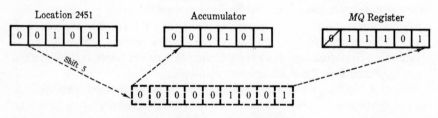

Corresponding stage of hand computation:

.01001
.10101
.00100 |1
01 |001
.00101 |101
|01001
.00101|11101

Figures 2–20

2.59 *Floating Point Arithmetic*

As described in the preceding chapter, in floating point arithmetic each number is represented as a mantissa and an exponent. The mantissa is a number less than one, and the arithmetic operations for mantissas as given in Chapter I are almost identical to those just described for fixed point operations. In fact, a fixed point machine is well suited to handle operations with mantissas, if only there were some automatic way of keeping track of the exponent. There are two principal ways of doing this: one is by use of special program in a machine with the fixed point circuits already described, and the other is by the provision of special circuitry within the machine.

The smaller, less expensive machines usually come equipped with circuitry only for fixed point arithmetic, so if they are to be used for floating point operations a special program must be written. A brief description will be given to show how such a program works. Two memory cells are used for the storage of each number, one for the mantissa and one for the exponent, properly scaled to be less than one. When two numbers are to be added, a series of steps similar to those of Theorem I of Chapter I are used. The exponents are checked for equality, and a mantissa shifted if necessary to make the exponents equal. Then the mantissas are added. If an overflow occurs, the sum mantissa is shifted one place to the left and the exponent increased by one. The other arithmetic operations are perfomed in an analogous fashion. Whenever an overflow on a mantissa occurs, it is handled by shifting and changing the exponent, as just described. Also, mantissas are checked for leading zeros after each operation, and, if there are any, the mantissa is shifted to the left and the exponent decreased. Thus the mantissa at all times is kept in the "normal form" as defined in Section 1.36, and so fills all the bit spaces in a word length. A program to accomplish all these operations is quite complex. To perform a single floating point operation, a whole sequence of fixed point operations must be performed by the machine, many of these being of types we have not yet even discussed. Floating point arithmetic will normally require the machine at least ten times as long as fixed point because of all the extra operations involved.

In larger machines some additional speed in floating point arithmetic is gained by the use of special circuitry. The memory cells are made longer so that more bits may be contained, and part of the cell is used for mantissa and part for exponent. When a "multiply" command is given, the mantissa parts of the numbers are put through the multiplication process, while the exponent parts are simply added. The circuitry takes care of shifting mantissas and changing exponents for all the details of floating point calculation as discussed in Chapter I.

Now that it has been at least indicated how a machine performs floating point arithmetic, an assumption will be made about the idealized computer to be used in the numerical analysis portion of this text. Each memory cell will accommodate a number with mantissa equivalent to eight decimal digits and exponent equivalent to two decimal digits. All arithmetic commands will cause floating point arithmetic to be done, completely and automatically, with the numbers involved. In the further work we will ignore all question as to how, in detail, the machine actually performs these operations and concentrate on the significance of the operations themselves for numerical mathematical analysis.

2.6 INPUT AND OUTPUT UNITS

It has been seen that a computer consisting of memory, arithmetic, and control units can be made to perform the elementary arithmetic operations in an automatic fashion. Some discussion of the input and output units is in order. Since these units perform operations which are peripheral to our major point of interest we will give only a very sketchy discussion of their nature and functions.

2.61 Input Units

Computers are normally equipped with a number of selections of input methods. The most common are typewriter, punched card, punched paper tape, and magnetic tape. The typewriter is the slowest but most direct: electrical connections are so arranged that a word typed on the keyboard can be transferred directly to the accumulator, and then automatically transferred from there to a memory cell. This method is extremely inefficient because the speed of filling the proper information into the memory is governed by the speed of typing—it may require several seconds to type in an instruction which will eventually be executed in a thousandth of a second. Other, faster, means of input are therefore preferred. Usually the numbers and instructions required are typed onto tape or cards utilizing an auxiliary unit, so that the machine can be performing other calculations while the input is being prepared. Then the problem can be read quickly into the memory and the new calculation commenced.

2.62 Output Units

The situation regarding output is similar to that regarding input. Electrical circuits can be arranged whereby the sequence of pulses stored in the accumulator can be made to operate the keys on a typewriter and by this method information can be extracted from the machine after the completion of a calculation. Even an electrical typewriter operates very slowly compared to computer speeds, however, so it is more efficient to have the computer place the information on cards or tape and then to print the information by means of auxiliary equipment. There are occasions, too, when the memory of the computer has insufficient storage capacity for all the numbers or instructions required in a calculation.   In such cases it may be necessary to put some of the intermediate results on tape and then read them back into the machine as required.   This process can be used to greatly increase the effective size of the memory, though with some loss in speed.

2.63   Control of Input and Output

Just as the arithmetic operations of the machine must be controlled, so must the input and output operations be controlled.   In order that the commands and numbers to start the calculations can be placed in the machine, some direct control by the human operator is required.   This is accomplished by a button or buttons on the control panel of the machine.   For example, there can be a button which will cause the numbers available in the input unit, whatever that unit may be, to be automatically transferred to the accumulator.   For most purposes, however, once the initial instructions are stored in the memory it is desirable to have the input and output operations controlled by instructions within the machine just as are the arithmetic instructions.   In order not to become too involved in the details of these operations, we shall introduce two idealized commands for this purpose. The command I 0000 will be assumed to cause the first available word on a prepared input tape to be stored in the accumulator, destroying the previous contents.   The command P 0000 will be assumed to cause the contents of the accumulator to be printed, and will leave the contents of the accumulator unaltered.   These two commands will serve to represent at least symbolically the input and output functions required in programs.   We shall assume that our programs themselves are placed in the memory by manual operations of the human operator but that any numbers required must be placed in memory by instructions within the program itself.

Example 1.   Write a program to find:

$$y = a^2 + ab + b^3$$

A suitable program is

    I   0000   (reads a into accumulator)
    C 1500   (stores a in 1500)
    I   0000   (reads b into accumulator)
    C 1501   (stores b in 1501)
    B 1500   (brings a into accumulator)
    A 1501   (adds b, giving $a + b$ in accumulator)
    M 1500   (multiplies by a, giving $a^2 + ab$ in accumulator)
    C 1502   (stores $a^2 + ab$ in 1502)

B 1501   (brings b into accumulator)
M 1501   (multiplies by b, giving b^2 in accumulator)
M 1501   (multiplies by b, giving b^3 in accumulator)
A 1502   (adds $a^2 + ab$, giving $a^2 + ab + b^3$ in accumulator)
P 0000   (prints $a^2 + ab + b^3$)

To perform the calculation, the machine operator would have to be provided with the two tapes, the first containing the program as listed above, and the second containing the constants a and b in order. For example, if the problem were to be performed for $a = .316, b = 2.73$, the constants tape, in accordance with our assumption that our machine handles eight place floating point numbers, would have the binary equivalents of:

31600000   50

27300000   51

On the other hand, if the calculation were to be performed with $a = 46.2$, $b = .03516$, the same program tape would be required, but the constants tape would have the binary equivalents of:

46200000   52

35160000   49

The procedure employed by the machine operator would be as follows: he would use control buttons on the machine to cause the program to read into the memory, and then again use control buttons on the machine to cause it to start executing the first instruction. Then the machine would automatically proceed through the list of instructions, executing them in order. The first instruction would cause the number a to enter the accumulator. The next would store a in memory cell 1500. The third would cause b, the next number on the input tape, to enter the accumulator, and so forth.

Example 2. Write a program to find:

$$x = a + ab \qquad \text{and} \qquad y = a + a^2 b^2$$

A suitable program is:

I 0000   (reads input tape, a into accumulator)
C 2100   (stores a in 2100)
I 0000   (reads b into accumulator)
C 2101   (stores b in 2101)

B   2100   (brings *a* into accumulator)
M   2101   (multiplies by *b*, giving *ab* in accumulator)
C   2102   (stores *ab* in 2102)
B   2102   (brings *ab* again to accumulator)
A   2100   (adds *a*, giving $a + ab$ in accumulator)
P   0000   (prints $x = a + ab$)
B   2102   (brings *ab* to accumulator)
M   2102   (multiplies by *ab*, giving a^2b^2 in accumulator)
A   2100   (adds *a*, giving $a + a^2b^2$ in accumulator)
P   0000   (prints $y = a + a^2b^2$)

This program also requires an input tape with *a* and *b* in sequence.

2.64   Input of Constants

In the two examples in the preceding section we referred to an input tape, which must be prepared in order that the command "I 0000" can be used to store away the numbers needed in the calculation. As noted in the examples, since our machine is assumed to perform its arithmetic in binary, these numbers would need to be on the input tape in binary form, unless the machine can automatically perform a conversion of a decimal input to a binary number for storage. As was seen in Chapter I, this conversion is a complicated one, which cannot be performed automatically by any very simple electrical circuit; it would thus not be fair to assume that our simple machine would make this conversion automatically. The most we can expect the machine to do automatically is make one of the easy conversions, as octal to binary or hexadecimal to binary. On the other hand, so that we will not become bogged down in the process of changing numbers from one system to another, we will give our input and output numbers only in floating decimal form in this text. In Chapter IV we shall obtain some understanding of how the machine can be made to perform the decimal to binary and binary to decimal conversion.

EXERCISE V

1. Write programs to input the necessary constants, to perform the calculations indicated, and print the results. Write the corresponding constants tapes (decimal) for $a = 2.6$, $b = .0351$, $c = 39.617$, $d = 9999.93$:

> a. $ab + cd$ d. $4(a + b)^2$
> b. $(ab + c)/d$ e. $a + 3(b + 2c)$
> c. $a + 2b + 3c$ f. $4a/b + 5c/d$

2. Write constants tapes for the calculations of Problem 1 for the case $a = 1$, $b = 2$, $c = 3$, $d = 4$. Calculate the results the machine should obtain with these inputs.

CHAPTER III *Accuracy in Numerical Calculations*

3.1 INTRODUCTION

We have just learned the basic facts about computers and the first steps of computer programming. At this point there is a strong temptation to plunge more deeply into the art of programming, to learn to write programs which will perform calculations far more difficult than the very simple ones described in the preceding chapter. It is probably better, however, to take time out at this very early stage to face up to one very serious problem associated with performing calculations on computers, one which is all too often neglected in everyday computer operations—the problem of accuracy in numerical calculations. When we set out to perform a calculation for some practical purpose, we usually start with numbers representing such quantities as length, weight, etc. These numbers are not ordinarily exact values, but instead are only approximations true to two, three, or more figures. It is possible in a complex machine program to do hundreds or even thousands of additions, subtractions, multiplications, and divisions with these inexact numbers, and it is also possible for the results to become succeedingly less and less exact, until the final results may be completely meaningless. Examples will be given later which will show that, in our hypothetical computer of the preceding chapter, in which computer all numbers are stored with eight significant digits, it is possible to obtain completely meaningless results after a relatively short and simple calculation. Such extreme cases are not common; however, the person who trusts the result of a computer calculation without some careful check for accuracy is running a grave risk. Therefore we shall cover the fundamental principles associated with accuracy in this chapter, and the problem of accuracy will be one of the major concerns throughout the remainder of this book. In order to remain on familiar ground as much as possible, the discussions will be given in terms of the decimal number system. The considerations are applicable in principle to other numbers systems as well.

63

3.2 APPROXIMATE NUMBERS

In the discussion of accuracy in calculations it is useful to make distinction between numbers that are exact and those that are only approximate values. Exact numbers are numbers whose values are completely represented by a symbol. All of the integers, for example, 1, 5, 179, are of this type. Fractions can be expressed exactly as the ratio of two integers, e.g., 1/2, 2/3, etc. Many other numbers can also be expressed completely by a symbol, for example, π, $\sqrt{2}$, e. All of the numbers mentioned have an exact meaning. Not all, however, can be exactly represented in the decimal system (or in any other place value number system, be it binary, octal, or any other.) For example, the decimal representation of 2/3 is .666666..., a decimal point followed by an infinite number of sixes. Since it is impossible to write an infinite number of sixes, it is impossible to write the number 2/3 exactly in the decimal system. We may write a number which is *approximately* 2/3, such as .6667, or, if we desire a closer approximation, .66666667. Likewise, we may write an approximate value for π, for example, 3.1416, but we cannot write the exact value. We shall term a decimal (or binary, or other number system) number an approximate number if it is used as a representation of some number it does not quite equal.

3.3 ABSOLUTE, RELATIVE, AND PERCENTAGE ERROR

The numerical difference between the true value of a quantity and the approximate number used to represent it is called the absolute error. The absolute error will ordinarily be regarded as positive if the approximate number is greater than the exact, and negative if the reverse is true. The relative error is the absolute error divided by the true value of the quantity. The percentage error is 100 times the relative error. For example, if Q is the true value of a number, and Q_1 the approximate number used to represent it, then:

$Q_1 - Q$ = absolute error of the approximate number,

$(Q_1 - Q)/Q$ = relative error of the approximate number, and

$100(Q_1 - Q)/Q$ = percentage error of the approximate number.

In nearly all cases, we will find that we use an approximate number Q_1 either:

(*1*) because we cannot write the exact number as a decimal number (as for π, 2/3, etc.), or

(*2*) because we simply do not know the value of the exact number (as when we have measured something with a rule, or scale, etc.)

In such cases, the error $Q_1 - Q$ cannot be written exactly in decimal form either; for if it could we could simply subtract it from the approximate number Q_1 to obtain the exact value Q. Our primary concern, however, will be how well or how poorly the approximate number describes the exact number. For this purpose, we would like to know the maximum possible size of the error. For practical purposes, then, it is better to speak not of the absolute error but of the upper limit on the magnitude of the absolute error. Let ΔQ be a number such that:

$$|Q_1 - Q| \leqslant \Delta Q$$

Then ΔQ is an upper limit on the magnitude of the absolute error. In the future we will frequently somewhat loosely refer to such an *upper limit* on the *magnitude* of the absolute error as *the* absolute error.

If we have an approximate number Q_1 and a value ΔQ for the absolute error, we would like to be able to find an upper limit for the relative error. By the definition above, we can say that:

$$\text{magnitude of relative error} = |(Q_1 - Q)/Q|$$
$$\leqslant |\Delta Q/Q| = \Delta Q/|Q|$$

Thus $|\Delta Q/Q|$ is an upper limit for the relative error. However, since we do not know the value of Q, the exact number, this formula is not of much use. We need a formula in terms of ΔQ and Q_1. We can write:

$$|Q| = |Q_1 - (Q_1 - Q)| \geqslant |Q_1| - |Q_1 - Q| \geqslant |Q_1| - \Delta Q$$

Hence $$|\Delta Q/Q| \leqslant \Delta Q/(|Q_1| - \Delta Q)$$

Thus if Q_1 is known, and an upper limit ΔQ on the absolute error is known, the quantity $\Delta Q/(|Q_1| - \Delta Q)$ can be calculated to give an upper limit on the magnitude of the relative error. In the future, we will frequently somewhat loosely refer to such an *upper limit* on the *magnitude* of the relative error as *the* relative error. If ΔQ is known to be small compared to $|Q_1|$, then the limit given above for the relative error is approximately $\Delta Q/|Q_1|$.

3.4 SIGNIFICANT FIGURES

In the decimal representation of a number, a significant figure is any one of the digits 1, 2, 3, ... , 9; and 0 is a significant figure except when it is used to fix the decimal point or fill the place of unknown or discarded digits. Thus in the number 0.0158, the significant figures are 1, 5, and 8. The zeros do nothing but fix the decimal point and hence are not significant. The number could just as well be represented as 1.58×10^{-2}. The number 4076 has four significant figures, the zero not being used in this number to fix the decimal point. In the number 38500, there is nothing to show whether the zeros are significant or whether they are simply for the purpose of fixing the decimal point. This ambiguity can be removed by writing the number as 3.85×10^4, if none of the zeros is significant, or 3.850×10^4 if one is significant, or 3.8500×10^4 if both are significant. Within our idealized computer, we have assumed that all numbers are recorded with eight significant figures.

3.41   Rounding of Numbers

If we attempt to represent the fraction 4/7 in decimal form, we obtain 57014285..., a nonterminating decimal. For purposes of practical computation this must be represented by an approximate number, such as .57, or .5701, or .570143, etc. The approximate number is obtained by dropping off certain of the lower order digits in the number, a process known as rounding off. An error is of course introduced in rounding off, and it is desirable to make this error be as small as possible. By using a proper method of rounding, it is always possible to make the absolute error no greater than half a unit in the last place retained. This is done by increasing by one the last digit kept if the discarded part is greater than half a unit in that digit position. If the discarded part is exactly one-half a unit in the last place kept, it is best to increase the last kept digit by one sometimes, and not other times, so that if several roundoffs are made during the problem, all will not introduce errors in the same direction. A simple way to do this is always to round the last kept digit to an even number when the discarded part is exactly half a unit in the last kept place.

Example 1.   Round the following numbers to the two decimal places:

	The answers are
46.12416	46.12
31.34792	31.35
52.27500	52.28
2.38500	2.38
2.38501	2.39

In the majority of calculations, the relative error is of more direct interest than the absolute error. It will be shown shortly that the relative error is closely associated with the number of correct significant figures. Hence it is frequently of interest to round off to some particular number of significant figures. The rule for doing this can be stated as follows:

To round off a number to n significant digits, discard all digits to the right of the nth significant digit. If the number discarded is less than half a unit in the nth place, leave the nth digit unchanged; if the number discarded is greater than half a unit in the nth place, increase the nth digit by one; if the number discarded is exactly half a unit in the *n*th place, leave the *n*th digit unaltered if it is an even number, but increase it by one if it is an odd number.

Example 2. Round off the following numbers to four significant figures:

	The answers are
316.8972	316.9
4.167500	4.168
.0011118	.001112
19.265001	19.27

3.42   Correct Significant Digits

When an approximate number is used to represent an exact one, it is of interest to know how many of the digits in the approximate number have meaning in the description of the exact number.   For example, one number which is approximately equal to 2/3 is .66667.   Another is .66699842593. Although the second number has many more significant digits, it is actually a worse representation than the first.   Many of the digits in the second number contribute nothing toward helping that number represent the fraction 2/3. Only the first few digits are of assistance in this representation.   We will call a significant digit in an approximate number "correct" if rounding the approximate number off to just after that digit position will cause the absolute error to be no more than half a unit in that digit position.   In the first representation of the fraction 2/3, above, all five of the significant digits are correct.   In the second, only the first three are correct.   In hand calculations, we usually try to write only the correct significant digits in writing an approximate number. The computer, on the other hand, will customarily carry all numbers to eight significant digits, whether these are correct or not.

3.43   Relative Error and Correct Significant Digits

It was mentioned earlier that the relative error of an approximate number was closely related to the number of correct significant digits.   If we know the number of correct significant digits in a given, approximate number we can calculate an upper limit for the relative error; vice versa, if we have an upper limit on the relative error for a given, approximate number we can determine something about the number of correct significant digits.   We shall consider each of these cases separately.

First consider the problem of estimating the relative error when the number of correct significant digits is known.   An example will make the process clear.

Example 1.   The number 34.152 is an approximate number, known to be correct to five significant digits.   Determine an upper limit for the relative error.

From the definition of correct significant digit, we know that the absolute error is no more than half a unit in the digit position of the lowest order correct significant digit, so in this case:

$$\Delta Q \leqslant .0005$$

Hence, from Section 3.3:

$$\text{relative error} = \frac{\Delta Q}{|Q_1| - \Delta Q} = \frac{.0005}{34.152 - .0005}$$

$$= \frac{.5}{34152 - .5} = \frac{1}{68304 - 1} = \frac{1}{68,303}$$

The process just demonstrated, while correct, is somewhat cumbersome. In addition, since the result is only an estimate of the relative error anyhow, there is some question as to the value of having such a careful determination. For example, for practical purposes we would probably be just as well off if, instead of knowing the relative error were less than one part in 68,303, we knew only that it were less than one part in 68,000, or even, say, only that it were less than one part in 10,000. To be sure:

$$\frac{1}{68,303} < \frac{1}{10,000}$$

so the first bit of knowledge is more complete than the last, but the extra knowledge may be of little practical value. Consequently it is worth asking ourselves whether or not there are easier methods of estimating the relative error, methods which may give cruder but still useful estimates. One such method is given by the following theorem:

Theorem I. *If the first significant digit in a number is K, and if the number is correct to* n *significant figures, then the relative error is less than or equal to* $1/(K \times 10^{n-1})$. *Equality occurs only in the trivial case in which* $n = 1$ *and* $K = 1$.

PROOF: Consider first the case in which the decimal point is just after the last correct significant digit. Let Q be the exact value of the number and ΔQ the absolute error. Then, by our definition of correct significant figures, ΔQ can be no greater than .5 in absolute value. The approximate number with n correct significant figures and K as the first figure must be at least equal to K followed by $n - 1$ zeros, or $K \times 10^{n-1}$. The number $|Q|$ might be smaller than this by the amount ΔQ, or by, at the most, .5. Hence $|Q|$ is at least $K \times 10^{n-1} - .5$. We now know that:

$$\Delta Q \leqslant .5$$

$$|Q| \geqslant K \times 10^{n-1} - .5$$

We are interested in the ratio $\Delta Q / |Q|$, or in the maximum value it could have. If we write a fraction whose numerator is as large as or larger than ΔQ and whose denominator is as small as or smaller than $|Q|$, then that fraction will have a value as large as or larger than $\Delta Q / |Q|$. Hence, from the above inequalities, we can state that:

$$\frac{\Delta Q}{|Q|} \leqslant \frac{.5}{K \times 10^{n-1} - .5}$$

or, multiplying both numerator and denominator by two:

$$\frac{\Delta Q}{|Q|} \leqslant \frac{1}{2K \times 10^{n-1} - 1}$$

Remembering that n is a positive integer and that K stands for any of the digits from 1 to 9 inclusive, we can show that $2K \times 10^{n-1} - 1$ is greater than $K \times 10^{n-1}$ in all cases except when $K = 1$ and $n = 1$, and then the two expressions are equal. The difference between the two expressions is:

$$2K \times 10^{n-1} - 1 - K \times 10^{n-1} = K \times 10^{n-1} - 1$$

which is equal to zero when K and $n = 1$, and greater than zero otherwise. Hence:

$$2K \times 10^{n-1} - 1 \geqslant K \times 10^{n-1}$$

and:

$$\frac{\Delta Q}{|Q|} \leqslant \frac{1}{K \times 10^{n-1}}$$

the equals sign applying only when $K = 1$, $n = 1$.

We have proved the theorem for the case in which the number has the decimal point following the last correct significant digit. To complete the proof, we note that the value of the relative error is unaffected by location of the decimal point. If we move the decimal point by m places (consider a positive value of m to indicate moving the point to the right and a negative value to indicate moving to the left) the effect is to multiply both $|Q|$ and ΔQ by 10^m, and leave the value of the relative error unchanged.

Example 2.   Find an upper limit on the relative error in the following numbers, assuming all the significant figures to be correct:

$$\text{a.}\quad 936.71$$
$$\text{b.}\quad 1.000$$

For part a, $n = 5$ and $K = 9$; hence the relative error is less than $1/9 \times 10^4$. For part b, $n = 4$ and $K = 1$; hence the relative error is less than $1/10^3$.

Some slightly stronger statements concerning the relative error can be made for special classes of numbers.   We shall state two of these as corollaries, leaving the proof to the reader.

Corollary 1.   Except in the case in which $K = 1$ and all the remaining significant digits zero, the relative error is less than $1/(2K \times 10^{n-1})$.

Corollary 2.   If $K \geqslant 5$, then except for the case in which all the remaining significant digits are zero, the relative error is less than $1/10^n$.

Application of Corollary 2 to part a of Example 2 shows that the relative error is less than $1/10^5$.   Application of Corollary 1 gives a limit on the relative error of $1/(1.8 \times 10^5)$.   Since the true number in that case is between 936.705 and 936.715, the closest limit we can give for the error is:

$$\frac{\Delta Q}{|Q|} \leqslant \frac{.005}{936.705} = \frac{1}{187,341}$$

Corollary 1 gave a limit almost as good as this one, but not quite.

The corollaries do not apply to part b of Example 2.

Let us now concern ourselves with the converse to the question we have just been studying—namely, if we have a number and an upper limit on its relative error, what can we say about the number of correct significant digits in its decimal representation.   Again, the basic method for answering such a question can be illustrated by an example:

Example 3.   The number 31.546824 is known to have a relative error no worse than one part in 100,000.   How many of the digits are known to be correct?

In this case we know that:

$$\frac{\Delta Q}{|Q|} \leqslant \frac{1}{100,000}$$

or

$$\Delta Q \leqslant \frac{1}{100,000} |Q|$$

We would like to know ΔQ. We do not know Q, but we do know Q_1, and we know that:

$$|Q| \leqslant |Q_1| + \Delta Q$$

Hence we can say:

$$\Delta Q \leqslant \frac{1}{100,000} (|Q_1| + \Delta Q)$$

or

$$\Delta Q \leqslant .00031546824 + \frac{1}{100,000} \Delta Q$$

or

$$\frac{99999}{100,000} \Delta Q \leqslant .00031546824$$

or

$$\Delta Q \leqslant .00032$$

Since ΔQ is less than half a unit in the thousandths place, the significant digit in the thousandths place (the digit 6) is correct, so the number has at least 5 correct significant digits.

As in the converse problem discussed previously, it would be helpful to have a less cumbersome method of estimating the number of correct significant digits when the relative error is known. One such method is given by the following theorem:

Theorem II. *If the relative error in an approximate number is less than $1/10^n$, where $n > 1$, then the number is correct to at least $n - 1$ significant digits.*

PROOF: Since the relative error is independent of the location of the decimal point, let us make the proof for the case in which the decimal point follows the first digit, that is to say:

$$1 \leqslant |Q_1| < 10 \tag{3-1}$$

Since:

$$\Delta Q/|Q| < 1/10^n \tag{3-2}$$

then:

$$\Delta Q < \frac{|Q|}{10^n} \leqslant \frac{|Q_1| + \Delta Q}{10^n} \tag{3-3}$$

Hence:

$$\Delta Q(10^n - 1) \leqslant |Q_1| < 10 \qquad \textbf{(3-4)}$$

or

$$\Delta Q < \frac{10}{10^n - 1} \qquad \textbf{(3-5)}$$

Now since $n > 1$, then surely:

$$\Delta Q < 1 \qquad \textbf{(3-6)}$$

Using this estimate in the right hand side of step (3–3), above, we can now say:

$$\Delta Q < \frac{11}{10^n} < \frac{50}{10^n} = .5 \times 10^{2-n} \qquad \textbf{(3-7)}$$

Thus the absolute error is less than half a unit in the $(n-2)$th place behind the decimal point, so that the number has one correct digit before the decimal point and $n-2$ correct significant digits after the decimal point, or a total of $n-1$ correct significant digits.

A stronger statement is the following:

Corollary 3. If the relative error is not greater than $1/(2 \times 10^n)$, the number is correct to n significant figures.

Example 4. The following numbers are listed with known limits on relative error. Round them so as to keep only the digits known to be correct.

	Number	Relative Error Less Than
(a)	4675.2179	$1/10^6$
(b)	3.6192815	$1/(2 \times 10^4)$

In (a), Theorem II applies directly. Five digits are known to be correct, and the number is to be rounded to 4675.2. In (b), Corollary 3 applies, so there are four correct significant digits. The number is to be rounded to 3.619.

EXERCISE VI

1. Round the following numbers to five significant digits:

a.	762.186	d.	.9999999
b.	9.23196	e.	192765001.
c.	.0189955	f.	3461.4612

2. Assuming all significant digits are correct, find the upper limit on the relative error by means of Theorem I or Corollary 1 or 2, whichever gives the smallest value:

a. 3728.14   c. 1.000

b. 614.2   d. 70.0

3. The following numbers are listed with known limits on relative error. Round them so as to keep only digits known to be correct, using Theorem II or Corollary 3:

a. 6.17926 10^{-4}

b. 576.8901 $1/(2 \times 10^6)$

c. .4912634 $1/(2 \times 10^4)$

d. .0499999 $1/(2 \times 10^3)$

e. .0006814269 10^{-4}

3.5 ACCUMULATION OF ERRORS IN ARITHMETIC

If two approximate numbers are added, multiplied, or otherwise combined, the result is again an approximate number. If estimates of the errors in the original numbers are available, it is possible to make an estimate of the error in the result. We shall consider this problem for both the absolute error and the relative error, for each of the fundamental operations of arithmetic. For these discussions, the numbers involved will be positive. The slight additional complication introduced by the use of signed numbers is left for the reader's investigation.

3.51   *Error Accumulation in Addition*

Let u_1 and u_2 be two approximate numbers, and Δu_1 and Δu_2 be the absolute values of their errors. Then the true values are no larger than $u_1 + \Delta u_1$, $u_2 + \Delta u_2$, and no smaller than $u_1 - \Delta u_1$, and $u_2 - \Delta u_2$. Hence the true sum is no larger than:

$$u_1 + \Delta u_1 + u_2 + \Delta u_2$$

and no smaller than:

$$u_1 - \Delta u_1 + u_2 - \Delta u_2$$

The sum of the approximate numbers is $u_1 + u_2$. Hence the absolute error of the sum is no greater than $\Delta u_1 + \Delta u_2$. From this absolute error an upper limit on the relative error is, according to Section 3.3:

$$\frac{\Delta u_1 + \Delta u_2}{u_1 + u_2 - \Delta u_1 - \Delta u_2}$$

It can be shown that the error as given by this relation is no more than the relative error of the least accurate of the two numbers. On the other hand, it is no less than the relative error of the most accurate number. These results can be extended to addition of several numbers, and we state the general result as a theorem:

Theorem III. *In the addition of approximate, positive numbers, the absolute error is the sum of their absolute errors, and the relative error is intermediate between the greatest and least of their relative errors.*

Example 1. Find the sum of the approximate numbers 467.6, 571.32, and 3.11918, each being correct to its last figure but no further.

Consider first our hypothetical digital computer doing this operation in floating point. A suitable program would be

```
I   0000
C   1000
I   0000
C   1001
I   0000
C   1002
B   1000
A   1001
A   1002
P   0000
```

The input tape would have the three numbers in order in floating point form, as follows:

```
46760000    53
57132000    53
31191800    51
```

The first add command would add the first two numbers, giving:

```
10389200    54
```

in the accumulator. In performing the next addition, the third number is first shifted to give it an exponent of 54. The last digit of the mantissa is lost since only eight digit mantissas are carried (we will assume the number is *not* rounded in the last place by the machine). Hence the number added to the above result is 00031191   54, giving as a final answer

```
10420391    54
```

or, writing with decimal point:

1042.0391

Since the absolute errors in the given numbers are .05, .005, and .000005 (half a unit in the last correct significant figure), the last three digits in the answer are worthless, and even the zero after the decimal point may be in error, because the absolute error is now .055005, or slightly greater than .05.

If the above calculation were to be performed by hand, one would take into account the fact that one of the numbers is known to only one decimal place and round the other numbers to two places before even commencing the calculation. The calculation would be:

$$
\begin{array}{r}
467.6 \\
571.32 \\
3.12 \\
\hline
1042.04
\end{array}
$$

By retaining two decimals in the more accurate numbers we eliminate the errors inherent in these numbers and thus reduce the error of the sum to that of the least accurate figure. In the final result, however, the last place is in error and the next to last place may be off by one unit.

3.52 *Error Accumulation in Subtraction*

Again, let u_1 and u_2 be two approximate numbers, and Δu_1 and Δu_2 be the absolute values of their absolute errors. Let us assume $u_1 > u_2$, and we desire the value of $u_1 - u_2$. The true value of the first number may be as large as $u_1 + \Delta u_1$, and that of the small one may be as small as $u_2 - \Delta u_2$. In this case the true difference could be as large as:

$$u_1 + \Delta u_1 - (u_2 - \Delta u_2), \quad \text{or} \quad u_1 - u_2 + \Delta u_1 + \Delta u_2$$

On the other hand, the true value of the first number could be as small as $u_1 - \Delta u_1$ and the second as large as $u_2 + \Delta u_2$. In this case the true difference might be as small as:

$$u_1 - \Delta u_1 - (u_2 + \Delta u_2), \quad \text{or} \quad u_1 - u_2 - (\Delta u_1 + \Delta u_2)$$

Thus we see that the true difference may be higher or lower than the approximate difference $u_1 - u_2$ by as much as $\Delta u_1 + \Delta u_2$. Thus the absolute error of the difference must be taken as $\Delta u_1 + \Delta u_2$. From this absolute error the relative error can be estimated from Section 3.42 as:

$$\frac{\Delta u_1 + \Delta u_2}{u_1 - u_2 - \Delta u_1 - \Delta u_2} \tag{3-8}$$

If u_1 and u_2 have nearly equal value, this expression for the relative error may give quite a sizable number.   In fact, it is possible for the denominator in the above expression to be smaller than the numerator, indicating a relative error greater than one.   This means the absolute error is larger than the number itself, so that the result of the subtraction is a meaningless number, one with no significant figures!   Examples of this occurrence will be given shortly.   First we summarize the situation concerning error accumulation during subtraction in a theorem.

Theorem IV.   *In the subraction of approximate, positive numbers, the absolute error is the sum of their absolute errors, and the relative error is given by* (3–8) *above.   The relative error may be so great as to render the result useless.*

As a first example of subtraction, we take one in which the errors do not become excessive.

Example 1.   Subtract 37.68151 from 754.8, where each number is approximate, and correct only to its last digit.

The calculation could be done by machine with the following program:

```
I  0000
C  0500
I  0000
S  0500
P  0000
```

The required input tape has the two numbers in order, as follows:

```
37681510    52
75480000    53
```

On the subtraction command the first number is shifted to make the exponents equal, giving:

```
03768151    53
```

The subtraction is then performed, giving:

```
71711849    53
```

In standard decimal form, the result is:

717.11849

Since one of the original numbers was accurate only to one decimal place, the result is not accurate to more than one decimal place.

If the calculation were to be done by hand, one would first round off the subtrahend to one decimal place, giving 37.7. There is no point in adding zeros after the 8 in 754.8 and carrying the calculation to more places, for the added places would be meaningless. Thus the hand calculation to the best possible accuracy, would be:

$$
\begin{array}{r}
754.8 \\
-\ 37.7 \\
\hline
717.1
\end{array}
$$

From the preceding example it is clear that the result in subtraction is accurate to about the same number of decimal places as the numbers being subtracted. The accuracy problem arises when the numbers are nearly equal, so that leading zeros are introduced in the process.

Example 2. Subtract 938.67814 from 938.67827, each number being accurate to the number of places given.

This problem can be solved by the machine program of Example 1. In this case, however, the input tape has the numbers:

93867814	53
93867827	53

On the subtract command, the machine subtracts the first from the second, obtaining:

00000013	53

and immediately shifts to remove the leading zeros, giving:

13000000	47

In some machines, instead of filling zeros in the lower six positions, contents from the upper digit position of the MQ register are shifted into the accumulator, so that numbers other than zero might appear in these locations. It does not matter because the result has only two significant digits anyway.

If this result is then to be combined with other numbers, the fact that it is accurate to only two figures may be a major influence in determination of the accuracy of the final result.   This problem of accuracy in subtraction is the most important accuracy consideration in many problems.

The loss of the leading significant figures in the subtraction of two nearly equal numbers is the greatest source of inaccuracy in most calculations, and forms the weakest link in a chain computation where it occurs.   Floating point arithmetic offers little or no protection against this form of accuracy loss.   Wherever it may occur, special programming precautions must be taken to avoid the difficulty or at least to make the programmer aware that a dangerous point in the calculation has arisen.

Further to illustrate how this loss of accuracy can jeopardize the results of a calculation, another example will be given, this time of an extreme case where all significant digits are lost.

Example 3.   Compute $a^2 - b^2 - c$, where:

$$a = 1.00020000$$
$$b = 1.00010000$$
$$c = 0.00020001$$

An apparently suitable routine would be

    I   0000
    C   0500
    I   0000
    C   0501
    I   0000
    C   0502
    B   0501
    M   0501
    C   0501
    B   0500
    M   0500
    S   0501
    S   0502
    P   0000

The input tape would contain the numbers:

    10002000   51
    10001000   51
    20001000   47

The instructions first square b, obtaining, for the eight-digit mantissa and exponent:

10002000   51

then a^2 is formed in like manner, giving:

10004000   51

The difference is:

00002000   51

which is immediately shifted to become:

20000000   47

When c is subtracted, the result is:

−00001000   47

which is then shifted to give:

−10000000   43

If the calculation is done by hand, carrying all significant digits, we have:

$$a^2 = 1.00040004$$
$$b^2 = 1.00020001$$
$$a^2 - b^2 = 0.00020003$$
$$a^2 - b^2 - c = 0.00000002$$

or, in floating decimal form:

20000000   43

The machine result was off by a factor of two and had the wrong sign!

Later examples will illustrate more natural ways in which this type of difficulty can arise.

3.54   Error Accumulation in Multiplication

Let u_1 and u_2 be two approximate numbers to be multiplied and let Δu_1 and Δu_2 be upper limits on the absolute value of their absolute errors.   Then the true values might be as great as $u_1 + \Delta u_1$ and $u_2 + \Delta u_2$, so that the true value of the product might be as large as:

$$(u_1 + \Delta u_1)(u_2 + \Delta u_2) = u_1 u_2 + u_1 \Delta u_2 + u_2 \Delta u_1 + \Delta u_1 \Delta u_2$$

On the other hand, the true values might be as small as $u_1 - \Delta u_1$ and $u_2 - \Delta u_2$, in which case the true value of the product might be as small as:

$$(u_1 - \Delta u_1)(u_2 - \Delta u_2) = u_1 u_2 - u_1 \Delta u_2 - u_2 \Delta u_1 + \Delta u_1 \Delta u_2$$

We notice a curious thing about the true product. It can be farther on the high side of the approximate product $u_1 u_2$ than it can be on the low side. Since the term $\Delta u_1 \Delta u_2$ has a positive sign in both of the above expressions, it contributes to the error portion of the first expression but detracts from it in the second. It is customary to simplify both of the expressions above by assuming that the errors in the original numbers are small compared to the numbers themselves. That is to say, $\Delta u_1/u_1$ and $\Delta u_2/u_2$ are small compared to one. If that is the case, then the term $\Delta u_1 \Delta u_2$ is so small in the above expressions it can be neglected. If this is done, the absolute error of the product becomes $u_1 \Delta u_2 + u_2 \Delta u_1$. The relative error, according to the formula of Section 3.42, is approximately:

$$\frac{u_1 \Delta u_2 + u_2 \Delta u_1}{u_1 u_2} = \frac{\Delta u_2}{u_2} + \frac{\Delta u_1}{u_1}$$

or, is roughly the sum of the relative errors of the numbers being multiplied. This rule can be extended to the product of several numbers, and provides the simplest method of evaluating errors of products. The rule can be stated as follows:

Theorem V. *The relative error of a product of* n *approximate numbers is the sum of the relative errors of the separate numbers. The absolute error, if desired, can be found by multiplying the relative error by the product.*

Example 1. Find the product of 369.7 and .0042131, assuming each of the numbers accurate to the number of significant figures given.

The calculation will be done by machine program. A suitable program would be:

```
I   0000
C   8000
I   0000
M   8000
P   0000
```

The input tape would contain the two numbers in the form:

```
36970000    53
42131000    48
```

The multiply command would cause the machine to perform binary multiplication of the mantissas outlined in Example 2, Section 2.57. In decimal equivalent, the operation would give the sixteen figure mantissa .1557583070000000. Only the first eight digits will be kept, so that the result in the accumulator, including exponent, will be:

```
15575830    51
```

Some machines round off the last place in the accumulator. Others do not. Even if the rounding occurs, it is in a binary bit position, so that the last decimal digit will be somewhat uncertain anyhow. From Theorem I, the relative error in the first of the two numbers being multiplied is $1/3 \times 10^3$, and that in the second number is $1/4 \times 10^4$. By Theorem V, the relative error of the product is about $1/3 \times 10^3 + 1/4 \times 10^4$, or, since the latter of these two errors is much less than the first, about $1/3 \times 10^3$, or 5 parts in 15,000. Hence the final answer above may be in error by five units in its fifth significant digit. The first three significant digits are correct, and the fourth might possibly be wrong by one unit.

The accuracy estimate in the above case suggests a rule which can be applied to multiplication problems. That is, that *the number of correct digits in the product is roughly equal to the number of correct significant digits contained in the least accurate of the figures being multiplied.* If two numbers, each having n significant digits, are multiplied, the product has $2n$ significant digits. However, Theorem V and the above statement indicate that not more than n of these can be expected to be correct. Half of the digits in the product are worthless.

It might be noted that, if ten numbers having the same number of correct significant digits are multiplied together, the product will have a relative error ten times that of the original numbers, i.e., will have about one less significant digit. Thus, as a rule of thumb, ten multiplications in numbers of equal accuracy will cost one significant digit in accuracy. If the individual numbers have errors in opposite directions, the accuracy in the product will not be as poor as indicated by this rule. If, on the other hand, a number is being raised to a power, the error in each multiplication *is* in the same direction and the worst case occurs. Thus we expect to lose one place accuracy in raising a number to the tenth power, two places in raising to the one hundredth power, etc.

3.55 Error Accumulation in Division

Again, let u_1 and u_2 be approximate numbers, and Δu_1 and Δu_2 be the upper limits on the absolute values of their absolute errors. The largest possible true value of the quotient is:

$$\frac{u_1 + \Delta u_1}{u_2 - \Delta u_2}$$

and the smallest possible value is:

$$\frac{u_1 - \Delta u_1}{u_2 + \Delta u_2}$$

If in the first of these expressions the numerator and denominator are multiplied by $u_2 + \Delta u_2$, that limit can be rewritten as:

$$\frac{u_1 u_2 + u_1 \Delta u_2 + u_2 \Delta u_1 + \Delta u_1 \Delta u_2}{u_2{}^2 - (\Delta u_2)^2}$$

In like manner, if the numerator and denominator of the second expression are multiplied by $u_2 - \Delta u_2$, that expression can be written:

$$\frac{u_1 u_2 - u_1 \Delta u_2 - u_2 \Delta u_1 + \Delta u_1 \Delta u_2}{u_2{}^2 - (\Delta u_2)^2}$$

If the errors are assumed small, so that the product $\Delta u_1 \Delta u_2$ and the square $(\Delta u_2)^2$ can be neglected, the upper limit becomes:

$$\frac{u_1 u_2 + u_1 \Delta u_2 + u_2 \Delta u_1}{u_2{}^2} \qquad \text{or} \qquad \frac{u_1}{u_2} + \frac{u_1}{u_2}\left(\frac{\Delta u_2}{u_2} + \frac{\Delta u_1}{u_1}\right)$$

and the lower limit:

$$\frac{u_1 u_2 - u_1 \Delta u_2 - u_2 \Delta u_1}{u_1{}^2} \qquad \text{or} \qquad \frac{u_1}{u_2} - \frac{u_1}{u_2}\left(\frac{\Delta u_2}{u_2} + \frac{\Delta u_1}{u_1}\right)$$

Thus the absolute error of the quotient is roughly:

$$\frac{u_1}{u_2}\left(\frac{\Delta u_2}{u_2} + \frac{\Delta u_1}{u_1}\right)$$

and the relative error, by Section 3.42, is roughly the absolute error divided by u_1/u_2, or:

$$\frac{\Delta u_2}{u_2} + \frac{\Delta u_1}{u_1}$$

But this is simply the sum of the relative errors of the two original numbers. Hence the accuracy rules for division are essentially the same as those for multiplication and can be stated as:

Theorem VI. *The relative error of a quotient is the sum of the relative errors of the separate numbers. The absolute error, if desired, can be determined by multiplying the relative error by the approximate quotient.*

The theorem shows that, in division as in multiplication, the result will have no more correct significant figures than the original numbers.

EXERCISE VII

1. The following sets of numbers are approximate and are correct only to the number of significant figures given. Find their sum, and state limits for the absolute error:

   a. $321.4 + 2.9613 + 12.72$
   b. $.19174 + 328.1 + 436$
   c. $17.91 + .00461 + .00542$

2. The following numbers are approximate and accurate only to the number of places given. Find their difference and state limits for the absolute error and relative error:

   a. $948.1 - 72.649$
   b. $367.5426 - 7.5$
   c. $43.196 - 43.19$
   d. $.16754 - .163$

3. The following numbers are approximate and are accurate only to the number of places given. Find the products and state limits on the relative error and absolute error:

   a. 2.50×2.5
   b. 1.11×1.11
   c. 1.74623×10.0
   d. $.93564 \times 2.000$

4. The following numbers are approximate and are accurate only to the number of places given. Find the quotients and state limits on the relative error and absolute error:

   a. $1728.0 \div 1.20$
   b. $4.0 \div 2.0000$
   c. $4.0000 \div 2.0$
   d. $4.0000 \div 2.0000$
   e. $6.96969 \div .0023$

5. The following calculations are parts of check calculations for a computer program. The numbers are accurate only to the number of figures given.

Find the correct computer result in each case, in floating decimal.   (Since you are checking for correctness of the program, you should carry the same number of significant digits the computer will carry.)   Indicate how many of the significant digits are correct.

a. $(.11111)^2 + (.22222)^2$
b. $(2.3456)(1.0101) - (1.1621)(2.0202)$
c. $(.10102)^3$
d. $9231.6 + .78149 + 3.015$
e. $46.842 + 132.7 - 179.51396$

CHAPTER IV *Computer Programming*

4.1 INTRODUCTION

In Chapter II we discussed the basic components of a digital computer and wrote programs for the performance of very simple calculations. The calculations discussed so far were so very simple that it would be pointless to use a digital computer to perform them. The true value of the computer becomes apparent only when the performance of more elaborate calculations is considered. In this chapter we will begin to consider calculations better suited for a digital computer. In order to do so, however, we must first introduce some additional commands that our computer will be able to perform. So far, two types of instructions have been used, the arithmetic instructions and those concerned with the input and output of information. There are definite advantages to having sufficient electrical circuitry within the control unit of the machine to allow it to respond to certain other types of instructions. We shall discuss some of these types and then equip our hypothetical computer with the ability to perform a very limited number of these. Then we can proceed to the more complex calculations.

4.2 CONTROL INSTRUCTIONS

It has been said that a computer which operates from an internally stored program does so by proceeding through memory locations sequentially beginning with memory cell 0000, executing in order the instructions it finds in these locations. Control instructions are instructions that will cause the machine to vary from this standard procedure of control. The first control action is taken by the machine operator when he presses the button which causes the machine to start executing the stored instructions. The first requirement for a stored control instruction becomes apparent if one looks closely at any of the sample programs given so far—it is the requirement for an instruction to cause the machine to stop when the calculation has been completed. At first glance it might seem to be sufficient to have the machine stop automatically after it executes a print instruction. As indicated in

Example 2 of Section 2.63, however, it is sometimes, and in fact frequently, desirable to print an answer and then continue to calculate. It is generally considered desirable to have a separate command which will cause the machine to halt. For our purposes we will assume that the command Z0000 will cause the machine to halt and do nothing further until the operator takes action utilizing the manual control buttons.

4.21   The Unconditional Transfer

Another important control instruction is the unconditional transfer. Sometimes it is desirable to have a machine, instead of continuing sequentially through the memory locations for its instructions, jump to another memory cell elsewhere in the machine for its next instruction. Such a capability can be used in many ways. For example, it can be used to cause the machine to return through the same set instructions repeatedly, so that the identical operation can be performed repeatedly with different sets of data. Also, if it is desired to add a sequence of new commands within a program for some reason, it is possible to do so without completely rewriting the program by transferring to another section of the memory to perform the added commands, and then transferring back to continue on with the program. The command used for this purpose will be:

> U XXXX   Take the next command from memory location XXXX and then continue sequentially from that point.

Some uses of this command will be illustrated.

Example 1.   Compute $y = ax + b$ for a set of given values of x.

At this point, in writing the program, it becomes necessary not only to list the instruction but also to indicate the memory location in which each instruction is to be stored. A suitable program is:

Memory Location	Instruction
0000	I 0000 (reads a into accumulator)
0001	C 1620 (stores a in 1620)
0002	I 0000 (reads b into accumulator)
0003	C 1621 (stores b in 1621)
0004	I 0000 (reads x into accumulator)
0005	M 1620 (multiplies by a, giving ax in accumulator)
0006	A 1621 (adds b, giving $ax + b$ in accumulator)
0007	P 0000 (prints $y = ax + b$)
0008	Z 0000 (stops machine)
0009	U 0004 (when operator restarts machine, returns automatically to 0004 for next instruction)

The constants tape to accompany this program would have *a* and *b* in sequence, followed by the successive values of *x*. When the operator has loaded the program into the machine and starts the machine, the values of *a* and *b* and the first value of *x* will be read into the machine and the first value of *y* will be calculated and printed. Then the machine will come to the "stop" instruction in memory location 0008 and will stop. When the operator presses the start button again, the machine will execute the instruction in memory location 0009, which causes it to return to location 0004 for its next instruction. The next value of *x* is on the input unit ready to enter the machine. The machine will continue through the instructions, once again printing the value of $y = ax + b$ and stopping at memory location 0008. Each time the operator restarts the machine a new answer will print out. The time requirements for computers will be discussed later, but it is worth pointing out now that, on nearly any modern computer, the instructions from 0004 to 0007 will be performed in a very small fraction of a second, so the answer is printed as soon as the operator presses the start button. The program given above is actually rather unwieldy, because a considerable amount or even most of the time may be wasted waiting for the operator to restart the machine. Some of the commands yet to be introduced will allow this calculation to be performed more efficiently.

Example 2. The program given below calculates $r = as^2 + bs + c$. Modify it, changing as few memory locations in the program as possible, to compute $r = as^4 + bs^2 + c$.

The given program is:

Memory Location	Instruction
0000	I 0000 (inputs *a*)
0001	C 2450 (stores *a*)
0002	I 0000 (inputs *b*)
0003	C 2451 (stores *b*)
0004	I 0000 (inputs *c*)
0005	C 2452 (stores *c*)
0006	I 0000 (inputs *s*)
0007	C 2453 (stores *s*)
0008	B 2453 (brings *s* into accumulator)
0009	M 2450 (multiplies by *a*, giving *as* in accumulator)
0010	A 2451 (adds *b*, giving $as + b$ in accumulator)
0011	M 2453 (multiplies by *s*, giving $as^2 + bs$ in accumulator)
0012	A 2452 (adds *c*, giving $as^2 + bs + c$ in accumulator)
0013	P 0000 (prints $r = as^2 + bs + c$)
0014	Z 0000 (stops machine)

This program requires a constants tape with *a*, *b*, *c*, and *s* located sequentially on the tape. A suitable modified routine is:

Memory Location	Instruction
0000	I 0000
0001	C 2450
0002	I 0000
0003	C 2451
0004	I 0000
0005	C 2452
0006	I 0000
0007	C 2453
0008	U 0015 (transfers to 0015 for next command)
0009	M 2450
0010	A 2451
0011	M 2453
0012	A 2452
0013	P 0000
0014	Z 0000
0015	B 2453 (brings *s* into accumulator)
0016	M 2453 (multiplies by *s*, giving s^2 in accumulator)
0017	C 2453 (clears s^2 into 2453)
0018	B 2453 (brings s^2 into accumulator)
0019	U 0009 (transfers to 0009 for next instruction)

Only one of the original instructions required change in preparing the new program, although several instructions had to be added. The advantages of accomplishing this change without interfering with the stored location of the majority of the instructions will become apparent in later, more complex, problems.

4.22 The Conditional Transfer

Another control instruction available on most computers is the conditional transfer. It can take many forms, but the one we will use for our purposes will be:

T XXXX   Take the next command from memory location XXXX and then continue sequentially from that point *if* the contents of the accumulator are negative. Otherwise, ignore this instruction and proceed to the next instruction in the present sequence.

It is seen that there is a condition placed on this transfer instruction. It is effective only if the contents of the accumulator are negative. In effect, this command gives the machine the ability to make a decision—a very simple decision, to be sure, but one of far-reaching consequences. The addition of this new control instruction opens a wide range of possibilities in programming, some of which will be demonstrated in the examples below.

Example 1. Compute $y = ax + b$ for a set of given values of x.

This is the same problem as Example 1 of Section 4.21. We will show, by the use of the conditional transfer, how we can make this calculation completely automatic. To do this, let us assume that we have first chosen a number c, larger than all the given values of x, and some number d larger than c. Then a suitable program is:

Memory Location	Instruction
0000	I 0000 (input a)
0001	C 1620 (store a in 1620)
0002	I 0000 (input b)
0003	C 1621 (store b in 1621)
0004	I 0000 (input c)
0005	C 1622 (store c in 1622)
0006	I 0000 (input x)
0007	C 1623 (store x in 1623)
0008	B 1622 (bring c into accumulator)
0009	S 1623 (subtract x, giving $c - x$ in accumulator)
0010	T 0016 (transfer to 0016 for next instruction if $c - x$ is negative, otherwise go to 0011)
0011	B 1620 (bring a into accumulator)
0012	M 1623 (multiply by x, giving ax in accumulator)
0013	A 1621 (add b, giving $ax + b$ in accumulator)
0014	P 0000 (print $y = ax + b$)
0015	U 0006 (transfer to 0006 for next instruction)
0016	Z 0000 (stop machine)

The routine requires a constants tape with a, b, c, and the sequential values of x in order with the number d listed at the end.

This routine will automatically compute and print y for all the values of x, whether there is one or ten thousand, and then will stop. The key to the whole operation is the conditional transfer instruction in memory location 0010. With our choice of the number c, the quantity $c - x$ is positive for all but the last value on the input list, which is our chosen number d. Hence the T instruction (sometimes called a "transfer on negative" instruction) will be ignored, and the machine will take its next instruction from memory location 0011. The instructions B 1620, M 1623, A 1621, P 0000 will then be executed, calculating and printing y. The machine will then return to 0006 and read a new value for x. When the machine reads in the final value d, and uses that for x, the quantity $c - d$ will be a negative number, so that when the T instruction memory location 0010 is reached, the machine will transfer, and will proceed to the "halt" instruction in memory location 0016.

A sequence of commands that the machine executes more than once without leaving the sequence is called a "loop." In the preceding example, the commands 0006 through 0015 form a loop. The T instruction in 0010 provides the exit from this loop. If we had used a U instruction instead of a T instruction in 0010, the loop would have had no exit, and the machine would have repeated the same instructions indefinitely, or until stopped by some action of the human operator. Such a procedure is not usually desirable, and a loop, to be of value, must have an exit.

Example 2. Compute and print $y = x^3$ for each integer value of x from $x = 1$ to $x = 500$.

Since the values of x are equally spaced, we do not need to read all 500 values of x in from a constants tape, but instead can compute them as we need them. A suitable program would be:

Memory Location	Instruction
0000	I 0000 (input the number "1")
0001	C 1500 (store "1" in 1500)
0002	I 0000 (input the number "500.5")
0003	C 1501 (store "500.5" in 1501)
0004	B 1500
0005	C 1502 (store "1" in 1502 as first value of "x")
0006	B 1502 (bring "x")
0007	M 1502 (multiply by x, giving x^2 in accumulator)
0008	M 1502 (multiply by x, giving x^3 in accumulator)
0009	P 0000 (print x^3)
0010	B 1502 (bring x)
0011	A 1500 (add 1, giving $x + 1$ in accumulator)
0012	C 1502 (store $x + 1$ in 1502 as new value of x)
0013	B 1502 (bring new x)
0014	S 1501 (subtract 500.5)
0015	T 0006 (transfer if $x - 500.5$ is negative)
0016	Z 0000 (stop if $x - 500.5$ is positive)

In this program the instructions from 0006 to 0015 form a loop that will be executed 500 times, each time with the value of x increased by one. After 500^3 is computed and printed, the instructions in 0010 through 0012 will cause the number 501 to be stored for x. The instructions in 0013 and 0014 will place $501 - 500.5$ or a positive $.5$ in the accumulator. The "transfer on negative" instruction in 0015 will then *not* cause a transfer, and so the computer will reach memory location 0016 and stop.

A question might be raised as to why we used the number 500.5 rather than 501 as a check number to determine whether 500^3 had yet been computed. After all, $500 - 501$ is negative, and $501 - 501$ is zero, so the transfer on negative instruction would cause the loop to be repeated for all values of x less than or equal to 500, but would stop the machine at $x = 501$. The answer is that we have said our machine uses its numbers internally in binary rather than decimal. As we saw in Chapter I, a terminating decimal number does not always convert to a terminating binary number. Thus it is possible that the floating binary numbers for $x = 501$, arrived at in the machine by different methods, not be precisely equal, but may differ by a roundoff error in the lowest bit positions. Thus the machine might compute $501 - 501$ as a very tiny negative number, and on this basis perform the loop once more, computing and printing 501 cubed. While this may not be a serious fault for the present problem, it is easily avoided by the simple artifice of using 500.5 instead of 501 as the test number.

Example 3. Compute $y = x^n$ where n may be any positive integer. (The program is to be so written that it will work for any value of n.)

The input information required for this problem will be numbers $x, n - 1/2$, and the integer 1. A suitable program would be:

Memory Location	Instruction	
0000	I	0000 (input x)
0001	C	5000 (store x)
0002	I	0000 (input $n - 1/2$)
0003	C	5001 (store $n - 1/2$)
0004	I	0000 (input 1)
0005	C	5002 (store 1)
0006	B	5000 (bring x into accumulator)
0007	C	5003 (first time, clears x to 5003; ith time, clears x^i to 5003)
0008	B	5001 (first time, bring $n - 1/2$ to accumulator; ith time, bring $n - 1/2 - i + 1$ to accumulator)
0009	S	5002 (subtract 1; first time, leave $n - 3/2$ in accumulator; ith time, leave $n - 1/2 - i$ in accumulator)
0010	T	0015 (transfer to 0015 if $n - 1/2 - i$ is negative, otherwise continue)
0011	C	5001 (store $n - 1/2 - i$ in 5001)
0012	B	5003 (first time, bring x to accumulator; ith time, bring x^i to accumulator)
0013	M	5000 (multiply by x, giving x^{i+1} in accumulator)
0014	U	0007 (transfer to 0007)
0015	B	5003 (bring x^n to accumulator)
0016	P	0000 (print $y = x^n$)
0017	Z	0000 (halt machine)

The loop in this case consists of the commands 0007 to 0014.   The exit is in location 0010.

This program is a little difficult to follow, and the explanatory remarks given beside the commands are somewhat involved.   To give a clearer picture of the way the program will function, the steps are written below as they would be executed by the machine for the case $n = 2$:

Memory Location	Instruction
0000	I 0000 (input x)
0001	C 5000 (store x)
0002	I 0000 (input $n - 1/2$, or 1.5)
0003	C 5001 (store 1.5)
0004	I 0000 (input 1)
0005	C 5002 (store 1)
0006	B 5000 (brings x into accumulator)
0007	C 5003 (clears x to 5003)
0008	B 5001 (brings 1.5 to accumulator)
0009	S 5002 (subtracts 1, leaving .5 in accumulator)
0010	T 0015 (does nothing since .5 > 0)
0011	C 5001 (stores .5 in 5001)
0012	B 5003 (brings x to accumulator)
0013	M 5000 (multiplies by x, giving x^2 in accumulator)
0014	U 0007 (transfers to memory location 0007)
0007	C 5003 (clears x^2 into 5003)
0008	B 5001 (brings .5 into accumulator)
0009	S 5002 (subtracts 1, giving $-.5$ in accumulator)
0010	T 0015 (transfers to 0015, since $-.5 < 0$)
0015	B 5003 (brings x^2 to accumulator)
0016	P 0000 (prints $y = x^2$)
0017	Z 0000 (halts machine)

Although there are only eighteen instructions in the original program, it is seen that the machine actually executed twenty-three instructions in finding x^2.   To find x^{1000}, the machine would repeat instructions 0007 through 014 a total of 998 more times, or in all would execute about 8000 instructions. (As indicated in Section 3.54, accuracy problems could become quite severe if the program were used to compute such a high power of x.)   The memory cell 5001 is in effect being used as a counter, to keep track of how many times the loop has been performed.   Such counter registers are frequently used to control exit from a loop.

EXERCISE VIII

1.   Write a program for the computation of y according to each of the following formulas, where a, b, and c are fixed constants and x will take on a sequence of values.

a. $y = (a + x)^3$

b. $y = a + bx + cx^2$

c. $y = a + bx^2 + cx^4$

d. $y = a^2 + b^4 + ac + x$

e. $y = \dfrac{ax + b}{ax + c}$

f. $y = a^2 + 2abx + b^2x^2$

2. Write a program for the computation of y according to each of the following formulas, where a, b, and c are constants and n may take on any positive integral value:

a. $y = a + c^n$

b. $y = (a + ab + c^2)^n$

c. $y = b^4 + c^n$

d. $y = a^n + b^n$

e. $y = 1 + a + a^2 + \cdots + a^n$

f. $y = 3 \times 1 + 4 \times 2a + 5 \times 3a^2 + \cdots + (n+3)(n+1)a^n$

3. Write a program for the computation of y according to each of the following formulas, where $a_0, a_1, \ldots, a_n$ are constants, n may take on any positive integral value, and x will take on a sequence of values:

a. $y = x^n$

b. $y = a_0 + a_1x^n$

c. $y = a_0 + a_1x + a_2x^2 + \cdots + a_nx^n$

4.3 LOGICAL INSTRUCTIONS

Just as the introduction of control instructions afforded programming whole new classes of calculations with slight effort, so the introduction of yet another type of instruction will provide for programming an even broader range of calculations. When a program is stored within the memory, it is possible to bring instruction words from the memory to the accumulator just as if they were numbers. Once in the accumulator, these instructions can be operated upon in various ways to alter them. Such operations are different in a sense from arithmetic operations, since they are not performed on pure numbers. Some have no resemblance at all to arithmetic operations, and are instead more akin to some of the operations of mathematical logic discussed earlier. All such operations are generally termed "logical" operations. They require special machine circuitry for their accomplishment, and new instructions are required to control this logical circuitry. A few of the most useful logical instructions will be defined for use in our hypothetical computer.

4.31 Modification of Address

It is of considerable value to be able to modify the address portion of an instruction during a calculation. This can be done by bringing the instruction from its location in the memory, adding a number to the address portion of the instruction, and then clearing it back to its location (or even to a different location in the memory if desired). The "bring" and "clear" steps can be accomplished utilizing the "B" and "C" arithmetic commands, since these commands merely transfer the word involved without regard to its nature. For most machines, however, the addition process required is not that of the ordinary addition command, since even the address portion of the instruction is not necessarily stored in memory as a number in binary form. It may be in binary-coded decimal or some other form. If this is the case, the circuitry for addition of numbers representing addresses may be somewhat more complicated than that already discussed for binary addition, but it can be constructed using combinations of the same basic "and" and "or" circuits described in Chapter II. We will assume that such an operation is performed by the command:

N XXXX   Increase the address portion of the word in the accumulator by the amount XXXX

For example, if the word A 6261 is stored in the accumulator, the command N 0003 will cause the word to be changed to A 6264. We will refer to this command as an "increment" command.

Example 1. The command B 5140 is stored in memory location 0651. Write a sequence of instructions that will cause this command to be changed to B 5165.

A suitable sequence of instructions is:

B 0651   (brings the instruction B 5140 to the accumulator)
N 0025   (increments the address part by 25, giving B 5165 in the accumulator)
C 0651   (stores the instruction B 5165 in memory cell 0651)

When an address is incremented by an amount which should cause it to exceed 10,000, say 12,632, we will assume that the leading digit will be ignored by the computer circuitry, leaving simply 2632.

Example 2. The command C 8631 is stored in memory location 1314. Write a sequence of instructions that will cause this command to be changed to C 2142.

A suitable sequence is:

B 1314   (brings the instruction C 8631 into the accumulator)
N 3511   (increments the address part by 3511; 3511 plus 8631 equals 12142, but the 1 is dropped so that C 2142 is now in the accumulator)
C 1314   (stores the instruction C 2142 in memory cell 1314)

Some more practical examples of the "increment" command will be given after the next section introduces another logical instruction.

4.32   Logical Conditional Transfer

The conditional transfer introduced in Section 4.22, the T command, provided what proved to be a very useful capability: to transfer or not transfer depending on the sign of a number in the accumulator.   It is quite valuable to have a somewhat analogous instruction for use in connection with the address portion of commands.   There are many possible variations of such a command. We choose the following:

> L XXXX   If the address portion of the word in the accumulator is the same as XXXX, skip the next instruction, otherwise perform the next instruction.   Contents of the accumulator are not altered.

Example 1.   Write a sequence of instructions that will input 3000 constants into the memory, and store them sequentially in memory locations 1001 through 4000.

In all the previous examples we have used a separate I 0000 instruction for each constant to be placed in the memory.   Clearly, in the present case the writing of this kind of program would be an onerous task, and a very large part of the computer memory would be used up in simply storing all the instructions required.   The new instructions just discussed afford a more elegant means of performing the task.   The program is as follows:

Memory Location	Instruction
0000	I 0000 (reads constant into accumulator)
0001	C [1001](stores in 1001 first time, 1002 second time, etc.)
0002	B 0001 (brings instruction C - - - - to accumulator)
0003	N 0001 (increments address by one)
0004	L 4001 (skips next instruction if accumulator contains C 4001)
0005	U 0007 (transfers to 0007 for next instruction)
0006	Z 0000 (stops machine)
0007	C 0001 (clears the command C - - - - to location 0001)
0008	U 0000 (transfers to 0000 for next instruction)

In this routine only eight commands are required to input and store 3000 constants.   There is only one input instruction, the one in memory cell 0000. It will be executed by the machine 3000 times.   Each time, however, the instruction in 0001 will be different.   The first time through, it is C 1001. The commands in 0002, 0003, 0004, 0005, and 0007 then cause this instruction to be changed to read C 1002.   The instruction in 0008 then causes the machine to return to memory location 0000, so that the input instruction will be performed once more.   Then the C 1002 will be executed.   The next time through the loop this instruction will be C 1003, then C 1004, etc.   On the three thousandth time through, the command C 4000 will be executed, and then will be changed to read C 4001.   At this point the L 4001 instruction in location 0004 will cause the machine to skip to 0006, where the Z 0000 instruction will cause it to stop.   If this were the first part of a longer problem, in which the numbers just put in the machine were to be used in some calculation, we could place a "U" instruction in 0006 to transfer to the other part of the problem.

There is one rather serious flaw with the above program: after it has been used, the instruction in memory cell 0001 reads "C 4001." and if we wish to use the program again we must first change the instruction back to C 1001. The brackets were placed on the address portion of the instruction to remind us of this fact.   We could do this by once more reading the program back into the machine, but in practice it is frequently necessary to restart a program already stored in the machine.   For this reason, whenever we have a command whose address will be modified during the calculation, it is advisable to write the program in such a way that the program itself will first ensure that the correct address is in place before the calculation is commenced.   This process, called *initialization*, is easily accomplished by the inclusion of a few more commands in the program.   For example, the above program could be replaced by the following:

Memory Location	Instruction
0000	C 1001 (dummy command, listed here to be available for storage in 0004)
0001	B 0000 (brings C 1001 to accumulator)
0002	C 0004 (stores C 1001 in 0004)
0003	I 0000 (reads constant into accumulator)
0004	C [1001](stores in 1001 first time, 1002 second time, etc.)
0005	B 0004 (brings instruction C - - - - into accumulator)
0006	N 0001 (increments address by one)
0007	L 4001 (skips next instruction if accumulator contains C 4001)
0008	U 0010 (transfers to 0010 for next instruction)
0009	Z 0000 (stops machine)
0010	C 0004 (clears command C - - - - to location 0004)
0011	U 0003 (transfers to 0003 for next instruction)

The very first instruction, C 1001, is a dummy instruction, not used directly in the calculation, but listed only to be available for placement in memory location 0004.   It could have been listed at any convenient point in the program where it would not interfere with the performance of the program.

Example 2. Write a sequence of instructions that will sum up the numbers already stored in memory locations 4000 to 5000, inclusive, and print the sum. Assume the first instruction in this sequence will be in memory location 0056.

A suitable sequence is:

Memory Location	Instruction
0056	C 3999 (clears accumulator to zero)
0057	A [4000] (adds content of 4000 first time, 4001 second time, etc.)
0058	C 3999 (stores partial sum in 3999)
0059	B 0057 (brings instruction A ---- to accumulator)
0060	N 0001 (increments address by 1)
0061	L 5001 (skips next instruction if accumulator contains A 5001)
0062	U 0066 (transfers to 0066 for next instruction)
0063	B 3999 (brings sum to accumulator)
0064	P 0000 (prints answer)
0065	Z 0000 (stops machine)
0066	C 0057 (clears A ---- to 0057)
0067	B 3999 (brings partial sum to accumulator)
0068	U 0057 (transfers to 0057 for next instruction)

This sequence of instructions builds up the sum by adding in the contents of 4001, 4002, 4003, etc. in order, storing the partial sum in memory location 3999 while the command in 0057 is altered. It performs the loop 0057, 58, 59, 60, 61, 62, 66, 67, 68 a thousand and one times, and then the instruction L 5001 tells it that another time through the loop would add in the contents of 5001, an undesired action, so control skips to 0063, where the sum is brought to the accumulator, the answer printed, and the machine stopped.

In the program, brackets were placed around the address of the command A 4000, as a reminder that this address is modified during the course of the problem. At the end of the problem, when the answer is printed, the contents of memory location 0057 are A 5000. As in the preceding example, this command should be initialized. The following commands are sufficient to perform this function:

Memory Location	Command
0054	A 4000 (dummy command, listed here to be available for storage in 0057)
0055	B 0054 (brings A 4000 to accumulator)
0056	C 0057 (stores A 4000 in 0057)

The command previously in 0056 is not needed when the above three commands are used since its only purpose was to clear the accumulator, a function now performed by the command C 0057.

Example 3. Write a program that will compute the values of y_1, y_2, y_3 from the equations:

$$y_1 = a_{11}x_1 + a_{12}x_2 + a_{13}x_3 + a_{14}$$
$$y_2 = a_{21}x_1 + a_{22}x_2 + a_{23}x_3 + a_{24}$$
$$y_3 = a_{31}x_1 + a_{32}x_2 + a_{33}x_3 + a_{34}$$

and print the values, for any list of sets of values, of x_1, x_2, x_3.

The equations given are for the transformation from one three-dimensional cartesian coordinate system to another. In effect, we are to write a program that will take sets of points (x_1, x_2, x_3) in one coordinate system and give back sets of points (y_1, y_2, y_3) in the other. Since we do not know how many points will be on the list, we will employ a system like that used in Example 1 of Section 4.21 to determine that all points have been completed. We will introduce a constant c larger than all of the values of x_1 we will be interested in (such as 90000000   99) and a still larger value d, and use these to allow the computer to determine when the list has been exhausted. Then the following program is a satisfactory one:

Memory Location	Instruction	
0000	B 0011	
0001	C 0003	
0002	I 0000	
0003	C [0051]	
0004	B 0003	
0005	N 0001	input "1" in 0051, "c" in 0052, a_{11} through
0006	L 0065	a_{34} in 0053 through 0064)
0007	U 0009	
0008	U 0012	
0009	C 0003	
0010	U 0002	
0011	C 0051	
0012	B 0046	(initialize 0027)
0013	C 0027	
0014	I 0000	
0015	C 0048	(store x_1 in 0048)
0016	B 0048	
0017	S 0052	(check to see if last set of x's have been used)
0018	T 0020	
0019	Z 0000	(stop, end of calculation)
0020	I 0000	
0021	C 0049	(store x_2 in 0049)
0022	I 0000	
0023	C 0050	(store x_3 in 0050)
0024	B 0047	
0025	C 0028	(initialize 0028)

Memory Location	Instruction	
0026	C 0065	(set contents of 0065 to 0)
0027	B [0053]	(bring a_{ij})
0028	M [0048]	(multiply by x_j)
0029	A 0065	
0030	C 0065	
0031	B 0027	
0032	N 0001	
0033	C 0027	
0034	B 0028	
0035	N 0001	
0036	C 0028	
0037	B 0028	
0038	L 0052	(check to see if a y value is completed)
0039	U 0027	(not complete; add on next term)
0040	B 0065	
0041	P 0000	(print y value)
0042	B 0027	
0043	L 0065	(check to see if y_3 has been computed)
0044	U 0024	(y_3 not computed; compute another y value)
0045	U 0012	(y_3 has been computed and printed; read in new x_1, x_2, x_3)
0046	B 0053	
0047	M 0048	

This program is quite complex, having a total of three loops. The complex structure was used to demonstrate the fact that the use of loops can lead to programs which are extremely involved and difficult to follow. A careful, step by step, study of the program will disclose that it does indeed do the required calculation. The calculation could also be accomplished by the following routine, which requires no modification of instructions. The program is much more straightforward, but involves more instructions.

Memory Location	Instruction
0000	I 0000
0001	C 0073 (store c)
0002	I 0000
0003	C 0074 (store a_{11})
0004	I 0000
0005	C 0075 (store a_{12})
0006	I 0000
0007	C 0076 (store a_{13})
0008	I 0000
0009	C 0077 (store a_{14})
0010	I 0000
0011	C 0078 (store a_{21})
0012	I 0000

Memory Location	Instruction
0013	C 0079 (store a_{22})
0014	I 0000
0015	C 0080 (store a_{23})
0016	I 0000
0017	C 0081 (store a_{24})
0018	I 0000
0019	C 0082 (store a_{31})
0020	I 0000
0021	C 0083 (store a_{42})
0022	I 0000
0023	C 0084 (store a_{33})
0024	I 0000
0025	C 0085 (store a_{34})
0026	I 0000
0027	C 0086 (store x_1)
0028	B 0086
0029	S 0073
0030	T 0032 (transfer if $x_1 < c$)
0031	Z 0000 (end of program)
0032	I 0000
0033	C 0087 (store x_2)
0034	I 0000
0035	C 0088 (store x_3)
0036	B 0074
0037	M 0086 (compute $a_{11}x_1$)
0038	C 0089
0039	B 0075
0040	M 0087 (compute $a_{12}x_2$)
0041	C 0090
0042	B 0076
0043	M 0088 (compute $a_{13}x_3$)
0044	A 0090
0045	A 0089
0046	A 0077
0047	P 0000 (print y_1)
0048	B 0078
0049	M 0086 (compute $a_{21}x_1$)
0050	C 0089
0051	B 0079
0052	M 0087 (compute $a_{22}x_2$)
0053	C 0090
0054	B 0080
0055	M 0088 (compute $a_{23}x_3$)
0056	A 0090
0057	A 0089
0058	A 0081

Memory Location	Instruction
0059	P 0000 (print y_2)
0060	B 0082
0061	M 0086 (compute $a_{31}x_1$)
0062	C 0089
0063	B 0083
0064	M 0087 (compute $a_{32}x_2$)
0065	C 0090
0066	B 0084
0067	M 0088 (compute $a_{33}x_3$)
0068	A 0090
0069	A 0089
0070	A 0085
0071	P 0000 (print y_3)
0072	U 0026

EXERCISE IX

1. Write a program to compute and print the value of y for each of the following cases, where a_1 through a_{100} are given numbers:

    a. $y = a_1 + a_2 + a_3 + \cdots + a_{100}$

    b. $y = a_1^2 + a_2^2 + a_3^2 + \cdots + a_{100}^2$

    c. $y = a_1^3 + a_2^3 + a_3^3 + \cdots + a_{100}^3$

    d. $y = a_1a_2 + a_2a_3 + a_3a_4 + \cdots + a_{99}a_{100}$

    e. $y = \dfrac{a_1}{a_2} + \dfrac{a_3}{a_4} + \dfrac{a_5}{a_6} + \cdots \dfrac{a_{99}}{a_{100}}$

2. Write a program to find and print out y for each integer value of x from 1 to 500. Describe the input required.

    a. $y = x + 2x^2$

    b. $y = \dfrac{1+x}{6+x^2}$

    c. $y = x^2 + 4x + 7$

    d. $y = \dfrac{3 + 2x + 6x^2}{1 + 9x + 16x^2}$

    e. $y = x - \dfrac{x^3}{3!} + \dfrac{x^5}{5!} - \dfrac{x^7}{7!} + \dfrac{x^9}{9!} - \dfrac{x^{11}}{11!} + \dfrac{x^{13}}{13!}$

4.4 FLOW CHARTS

It can be seen at this stage that, since we have added the logical instructions and control instructions, our programs have been becoming more complex in structure. The commands are not simply executed in the sequence in which they appear in the program: instead there are loops, transfers, and branch points where the machine proceeds sometimes to one set of instructions and sometimes to another. As we proceed to still more complex problems, we shall find ourselves faced with more complex programs whose structure will not be at all readily apparent. In order to display the structure of a machine program more clearly, a device known as a "flow chart" is commonly used. This is a diagram showing in boxes the calculations to be done and with connecting lines the order in which they are to be done. The chart can be detailed or gross, depending on its purpose. For more complex problems, it is advisable to draw a flow chart first and to use it as a guide in preparation of the machine program.

The flow chart will be of major value to us for another reason. It is in essence a presentation of the instructions for a calculation in a universal language, one independent of the particular computer to be used. In this text we have been making use of an idealized computer, and have solved problems in terms of the "machine language" of this particular computer. Such a procedure has been necessary in order to give some first hand feel for the capabilities and limitations of digital computers. However, it is unlikely that the reader will ever find it necessary to write a program directly in machine language, so in the remainder of this text we will use machine language only when it is needed to demonstrate some inner property of a computer, and will present solutions to problems in terms of more general languages, such as the flow chart.

4.41 Flow Chart Symbols

As yet there is no uniformity in the symbols used within flow charts. We shall restrict ourselves to a bare minimum of such symbols. Flow charts will begin with a box labeled START and end with a box labeled STOP. The progression from START to STOP is traced by following the connecting lines through the other boxes in the chart. The other types of boxes are:

a. *The assertion box.* ⟶ | $y = ax + b$ | ⟶

This box asserts that the operations contained therein are to be executed at this time. These operations may involve the calculation of a numerical quantity, the replacement of a quantity by another, the input of certain quantities into the memory, or the printing of certain results. The above assertion box indicates that the value of y is to be computed by taking a times x, plus b, the quantities a, x, and b already stored in the memory.

b. *The test box.* ⟶ ($x - 16 < 0$?) —yes→   no↓

This box represents the use of a conditional transfer instruction of some type. It has one input line and two output lines. Either output is selected, depending on whether the answer to the question contained in the box is affirmative or negative.   It represents a branching point in the program.

c.   *The remote connector.*   ⟶ (3)

This circle indicates that the logical control is transferred to the point at which another such circle appears with the same number in it. It is used to keep the flow chart uncluttered by connecting lines criss-crossing the diagram to join boxes.

d.   *The variable remote connector.*   ⟶ (α)

This circle indicates that the point to which control is transferred is set by the program itself.   Somewhere prior to the position of this symbol in the flow chart there must be an assertion box which assigns a numerical value to α.   Then this connector will indicate a transfer to the entry circle with that particular numerical value in it.

4.42 Examples of Flow Charts

The use of the symbols just described will be demonstrated with a few examples.

Example 1.   Draw a flow chart for the calculation of $y = a^2 + ab + b^3$ (see Example 1 of Section 2.63).

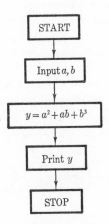

Figure 4–1

Figure 4–1 shows a suitable flow chart.   This flow chart is extremely simple, requiring only assertion boxes.   Since each of the boxes is a simple assertion, there is no real advantage in having a separate box for each item.   All the statements could be placed in a single box, as in Figure 4–2.   When several statements are included in a single box, they should be taken in order from top to bottom.

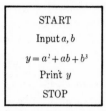

Figure 4–2

Example 2.   Draw a flow chart for the calculation of $y = ax + b$ for a set of given values of x (see Example 1 of Section 4.21).

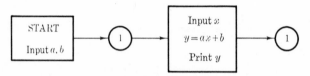

Figure 4–3

A suitable flow chart is shown in Figure 4–3.   Following this flow chart, the machine will input a and b, then input x, compute $y = ax + b$, print y and input x again, continuing without any stop command.   Ordinarily a machine following such a program would use up all available values of x and then continue trying to read a new value of x until the human operator takes some action to stop it.   In Example 1 of Section 4.22, this same problem was done, using a test to determine when the last value of x was used.   In that example a constant c, larger than all the given values of x, was used for the test, and another constant d, larger than c, was put at the end of the input tape of x values.   A flow chart for that program is shown in Figure 4–4.

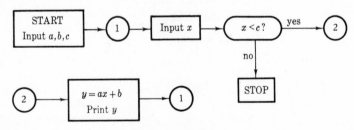

Figure 4–4

Example 3. Draw a flow chart for a program that will read 3000 values of x into the machine and then stop (see Example 2, Section 4.32).

A suitable flow chart is shown in Figure 4–5. This flow chart contains some features not present in the preceding examples. One is the use of the arrow, in $i + 1 \rightarrow i$. This expression would be read "$i + 1$ replaces i." Another feature is the use of the variable subscript "i" to indicate which value of x is being used. This is somewhat typical of a program in which a loop is to be performed using "logical" instructions and modifying an address. In the program of Example 2, Section 4.32, the 3000 values of x are not identified by numbers 1 to 3000, so the quantity "i" as such does not appear in the

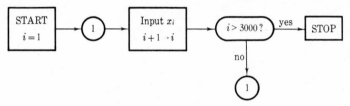

Figure 4–5

program. The values of x are, however, identified by the memory locations in which they are stored; the first is in location 1001, the second in 1002, etc., and the 3000th in location 4000. As far as the program is concerned, the flow chart instruction "$i + 1$ replaces i" translates into "increase by one the number of the memory location into which the value of x is to be placed." The test "is $i > 3000$" becomes the command L 4001, or skip (to the stop command) if the next x would go in memory location 4001.

Example 4. Draw a flow chart for the first program of Example 3, Section 4.32.

A suitable flow chart is shown in Figure 4–6. There are several new features in this flow chart. First, the input of a_{11} through a_{34} is described only by a statement in a single insertion box. It could have been described in more detail by utilizing a set of boxes such as were used in Example 3 above, if such detail were considered necessary. Decisions as to how much detail must be included in a flow chart depend upon the purpose for which the chart is constructed: if as a guide for an inexperienced coder who is to prepare the actual machine program, great detail will be necessary; if for the use of a more experienced coder, some of the more elementary parts of the flow chart can safely be abbreviated.

Another new feature of the above flow chart is the use of the arrow in two different manners. It is used in $i + 1 \rightarrow i$ and $j + 1 \rightarrow j$. In these two instances its use is precisely as in Example 3, above: to indicate modification of an address in a logical loop. It is also used, however, in the expression

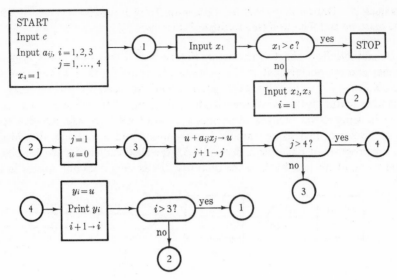

Figure 4–6

$u + a_{ij}x_j \rightarrow u$, which is read "$u + a_{ij}x_j$ replaces u." The quantity u is a number, which is changed in value each time through the loop. The term "replaces" in this circumstance means that, in the memory location where the number u was stored, the quantity $u + a_{11}x_1$ will now be stored. We start out at connector 3 with $u = 0$. The first four times through this section, we will obtain:

$$u = a_{11}x_1$$
$$u = a_{11}x_1 + a_{12}x_2$$
$$u = a_{11}x_1 + a_{12}x_2 + a_{13}x_3$$

and finally:

$$u = a_{11}x_1 + a_{12}x_2 + a_{13}x_3 + a_{14}$$

At this point the test box for j will cause us to go to connector 4, where we will set $y_1 = u$ and print y.

EXERCISE X

Draw flow charts for the programs of Exercise IX.

4.5 ADDITIONAL INSTRUCTIONS

In our examples of computer programming we have assumed that the wiring of our hypothetical computer was such as to allow it to execute about a dozen different commands, or instructions. These commands formed the "language" of our hypothetical computer. More expensive computers ordinarily have additional wiring in their control units, which enables them to have a larger vocabulary, i.e., to recognize and execute a larger number of basic commands. Some of the instructions frequently made available by added circuitry are the following:

(*1*) "Shift" instructions, which cause the contents of the accumulator to shift to the right or left a prescribed number of bits.

(*2*) A variety of "Store" instructions, which perform variations of the operation done by our "Clear" instruction. These may perform such varied functions as storing the contents of the accumulator in some memory cell while also retaining them in the accumulator, or storing only the bits in a certain portion of the accumulator into a certain portion of a memory cell such as only the address portion of a command.

(*3*) A variety of "Load" instructions, which are similar to our "Bring" instruction, but which may load into the accumulator only a portion of some word stored in the memory.

(*4*) A variety of "Transfer" instructions, similar in character to our "Transfer on negative" instruction. For example, there may be one causing transfer if the contents of the accumulator are exactly zero, or one causing transfer if the contents are positive, or one causing transfer if only the address portion is zero, and so forth.

Further flexibility in commands is frequently made available by the use of special memory cells, or registers, within the control unit. These registers, called index registers, can be used in a variety of ways. A number may be placed in an index register and used as a modifier for the address portion of instructions used in a program. When used in this fashion, each instruction word for the computer contains not only an operation and an address, as do the instructions for our hypothetical computer, but also an indicator to let the computer know if the address portion given in the instruction word is to have added to it the contents of an index register before the instruction is executed. Such an arrangement gives the programmer greatly increased ease and flexibility in programming loops, a task which was rather difficult on our simple, hypothetical computer. Index registers can also be used as counters in causing a command or group of commands to be executed a prescribed number of times. Such a capability greatly simplifies the process of writing a general program for solving, say, an n by n system of linear equations.

The above list of examples of added capabilities attainable with improved computer circuitry is by no means exhaustive, nor is it even indicative of all the avenues open for improvement. The science of computer circuit design is a rapidly developing one, and one can expect the "machine language" of computers to expand at a rapid rate. It should be noted, however, that, while such advances may aid in performing the mathematical calculations described in later chapters, the mathematical methods which will be described are of a more permanent nature, and will probably continue to form the basis of a large amount of scientific and engineering work for many years to come.

4.6 ADVANCED PROGRAMMING TECHNIQUES

It would carry us too far afield to trace in detail the development of the art of programming from the rudimentary examples given in the early part of this chapter to the advanced stage it has now reached. In this section we will sketch some aspects of this development in order to introduce an important type of program known as a compiler. Then in the next chapter we will describe one of the most widely used compilers, known as FORTRAN, and will use FORTRAN extensively in the remainder of the text.

4.61 *Interpretive Routines*

On a computer with limited circuitry, and hence a limited vocabulary of basic instructions, it is possible to write programs that will in effect increase the vocabulary. Such programs are referred to as interpretive routines, because they allow a computer to "interpret" commands which are not part of its basic language. Such a routine can give a small, inexpensive computer some of the capabilities of a larger, more expensive one. They are frequently used to do floating point arithmetic on a fixed point machine as mentioned in Section 2.58, and to convert decimal input numbers to binary, a problem mentioned in Section 2.64. In order to use an interpretive routine, we must have two programs in the computer memory simultaneously: the interpretive routine, and the program we wish to have executed. Then we actually start the computer on the first command of the interpretive routine. As the computer works its way through the commands in the interpretive routine, it will look in turn at each of the instructions in our program, decide what instructions in its own language it must execute in order to obtain the result required by the "foreign" instruction, and perform these. It is worth while to demonstrate this process on our hypothetical computer. Unfortunately, as our computer now stands, its vocabulary is so limited that it would be extremely difficult to write a meaningful interpretive routine for it. This situation can be remedied by adding two more instructions to the vocabulary of our hypothetical computer. We choose to add the following:

E XXXX   Compare, bit by bit, the operation portion of the instruction in the accumulator with the operation portion of the word located in memory cell XXXX If they are different, disregard this instruction and continue to the next. If they are the same, skip the next instruction. Leave the contents of the accumulator unaltered.

In order to understand this instruction, let us first remind ourselves that for our hypothetical computer each instruction is a series of bits, in binary-coded decimal, as described in Section 2.53. One portion of these bits will be the binary coding for the operation to be performed. It would be easy to construct gating circuits to compare these few bits with the corresponding ones from memory cell XXXX, and cause the next instruction to be skipped if all these bit positions agree. Note that for this purpose the bits involved need not be the binary coding for any of the standard operations which the machine performs. In essence, this command gives the computer the ability to recognize any combination of bits in the operation portion of a command and to act differently depending on what these bits may be.

The second instruction we will add is:

> Y XXXX Store the address portion of the word in the accumulator in the address portion of memory location XXXX. Leave the operation portion of XXXX unchanged.

This instruction allows us to handle the address portion of an instruction word separately from the operation portion. It would be easy to incorporate such a capability into a computer by means of gating circuits.

We will demonstrate the use of these new instructions in the preparation and use of an interpretive routine.

Example 1. With the aid of the above new instructions, write an interpretive routine that will allow our computer to use a program containing the following set of commands:

> F XXXX Bring the contents of memory location XXXX to the accumulator, destroying the previous contents.
> H XXXX Store the contents of the accumulator in memory location XXXX, leaving the contents of the accumulator unaltered.
> A XXXX Add the contents of memory location XXXX to the contents of the accumulator and leave the result in the accumulator.
> M XXXX Multiply the contents of memory location XXXX by the contents of the accumulator and leave the result in the accumulator.

We will not ask why anyone might want a machine to have such an odd vocabulary as that just given. We will merely use it to obtain a firmer idea of what an interpretive program is and how it works. The following routine, stored in memory location 0900, will allow the machine to perform a program starting in 0000 and made up of the above commands:

Memory Location	Instruction	
0900	B 0000	(dummy instruction)
0901	B 0900	(initialize 0903)
0902	C 0903	
0903	B [0000]	

Memory Location	Instruction	
0904	E 0917	⎫
0905	U 0907	⎬ (if an "F" command, go to 0921)
0906	U 0921	⎭
0907	E 0918	⎫
0908	U 0910	⎬ (if an "H" command, go to 0925)
0909	U 0925	⎭
0910	E 0919	⎫
0911	U 0913	⎬ (if an "A" command, go to 0929)
0912	U 0929	⎭
0913	E 0920	⎫ (if an "M" command, go to 0934;
0914	U 0916	⎬ if not, STOP)
0915	U 0934	⎭
0916	Z 0000	
0917	F 0000	⎫
0918	H 0000	⎬
0919	A 0000	⎬ (dummy commands)
0920	M 0000	⎭
0921	Y 0922	⎫
0922	B 0000	⎬ ("bring")
0923	C 0943	⎬
0924	U 0939	⎭
0925	Y 0927	⎫
0926	B 0943	⎬ ("Store")
0927	C 0000	⎬
0928	U 0939	⎭
0929	Y 0931	⎫
0930	B 0943	⎬
0931	A 0000	⎬ ("add")
0932	C 0943	⎬
0933	U 0939	⎭
0934	Y 0936	⎫
0935	B 0943	⎬
0936	M 0000	⎬ "(multiply")"
0937	C 0943	⎬
0938	U 0939	⎭
0939	B 0903	⎫
0940	N 0001	⎬ (advance to next command in program)
0941	C 0903	⎬
0942	U 0903	⎭
0943	[ ]	(interpretive routine "accumulator")

Note that this routine uses memory location 0943 as a false "accumulator." Any time an instruction in the basic program calls for placing something in the accumulator or removing something from it, the interpretive routine uses memory location 0943 instead. It must do this, because the interpretive routine itself needs to use the computer accumulator.

Example 2. Write a program in the new language given above to compute:

$$y = x_1 + x_1x_2 + x_1x_2x_3$$

where x_1, x_2, and x_3 are already stored in 0500, 0501, and 0502.

A suitable program is:

Memory Location	Instruction
0000	F 0500
0001	M 0501
0002	H 0503
0003	M 0502
0004	A 0503
0005	A 0501

We would use this program by placing it in memory, then starting the machine at memory location 0900. The interpretive routine would then proceed through the instructions one at a time, determining what each one meant, and performing the required operation. For example, when the machine is started, and 0903 is reached, it will bring F 0500 into the accumulator. The instructions in 0904 to 0906 will determine that this is indeed an "F" command. The U command in 0906 will cause the machine to transfer to 0921, where the "Y" command will cause the address 0500 to be placed in the address portion of the "bring" command in 0922. The machine will then execute the bring command in 0922 and then clear the result to 0943, the interpretive routine "accumulator." The U command in 0924 will then cause transfer to 0939, where the B 0000 in 0903 will be changed to B 0001, so that the next command can be interpreted and executed. Note that, in order to perform one of the commands in the new language, the computer must perform many, many instructions in its own language. This means that the time requirement using an interpretive routine will be much longer than that in direct machine language.

The examples just given are clearly of no practical value, but they do serve to demonstrate the nature of interpretive routines. Interpretive routines of practical value are usually quite long and complex, and are prepared by professional programmers and provided as ready-to-use packages. The user need only know the commands the routine can handle, not the basic machine language or details of the interpretive routine itself.

4.62 Assembly Programs

An assembly program is a different type of aid to programming. It is a routine that automatically assigns memory locations to the quantities being used in a calculation, so that the programmer only uses a symbol for each quantity involved, and does not keep track of the memory location where it is located. For example, the program to calculate $y = x_1 x_2 + x_2 x_3$ might appear as follows:

I   0000
C   X1
I   0000
C   X2
I   0000
C   X3
B   X1
M   X2
C   X4
B   X2
M   X3
A   X4
P   0000

In the address portion of each command, there is given not an address, but a symbol to indicate the quantity involved. This program would be placed in the computer, along with the assembly program; when the assembly program is run it will look at each of the above commands and, where the address is a symbol, replace the symbol by the number of some actual memory cell. Then the above program as modified would be run in order to perform the desired calculation.

While assembly programs do have some applications, they have largely been replaced by a more sophisticated and powerful programming aid, the compiler program. They are of interest chiefly as a logical step in the development of programming aids.

4.63   Compilers

A compiler can be described as a routine that takes a program written in the form of symbolic expressions, or statements, and develops from it another program, in the basic machine language, that will perform the required calculation. The original program is referred to as the source program and the resultant machine language program as the object program. If the compiler is a good one, the source program can look almost like the actual mathematical expressions in the original problem.

For example, the source program might contain statements like:

$$X = Y \cdot Z$$

These would be placed in the computer in, say, the six-bit binary code described in Section 1.72. The computer would first look through the statement and assign a memory location for each of the quantities involved, say:

$$0600 \text{ for } X$$
$$0601 \text{ for } Y$$
$$0602 \text{ for } Z$$

It would then look through the statement again for the operations involved. In the above statement the only operation involved is a multiplication. The compiler would then generate the commands:

```
B   0600
M   0601
C   0602
```

to fit into the object program. If more than one operation had been involved in the statement, the compiler would have programmed each one of them individually, storing the intermediate result in working storage. As with interpretive routines, the user need not know the inner workings of a compiler, but only the symbols and statements it is able to recognize and to convert to machine language commands. The better compilers will automatically perform tests, program loops, and so forth. With a good compiler, writing the source program is not much harder than drawing a flow chart. The machine does nearly all the work.

CHAPTER V *FORTRAN Systems*

5.1 INTRODUCTION

In Chapter IV it was indicated that computer programming has progressed to the point at which it is no longer necessary for the programmer to write a set of commands in machine language in order to have a calculation performed. Instead, ready-made compiler programs can be used to convert a set of statements that describe the problem into a set of machine language commands that will actually cause the machine to solve the problem. The task of the programmer, then, is to write the problem in the form of a set of statements which the compiler is capable of converting. He need not know how the compiler does this conversion, but he must know those symbols and statements the compiler can handle, and must adhere religiously to them. One of the earliest compilers for scientific use was the IBM FORTRAN. The original FORTRAN compiler was so successful that FORTRAN compilers now exist for most machines. In this chapter we will describe the FORTRAN language; that is to say, we will define those symbols and statements the typical FORTRAN compiler is capable of converting to machine language. Unfortunately, even FORTRAN compilers vary somewhat from one machine to another, so the language described below is not really universal. However, the modifications required for particular machines are generally small, so this FORTRAN language will be used in describing solutions to problems in later chapters. In using this material in connection with some particular computer, the reader would be wise to consult the FORTRAN programming manuals for that particular computer, in order that he can make modifications if any are required.

A FORTRAN program consists of a series of statements of different types. One describes arithmetic operations to be performed, such as $Z = X + Y$. A second type causes the machine to call for input, say from a data card or a magnetic tape, or to provide output, say on a printed page or a magnetic tape. Another specifies the flow of control through the set of statements, that is to say, the order in which the statements are to be executed. Still

114

another type of statement simply provides information about the procedure without causing any action. The following sections will describe these statements and demonstrate how they are used to form a program.

5.2 ARITHMETIC STATEMENTS

The heart of a FORTRAN program is the set of arithmetic statements which describes the calculations to be performed. These statements involve arithmetic operations on constants and variables stored in the machine.

5.21 *Constants*

The FORTRAN compiler allows arithmetic to be done in either fixed point or floating point form. In the fixed point arithmetic, the operations are done as if the numbers involved are integers.* Any positive or negative integer (not too large to fit in a memory cell of the machine) used in a FORTRAN statement will be stored as an integer and can be used in fixed point arithmetic. To be recognized as an integer, the constant must be written without a decimal point. For example, the constants:

$$5$$
$$0$$
$$-150$$
$$+4361$$

if appearing in FORTRAN statements would be recognized as fixed point numbers and stored as such.

Floating point constants may be written in FORTRAN statements in either of two forms. Any number written with a decimal point will be recognized by FORTRAN as a floating point number and stored as such. For example, the numbers:

$$+5.$$
$$0.$$
$$16.793$$
$$-.0001985$$

if appearing in FORTRAN statements would be stored as floating point constants. If the number is so large or so small that it is inconvenient to

---

* In Chapter II, a system of fixed point arithmetic was demonstrated where the binary point was assumed to occur just before the first bit position. In FORTRAN fixed point arithmetic, the binary point is assumed to occur just after the last bit position. The former system is somewhat more typical of normal circuitry in small, inexpensive computers. The type of fixed point arithmetic used in FORTRAN might more aptly be termed "integer arithmetic."

write it in the above form, it can be followed by the letter E and a one or two digit positive or negative power of 10 by which the number is to be multiplied. For example:

$$5.1E6 \text{ is recognized as } 5.1 \times 10^6$$
$$-.32E-12 \text{ is recognized as } -.32 \times 10^{-12}$$

A floating point constant can be written with any number of digits, but since a memory cell in the machine will not ordinarily hold a number more than 8 or 9 decimal digits in length, additional digits beyond 8 or 9 are usually wasted.

5.22   Variables

Any number to be used in a FORTRAN statement whose value is unknown or whose value may change during the calculation is termed a variable. Just as in an ordinary algebraic calculation we give a name such as x or y or t to any unknown or any variable, so in FORTRAN we must give names to any variables used.   FORTRAN will recognize any combination of six or less letters or digits, beginning with a letter, as a name of a variable, and will save a memory cell within the computer for storage of that particular quantity. The quantities:

A

B1

CLOCK

K

M589C

are all acceptable names for FORTRAN variables.

As for constants, a FORTRAN variable can be either a fixed point number or a floating point number, and the name indicates which it is.

Any variable whose name begins with I, J, K, L, M, or N is treated by FORTRAN as a fixed point number.   A variable whose name begins with any other letter is treated as a floating point number.

5.23   Expressions

In FORTRAN, each of the four basic arithmetic operations is represented by a distinct symbol:

Additon: +
Subtraction: —
Multiplication: *
Division: /

FORTRAN will recognize mathematical expressions made up of mathematically proper combinations of constants, variables, and these symbols. Parentheses can be used to indicate the order in which operations are to be performed but not to replace an operation's symbol.   For example, a FORTRAN expression for the algebraic expression $a(b + c)$ would be A*(B + C). A(B+C) would not be a correct expression, since no operation is indicated between A and B.   When there are no parentheses to indicate the order of operations, the multiplications and divisions would be performed first, working from left to right, and then the additions and subtractions, also working from left to right.   Thus A/B*C would be interpreted to mean $\left(\dfrac{A}{B}\right)C$ and not $\dfrac{A}{BC}$.

Fixed and floating point quantities cannot be mixed in the same expression. Thus the expression:

$$DOG + CAT$$

will cause the two quantities named DOG and CAT to be added floating point fashion.   The expression:

$$MICE + MOOSE$$

will cause the two quantities called MICE and MOOSE to be added fixed point fashion.   The expression:

$$CAT + MICE$$

is illegal because CAT is stored in floating point form and MICE is in fixed point form.

5.24   Arithmetic Statements

An arithmetic statement in FORTRAN is written in the form:

some FORTRAN variable = some FORTRAN expression

Although it contains an equals sign, the statement is not really an equation. FORTRAN interprets the equals sign to mean: compute the numerical value of the FORTRAN expression on the right and store the result in the memory location reserved for the variable named on the left.   Thus the statement:

$$A = DOG + CAT$$

means compute the sum of the numbers in the memory locations reserved for the variables named DOG and CAT and store the result in the memory location reserved for the variable named A. The previous contents of that memory location are lost. The statement:

M = M + 1

means add one to the fixed point constant in the memory location reserved for the variable named M and store the result back in the same location. (It is quite clear that this last statement cannot be interpreted as an equation in the normal sense.) The statement:

B = 3.75*A

means multiply by 3.75 the contents of the memory location reserved for the variable named A and store the result in the memory location reserved for the variable named B.

5.3   INPUT AND OUTPUT STATEMENTS

Special FORTRAN statements can be used to cause input of data or output of results. The most important of these statements are described below. When they are used, the compiler expects input numbers to be in decimal form and causes them to go through a conversion to binary. Likewise, it causes binary numbers to be converted to decimal before output.

5.31   READ and FORMAT

Input is caused by a statement which begins with the READ, followed by the names of the variables to be read into the machine. Data input with FORTRAN is normally from punched cards, and each READ statement initiates the reading of a new card. Values for the variables must be punched on the card in the order the names appear in the READ statement. The READ statement then causes these values to be put in memory in the proper locations.

A READ statement by itself does not contain all the information required for reading a number from a punched card. The card contains eighty columns, each of which may contain a decimal digit. The machine must be told which of these columns contain the particular number to be stored, and whether this number is fixed or floating point, and where the decimal point is located. This information is placed in a separate statement, called a FORMAT statement. The FORMAT statement consists of the word "FORMAT," followed by parentheses containing the description of each number to be read in by the corresponding READ statement. If the number is fixed point, this description would consist of the letter I followed by a number that indicates the number of card columns reserved for the number. If the number is floating point, it was mentioned earlier that it might appear in either one of two forms: either as an ordinary decimal number with decimal point or as a number followed by the letter E and a power of 10 by which the number is to be multiplied. In the first case, the description in the FORMAT statement is the letter F, then a number representing the number of card columns reserved for the number, then a period, then a number representing the number of digits after decimal point in the number as it appears on the card. In the second case, the letter E is used rather than the letter F. For example, the statement:

$$\text{FORMAT(I5,F8.4,E12.2)}$$

would indicate that the first five columns of the card contain a fixed point number, the next eight contain a floating point number having four digits after the decimal point, and the next twelve contain a floating point number having two digits after the decimal point and followed by a power of ten as described in Section 5.21.

Any FORTRAN statement can be given a statement number that can be used for reference by other statements. The statement number is placed at the beginning of the statement. A FORMAT statement *must* be given a statement number so that READ statements can refer to it. Then each READ statement, immediately after the word "READ," contains the number of the FORMAT statement that describes how the reading is to be done. A few examples will serve to clarify the way in which this combination works.

Example 1. Write input statements to read from a card values for the variables A, B, and X, where A covers 10 columns of the card and has 4 digits after the decimal point, B covers 8 columns of the card and has 2 digits after the decimal point, and X covers 12 columns of the card and has 6 digits after the decimal point.

A suitable set of statements is:

```
    READ 15,A,B,X
15  FORMAT(F10.4,F8.2,F12.6)
```

Note that there are commas after the 15, A, and B in the READ statement and commas separating the three descriptions of numbers in the FORMAT statement. These commas are required, and FORTRAN could not correctly interpret these statements without them.

Example 2. Write input statements to read from a card values for the variables MAT, A1, A2, A3, A4, where MAT is a fixed point number occupying 5 columns on the card and A1 through A4 are floating point, each occupying 10 columns and having 5 digits after the decimal point.

A suitable set of statements is:

        READ 123,MAT,A1,A2,A3,A4
    123 FORMAT(I5,F10.5,F10.5,F10.5,F10.5)

In this case we have four identical descriptions F10.5. In such cases these can be grouped and written as 4F10.5. Thus another suitable solution is:

        READ 73,MAT,A1,A2,A3,A4
     73 FORMAT(I5,4F10.5)

Example 3. Write input statements that will read values for A1, A2, A3, A4 from a card and then read values for B1, B2, B3, B4 from a second card, where each number occupies 8 columns on the card and has 4 digits after the decimal point.

A suitable set of statements is:

        READ 101,A1,A2,A3,A4
        READ 101,B1,B2,B3,B4
    101 FORMAT(4F8.4)

Note that both READ statements refer to the same FORMAT statement. It is permissible to have many READ statements referring to the same FOR-MAT statement.

5.32 PRINT

Output is normally accomplished by a PRINT statement, which causes the desired values to be listed on a printer, usually one capable of printing 120 characters in a line. Alternatively, depending upon the particular machine, the PRINT statement may cause the output values to be recorded on magnetic tape for later printing in a separate operation. In either event, the PRINT statement is quite similar to the READ statement, consisting of the word PRINT, followed by the statement number of the FORMAT statement which describes how the printing is to be spaced across the page, followed by the names of the variables whose values are to be printed.

Example 1. Write a set of FORTRAN statements that will cause the machine to print the quantities I and A, where I is a fixed point number having at most 5 digits and A is a floating point number less than 500, and we wish to print the value to 4 decimal places.

A suitable set of statements is:

```
    PRINT 150,I,A
150 FORMAT(I5,F8.4)
```

This set of statements will cause I to be printed in the first five character positions and A to be printed in the next eight (one space will be used to print a decimal point). Since this way of printing would cause the values of I and A to run together on the page, a better FORMAT statement might be:

```
150 FORMAT(I5,F20.4)
```

With this FORMAT statement, twenty spaces will be reserved for A. Since the number requires only eight of these, there will be vacant spaces between the value of I and the value of A, making the outputs easier to read. This same result can be obtained by use of another symbol allowed in a FORMAT statement: the symbol X means leave a blank space; 5X means leave five blank spaces, etc. Thus the statement:

```
150 FORMAT(I5,12X,F8.4)
```

would also cause space to be left open between the two printed numbers.

5.33   Hollerith Characters

Frequently it is desirable to have the computer print out just a set of characters or words, as page headings or titles, or as indicators that the calculation has reached a certain stage. Such symbols or characters are referred to as "Hollerith" characters, after Hollerith, former director of the Bureau of Census, who introduced the use of binary coding of letters and characters on punched cards. Hollerith characters can be included in a FORMAT statement, and will be printed out just as written in the FORMAT statement whenever a PRINT statement is executed which uses that format. The Hollerith characters must be preceded by a number which is the actual number of characters to be printed, and then the letter H. For example, the statements:

```
    PRINT 105
105 FORMAT(I5H END OF PROBLEM)
```

would cause the computer to print "end of problem." Note that the number of Hollerith characters is listed as 15. The blank space after H and the two blank spaces between words must be included in the count.

5.4 SIMPLE FORTRAN PROGRAMS

Only two more FORTRAN statements are necessary before we will be able to write simple programs in FORTRAN. The first of these is the STOP statement. The word STOP is used to indicate to the computer that the calculation is over, and the machine should stop and wait for its next task. The second is the END statement. This statement is used to tell the FORTRAN compiler that there are no more statements in the program, so that the compiler can complete its task of constructing an object program.

5.41 Examples

Example 1. Write a FORTRAN program to read in three numbers A, B, and C, and compute and print their sum and their product.

A suitable program is:

```
      READ 101,A,B,C
      X = A + B + C
      Y = A*B*C
      PRINT 101,X,Y
      STOP
  101 FORMAT(3E12.4)
      END
```

This program would be used by punching the statements on cards, one statement per card. The FORTRAN compiler would be placed in memory, and the deck of cards with the above program, or source deck, in the card reader. The compiler would then write a machine language program, or object program, which could either be punched on cards for use at a later time, or left in the machine memory and executed as soon as the compilation was complete. This object program, when executed, would, in effect, cause the machine to execute the FORTRAN statements in the order in which they are listed in the above FORTRAN program.

Since the FORMAT statement is not executed but only provides information, its location in the program does not matter. We have chosen to place it at the end. Note also that the FORMAT statement provides formats for three numbers and the PRINT statement uses only two of these. The format E12.4 requires that the input numbers be in floating point form and that A be punched in the first twelve columns of the card, B in the next twelve columns, and C in the next twelve. Exponential form is used because we have no idea of the sizes of A, B, and C.

If we wanted a fancier printed output, we might replace the above PRINT statement by:

```
      PRINT 102,X,Y
```

and add another FORMAT statement:

102 FORMAT(6H SUM =,E12.4,10X,9HPRODUCT =,E12.4)

With these statements, the printed results will be a line containing the words SUM =, followed by the value of the sum, then ten blank spaces, then the words PRODUCT =, followed by the value of the product.

Example 2. Write a FORTRAN program which will read in the quantities XENGTH, WIDTH, HEIGHT, which are dimensions of a box in inches, and print out the total surface area in square feet and volume in cubic feet.

A suitable program is:

```
    READ 101,XENGTH,WIDTH,HEIGHT
    AREA=(XENGTH*WIDTH+WIDTH*HEIGHT+XENGTH
                                      *HEIGHT)/72.
    VOLUME=XENGTH*WIDTH*HEIGHT/1728.
    PRINT 101,AREA,VOLUME
    STOP
101 FORMAT(3E12.4)
    END
```

(In this program, the word LENGTH could not be used for length of a side because, beginning with "L," it would be treated by the machine as a fixed point variable.)

EXERCISE XI

1. Write a FORTRAN program that will read in four numbers A, B, C, and D and compute and print their average.

2. Write a FORTRAN program that will read in the radius and height of a cylinder and compute and print its total area and volume.

3. Write a FORTRAN program that will read in two numbers x and y, and compute and print the following quantities:

$$u = 2x + 4y$$
$$v = x^2 + 5xy + 4y^2$$
$$w = 3 + 4x + 5x^2 + 6x^3$$
$$z = (x + 2y)/(6x - 4y)$$

5.5 TRANSFER OF CONTROL

In the FORTRAN programs we have written so far the statements are executed in the same order in which they appear in the program. In Chapter IV we found many advantages in having machine language commands which could transfer control to other points in the program. There are similar advantages in being able to alter the order in which FORTRAN statements are executed. There are several FORTRAN statements designed for this purpose.

5.51   The "GO TO" Statement

The FORTRAN statement:

$$\text{GO TO } n$$

where n is the statement number of some other statement in the program, will cause statement n to be executed next.

Example 1. Write a program that will read in sets of three numbers A, B, and C, and compute and print their sum and product.

This is Example 1 of Section 5.41, except that the calculation is to be repeated for several sets of numbers A, B, and C. A suitable program is:

```
  1 READ 101,A,B,C
    X=A+B+C
    Y=A*B*C
    PRINT 101,X,Y
    GO TO 1
101 FORMAT(3E12.4)
    END
```

This program will read in a card, compute and print X and Y, and then the statement GO TO 1 will cause the calculation to return to statement 1 and read the next card. This process will continue until all cards are used up.

5.52   The "IF" Statement

The "GO TO" statement just discussed is analogous to the unconditional transfer in machine language. A FORTRAN statement analogous to the conditional transfer is also extremely useful. The "IF" statement serves this purpose. It is of the form:

$$\text{IF}(e) \; n_1, n_2, n_3$$

where e stands for any expression as described in Section 5.23, and n_1, n_2, and n_3 are statement numbers. If the value of the expression in parentheses is negative, control is transferred to n_1. If it is zero, control is transferred to n_2. If it is positive, control is transferred to n_3.

Example 1. Write a program that will read in pairs of numbers, A and B, and print out the smaller, or, if the numbers are equal, that will print the word "EQUAL."

A suitable program is:

```
  1 READ 101,A,B
    IF(A−B)2,3,4
  2 PRINT 101,A
    GO TO 1
  3 PRINT 102
    GO TO 1
  4 PRINT 101,B
    GO TO 1
101 FORMAT(2E12.4)
102 FORMAT(6H EQUAL)
    END
```

Statement 1 reads in a set of values for A and B, and the IF statement computes the difference A − B. If this number is negative, control is transferred to statement 2, which causes A to be printed. Then the GO TO 1 statement returns control to statement 1, and another set of values is read in. If A − B is zero, the IF statement transfers control to statement 3, which causes a print according to FORMAT statement 102, which is simply the word "EQUAL." Again there is a GO TO 1 statement to return control to statement 1 to read in another card. If A − B is positive, the IF statement transfers control to statement 4, which causes B to be printed. Again, there is a GO TO 1 statement to return control to statement 1 to read in another card. The "IF" statement serves as a branch point in the program switching control to 2, 3, or 4 depending on the value of A − B. The process continues as long as input cards are available.

Another use of the IF statement is to cause the machine to stop properly when the last data card has been executed. In the last few examples we have used the GO TO statement to cause the machine to return to a READ statement to read new input. This was a loop with no end, and we have said that the machine would stop when there was no input available. This is not a very desirable way of stopping, since so far as the machine is concerned it does not know the problem is completed, and hence sits waiting for more input. It is more efficient to stop the machine with a STOP command, which clearly indicates that the problem is completed and that the machine may proceed immediately to the next problem. This can be done with an IF statement as demonstrated in the following example.

Example 2. Write a program that will read in sets of three numbers A, B, and C, and compute and print their sum and product.

This is Example 1 of Section 5.51.   Suppose we know that the value of A never exceeds 10^{30}.   (For most problems such an assumption would be quite reasonable.   At least we will know something about A, and can use that knowledge to construct a test such as the one in the program below.)   Then we can use the program below to make the desired computation:

```
 1  READ 101,A,B,C
    IF(A−1.E30)2,3,3
 2  X=A+B+C
    Y=A*B*C
    PRINT 101,X,Y
    GO TO 1
 3  STOP
101  FORMAT(3E12.4)
    END
```

Here the IF statement is used as an exit from the loop.   In order to utilize it, we must place behind the real data cards a false data card with a value for A greater than 10^{30}.   Then when the machine reads this data card, the IF statement will cause a transfer to statement 3, which will stop the machine.

5.53   The Computed "GO TO" Statement

Another kind of conditional transfer statement is available in the FORTRAN language, the computed GO TO statement.   This statement has the form:

$$\text{GO TO } (n_1, n_2, \dots, n_m), i$$

where i is a fixed point variable and $n_1, n_2, \dots, n_m$ are statement numbers. If the value of i is 1 at the time this statement is reached, control will be transferred to statement n_1.   If i is 2, control will be transferred to statement n_2, etc.   This kind of statement is useful when the program may branch in any of several different directions.

Example 1.   Write a program that will input a value X, which may be in inches, feet, yards, or miles, and print out its value in yards.

Let us assume that each input card contains a value for X and also a fixed point constant I, which has the value 1 if X is in inches, 2 if it is in feet, 3 if it is in yards, and 4 if it is in miles.   Then a suitable program is:

```
 1  READ 101,X,I
    IF(X−1.E30)2,3,3
 2  GO TO(4,5,6,7),I
```

```
  4 X=X/36.
    GO TO 6
  5 X=X/3.
    GO TO 6
  7 X=1760.*X
  6 PRINT 101,X
    GO TO 1
  3 STOP
101 FORMAT(E12.4,I1)
    END
```

In this program we have again used an IF statement to stop the problem when all input cards have been used. The computed GO TO statement functions as follows: If X is in inches, $I = 1$, and transfer is to statement 4, which divides X by 36 to convert to yards. Then a transfer to 6 allows the value to be printed. If X is in feet, $I = 2$, and transfer is to statement 5, which divides X by 3 to convert to yards. Again a transfer to 6 allows the value to be printed. If X is in yards, $I = 6$, and transfer is to statement 6 for immediate printing. If X is in miles, transfer is to statement 7, which multiplies X by 1760 to convert to yards, and control proceeds to the next statement, statement 6, where X is printed. Note that the statements in this program are not numbered sequentially. Statement numbers are for identification only and need not appear in order throughout a program.

5.6 SUBSCRIPTED VARIABLES

It is common in mathematics to use subscripts on variable names in order to economize on notation. For example, if we wish to speak of a set of values of x, we may label them $x_1, x_2, x_3, \dots, x_n$. Sometimes such a set of quantities is referred to as an array, and each individual quantity as an element in the array. FORTRAN provides for the use of subscripts in variable names. The subscript is a positive fixed point constant or variable placed in parentheses after the variable name, thus:

$$X(1), X(2), \text{etc.} \quad \text{or} \quad X(I), X(M), \text{etc.}$$

(Note that zero is not allowed as a subscript.) A subscripted variable name can be used in FORTRAN statements just as any other variable name. For example, a statement to calculate a quantity $y = x_1 + x_2 + x_3$ might be written $Y=X(1)+X(2)+X(3)$. The subscript notation is of no particular value in a statement such as this one, however. Its chief value is that it frequently allows lengthy calculations to be programmed as loops. For example, the quantity $y = x_1 + x_2 + \cdots + x_{100}$ can be computed by the set of statements:

```
    Y=0.
    I=1
  5 Y=Y+X(I)
    I=I+1
    IF(101−I)6,6,5
  6 PRINT 10,Y
```

This FORTRAN loop is similar in many respects to the machine language loops described in the previous chapter.   The required sum is built up a term at a time in the memory location reserved for Y.   The fixed point number I serves as a counter to keep track of how many terms have been added, as well as a subscript for X to assure that the proper term is added at each step. The statements $Y = 0$ and $I = 1$ initialize the values of Y and I.   Statement 5 does the actual calculation, and the next statement advances by one the value of I.   The IF statement serves as an exit for the loop, sending the calculation back to statement 5 each time until X(100) has been added into the sum, then sending the calculation to statement 6 for printing the answer.

5.61   The DIMENSION Statement

So far we have written a few statements using subscripted variables, but have written no complete programs using subscript notation.   The reason for this is that a FORTRAN compiler is unable to compile a program containing subscripted variables unless it is given some advance information.   In compiling the program, it will need to know which variables are subscripted, and how many different values each subscript may have, so that it can save a memory location for each quantity to be stored.   This information is provided by a DIMENSION statement.   Before any subscripted variable appears in a program, it must be mentioned in a DIMENSION statement.   Usually a DIMENSION statement listing all the subscripted variables is placed at the beginning of the program.   This statement is of the form:

$$\text{DIMENSION } V_1, V_2, V_3, \cdots ,$$

where $V_1, V_2, V_3, \cdots$ are the names of the subscripted variables.   Each variable name must be followed, in parentheses, by the maximum value the subscript will have.   For example, a program involving a subscripted variable x_i, where i can be any integer from 1 to 100, would require a DIMENSION statement:

$$\text{DIMENSION } X(100)$$

Example 1. Write a dimension statement for a program that will use the subscripted variables $X(I)$, where I may be as large as 50, $ZAV(J)$, where J may be as large as 25, and $MOX(K)$, where K may be as large as 10.

A suitable statement is:

DIMENSION X(50),ZAV(25),MOX(10)

It should be noted that, when subscripted variables are used, a separate memory location is saved for each value of the subscript. This can use up available memory space very quickly, so subscripted variables should not be used unless they are actually needed. The following example demonstrates an unnecessary use of a subscripted variable.

Example 2. Write a program that will input the quantities x_1, x_2, ... , x_{100} and find and print their sum.

One program which will perform this task is the following:

```
   DIMENSION X(100)
   Y=0.
   I=1
 1 READ 50,X(I)
   Y=Y+X(I)
   I=I+1
   IF(101−I)2,2,1
 2 PRINT 50,Y
   STOP
50 FORMAT(E12.4)
   END
```

In this program, 100 memory locations are saved for the quantities $X(I)$. Each time statement 1 causes a new value of $X(I)$ to be read in, it will go into a new memory location. Immediately it is added into the value of Y, and then is no longer needed. The following program would do the calculation just as well, and without the wasted memory space:

```
   Y=0.
   I=1
 1 READ 50,X
   Y=Y+X
   I=I+1
   IF(101−I)2,2,1
 2 PRINT 50,Y
   STOP
50 FORMAT(E12.4)
   END
```

In the following example, the subscripted variable is really needed, since all 100 values are needed in memory at the same time.

Example 3. Write a program that will input 100 quantities $x_1, x_2, \ldots, x_{100}$ and print them out in order of size, from smallest to largest.

The following program will suffice:

```
      DIMENSION X(100)
      I=1
    1 READ 50,X(I)
      I=I+1
      IF(101-I)2,2,1
    2 A=1.E30
      I=0
    3 I=I+1
      IF(101-I)6,6,4
    4 IF(X(I)-A)5,3,3
    5 J=I
      A=X(I)
      GO TO 3
    6 IF(.9E30-A)8,8,7
    7 PRINT 50,A
      X(J)=1.1E30
      GO TO 2
    8 STOP
   50 FORMAT(E12.4)
      END
```

In this program, first all 100 values x_i are read in. Then a number A is used for comparison. It is first set equal to 10^{30} (we have assumed that all the x_i values are known to be less than this number). Each x_i in turn is compared to A, and, when one smaller than A is found, A is given that value, and the corresponding subscript is stored as the quantity J. After all 100 values x_i have been gone through in this fashion, the value A is equal to the smallest x_i. A is printed, and then the value of that particular x_i is set to 1.1×10^{30}, so that it cannot again be selected as the smallest. A is then reset to 10^{30}, and the process repeated. When all the x_i's have been selected as smallest, printed, and set equal to 1.1×10^{30}, the test in statement 6 will transfer control to 8, where the program will be stopped. In a later chapter, the subject of machine time is discussed. The astute reader may be able to find a method of rearranging the numbers which is faster than the method in the above program.

5.62 Double and Triple Subscripts

Sometimes it is convenient to have more than one subscript on a variable. For example, the transformation from one rectangular coordinate system to another is conveniently represented by the equations:

$$y_1 = a_{11}x_1 + a_{12}x_2 + a_{13}x_3$$
$$y_2 = a_{21}x_1 + a_{22}x_2 + a_{23}x_3$$
$$y_3 = a_{31}x_1 + a_{32}x_2 + a_{33}x_3$$

If the elements in an array have a single subscript, the array is called one-dimensional. If they have two subscripts, the array is two-dimensional, etc. Thus the nine coefficients a_{11}, a_{12}, etc. form a two-dimensional array. FORTRAN provides for the use of two- and three-dimensional arrays as well as one-dimensional arrays. A doubly subscripted variable is written in the form A(I,J), and a triply subscripted one in the form B(I,J,K). The DIMENSION statement must prescribe the maximum value for each subscript in a subscripted variable. Thus, if a program contains the subscripted variable B(I,J,K), where I may be as large as 10, J as large as 15, and K as large as 20, the DIMENSION statement should appear as:

DIMENSION B(10,15,20)

Example 1. Write a program that will input sets of values x_1, x_2, x_3, and compute and print y_1, y_2, y_3 according to the equation:

$$y_1 = a_{11}x_1 + a_{12}x_2 + a_{13}x_3$$
$$y_2 = a_{21}x_1 + a_{22}x_2 + a_{23}x_3$$
$$y_3 = a_{31}x_1 + a_{32}x_2 + a_{33}x_3$$

A suitable program is:

```
      DIMENSION X(3),Y(3),A(3,3)
      READ 101,A(1,1),A(1,2),A(1,3)
      READ 101,A(2,1),A(2,2),A(2,3)
      READ 101,A(3,1),A(3,2),A(3,3)
    1 READ 101,X(1),X(2),X(3)
      IF(X(1)-1.E30)2,3,3
    2 Y(1)=A(1,1)*X(1)+A(1,2)*X(2)+A(1,3)*X(3)
      Y(2)=A(2,1)*X(1)+A(2,2)*X(2)+A(2,3)*X(3)
      Y(3)=(3,1)*X(1)+A(3,2)*X(2)+A(3,3)*(3)
      PRINT 101,Y(1),Y(2),Y(3)
      GO TO 1
    3 STOP
  101 FORMAT(3E12.4)
      END
```

The above program makes use of subscript notation in identifying the quantities involved but does not take advantage of the capabilities of subscript notation for reducing the amount of writing required in the program. In Section 5.7 a somewhat neater way of programming this calculation will be given.

5.7   THE "DO" STATEMENT

It was seen earlier that loops may be constructed in FORTRAN by means of the IF statement.   Another extremely useful way of programming loops is provided by the DO statement.

This statement has the form:

$$\text{DO } n \; i = m_1, m_2, m_3$$

where n is the statement number of some later statement in the program, i is a fixed point variable, and m_1, m_2, and m_3 are positive fixed point constants or variables.   This statement is a command to repeat the sequence of FORTRAN statements which follow it, up to and including statement number n, altering the value of i each time.   The first time through, i is set equal to m_1.   Each successive time through the statements, i is increased by an amount m_3, until it exceeds m_2.   At that point control proceeds beyond statement n to the remainder of the program.   The quantity m_3 can be omitted, and, if it is, FORTRAN assumes the value of m_3 to be 1.

Example 1.   Write a program that will input the quantities $x_1, x_2, \ldots, x_{100}$ and find their sum.

This is Example 2 of Section 5.61.   Suitable programs were given there. Another suitable program is:

```
     Y=0.
     DO 4 I=1,100
     READ 50,X
   4 Y=Y+X
     PRINT 50,Y
     STOP
  50 FORMAT(E12.4)
     END
```

The DO statement sets $I = 1$.   Then the program reads a value of X and adds it to Y.   After statement 4 is executed, I is increased to 2, and the next value of X is read in and added to Y.   When finally $I = 100$, the 100th value of X is read in and added to Y.   Then control proceeds to the print statement.

Example 2. Write a program that will input sets of values x_1, x_2, x_3, and compute and print y_1, y_2, y_3 according to the equations:

$$y_1 = a_{11}x_1 + a_{12}x_2 + a_{13}x_3$$
$$y_2 = a_{21}x_1 + a_{22}x_2 + a_{23}x_3$$
$$y_3 = a_{31}x_1 + a_{32}x_2 + a_{33}x_3$$

This is Example 1 of Section 5.62. A suitable program was given there. Another suitable program is:

```
      DIMENSION X(3),Y(3),A(3,3)
      DO 1 I=1,3
    1 READ 101,A(I,1),A(I,2),A(I,3)
    2 READ 101,X(1),X(2),X(3)
      IF(X(1)-1.E30)3,4,4
    3 DO 5 I=1,3
      Y(I)=0.
      DO 5 J=1,3
    5 Y(I)=Y(I)+A(I,J)*X(J)
      PRINT 101,Y(1),Y(2),Y(3)
      GO TO 2
    4 STOP
  101 FORMAT(3E12.4)
      END
```

5.71 Restrictions on DO Loops

Certain rules must be observed in using the DO statement. The more important of these rules are listed below:

1. The last statement in a DO loop must not be GO TO, IF, or another DO statement. In order to assist in obeying this rule, FORTRAN provides a dummy statement which can be used when necessary as the final statement in a DO loop. This statement is simply the word CONTINUE.

2. The statement following a DO statement must not be a DIMENSION or FORMAT statement.

3. DO loops may be nested, but may not overlap. That is to say, if a DO statement occurs within a DO loop, it must set up a loop which terminates before or on the same statement as the other DO loop.

4. No statement may cause transfer of control from outside a DO loop to the interior of the loop.

5. No statement in a DO loop:

$$\text{DO } n \ i = m_1, m_2, m_3$$

may alter the values of i, m_1, m_2, or m_3.

5.8   FURTHER REMARKS

The preceding sections have covered the main characteristics of the FOR-
TRAN language.   Despite the universal character of this language, there are
a number of subtleties not mentioned above.   The reader should consult
the programming manuals for the particular machine he is using in order to
become properly aware of these subtleties.

EXERCISE XII

1.   Write FORTRAN programs which will read in values of x and compute and
     print corresponding values of y for each of the following equations:

$$\text{a.} \quad y = 3x + 5$$
$$\text{b.} \quad y = x^2 + 6x - 4$$
$$\text{c.} \quad y = 4x^3 + 6x^2 + 3x - 1$$

2.   Write FORTRAN programs that will read in values of x and compute and
     print corresponding values of y for each of the following equations.   In each
     case, there is some value or values of x which will make the denominator zero;
     have your program test for this, and in such cases, instead of trying to compute y,
     print "DENOMINATOR IS ZERO" and proceed to the next value.

$$\text{a.} \quad y = (3x + 2)/(x - 1)$$
$$\text{b.} \quad y = (x^2 + 2x + 7)/(x^2 - 3x + 4)$$
$$\text{c.} \quad y = (x^2 - 2x + 3)/(x^2 - x + 1)$$

3.   Write a program to read in 100 sets of values (x_i, y_i) and print them out in order
     of increasing value of $x_i^2 + y_i^2$ (i.e., increasing distance from the origin).

4.   Write a program to read in sets of values $x_1, x_2, \ldots, x_6$ and compute and print
     sets of values $y_1, y_2, \ldots, y_6$ according to the equations:

$$y_1 = a_{11}x_1 + a_{12}x_2 + \cdots + a_{16}x_6$$
$$y_2 = a_{21}x_1 + a_{22}x_2 + \cdots + a_{26}x_6$$
$$\cdot$$
$$\cdot$$
$$\cdot$$
$$y_6 = a_{61}x_1 + a_{62}x_2 + \cdots + a_{66}x_6$$

CHAPTER VI *Machine Time and Program Checkout*

6.1 INTRODUCTION

The successful performance of numerical calculations with a digital computer involves more than simply writing a program for the calculation. Blindly to write a program and place it on the computer with the expectation of immediate and correct answers is to invite trouble of many sorts. Before the program is placed on the machine, or even written down in detail for more complex calculations, it should be evaluated from three standpoints. They are:
- (*1*) How much computer time will the program require?
- (*2*) How can the program be tested for correctness?
- (*3*) How accurate will the results of the calculation be?

The method of evaluation of the program from the first two standpoints will be discussed in this chapter. The accuracy problem, which is by far the most difficult, was introduced in Chapter III and will be treated in more detail in later chapters.

6.2 COMPUTER TIME

If there is a single aspect of the digital computer which is most responsible for its growth and development in the last several years it is the speed with which it can calculate. This speed allows not only standard problems to be solved more quickly and easily than would be the case with hand calculators, but also the solution of complex problems whose solution would not even be attempted or considered without computers. If it takes a man ten seconds to multiply two eight digit numbers the man would not even consider attempting a calculation involving one billion multiplications by hand, for it would require working eight hours a day for nearly one hundred years. If a computer can perform a multiplication in one microsecond, this same calculation would require less than twenty minutes on the computer, so the problem is quite feasible on the computer.   On a slower computer which requires one millisecond to perform a multiplication, this same calculation would require one million seconds, or a little over ten days at twenty-four hours a day, or roughly one month utilizing eight-hour days.   Thus the time requirement for a particular problem determines whether or not it may be feasible to perform the calculation on a particular machine.   Since machine time is usually obtainable at a certain cost per hour (which varies greatly with the size and speed of the machine), the time required for the calculation determines the cost of obtaining the answers, and even for a calculation which is quite feasible the answers may not be worth the cost involved.   Hence it is worth while to be able to estimate the time required to perform the program. It would be extremely difficult to make an accurate prediction of the time requirement, and such a prediction is not needed in most cases.   However, a rough value, probably correct within about a factor of four, can be obtained by merely assigning a time for execution of each of the basic instructions, and then adding up the times for all the instructions involved in a program. If an instruction is in a loop to be performed fifteen times, for example, that instruction would have to be counted fifteen times.

6.21   Factors That Determine Machine Time

In order to estimate how long a computer will take to perform a calculation, we need to know how long is required to execute each of the basic commands. Generally speaking, except for input and print instructions, each command involves obtaining access to one or more memory locations (depending on whether the machine uses single address or multiple address commands) to read out the contents or store a result, and performing operations of some sort in the arithmetic unit.   The time required to execute, e.g., an "add" command, then, will depend upon how long it takes to obtain a number from a memory cell and how long it takes to send this number and the contents of the accumulator through the adder circuits.   For most commands, the time required to obtain a number from a memory cell is the longer time.   This "access time" can be used as an estimate of the time to execute most commands.   The access time depends very strongly on the type of memory used by the machine.   For a magnetic drum memory, where the memory cells are areas on a drum rotating at thousands of revolutions per minute, the access time will vary from one instruction to the next, depending upon how far the drum must rotate before the memory cell will be under a reading head. On the average, unless special pains are taken in the programming, the drum will have to turn half a revolution to get to the memory cell required by the next command.   The average access time in this type of memory is ordinarily on the order of a few milliseconds.   This time might be reduced considerably by clever programming based on an intimate knowledge of the internal timing of the computer to be used, for example, by choosing for storage locations for constants memory cells which will arrive under a reading head just when access will be required. Such "optimized" programming is done on routines which will be subject to much repeated usage on a machine, but the amount of effort involved in such programming is so great that it is not ordinarily attempted for the performance of every-day calculations. For other types of storage, such as magnetic core storage, the time required for access is appreciatively smaller than that for the magnetic drum. Such memories are much more expensive, but the additional speed ordinarily more than makes up for the added cost.

It was said above that access time usually governs the time to execute an instruction. This is not ordinarily true for the "multiply" and "divide" commands. As was seen in Chapter II, the multiplication and division operations are essentially a repetition of several addition or subtraction operations. Generally, the "multiply" and "divide" commands require several times the access time for their execution.

The other slow commands on a computer are input and output. These depend on the particular type of hardware being used as input and output units. Ordinarily these are by far the slowest commands for a machine to execute, even with the fastest of the input and output units, such as magnetic tape. Punched card or punched paper tape units are much slower, and direct printing output units are very much slower yet. In order to speed the output operation, results are frequently put on a magnetic tape and then typed on paper from the tape by a separate unit, so as not to tie up valuable computer time with this very slow operation. To gain still more speed, some machines are so constructed that, when "input" or "print" command is given, the machine can proceed to the execution of the next command without awaiting the completion of the input or output operation. This arrangement, called "buffering," requires more complex and expensive circuitry, but can result in quite considerable increases in speed.

6.22 Time Requirement for an Idealized Computer

In order that we may make somewhat realistic time estimates for problems later in this text, we introduce at this point some timing information for an idealized computer. We will consider that the operations of multiplication and division require a time t_m for execution, which we will call the multiplication time. All other commands, except "print" and "input," require a lesser time t_a for execution, which we will call the addition time. The "input" instruction will be assumed to require ten multiplication times. The print instruction will require some other time t_p, depending on the output method used. For simplicity we shall assume $t_p = 10t_m$ if the answers are going onto tape or other device, and $t_p = 100t_m$ if answers are being printed directly. The first method will be referred to as "off-line" printing and the second as "on-line" printing. We will further assume that multiplication takes 10 times as long as addition, that is $t_m = 10t_a$. Thus the number of multiplication times for a program can be determined by adding up all the multiplication and division instructions to be executed, then adding on 10 multiplication times for each input number, and 10 or 100 multiplication times for each "print," depending on the output unit, and adding on the total of all other instructions, divided by 10. Then, if the actual multiplication time for a particular machine is known, the problem time can be quickly estimated by multiplying this number by the number of multiplication times determined for the program. It is to be remembered that the time obtained will be only crude estimate, not an exact figure. However, it will be good enough to give a feel for the capabilities of current computers. For purposes of illustration, in the problems to follow we will estimate time for a "slow" machine, for which $t_m = 10$ milliseconds, and a "fast" machine, for which $t_m = 10$ microseconds. Our "fast" machine is not as fast as some already on the market, and machines 10 to 100 times this fast are not out of the question.

Example 1. Find the computer time required for Example 2 of Section 4.32 assuming on-line printing of the answers.

That program contained a loop of 9 instructions, each of which requires an addition time. The loop is to be performed about 1000 times. The instructions not in the loop are performed only once and so can be neglected timewise, except for the print command. The total time for the loop is:

$$9 \times 1000t_a = 9000t_a = 900t_m$$

The print command adds $100t_m$, giving a total of $1000t_m$. If t_m is 10 milliseconds, then the running time for the machine is about:

$$1000 \times 10 \times .001 = 10 \text{ seconds}$$

If $t_m = 10$ microseconds, then the time required is:

$$1000 \times 10 \times 10^{-6} = .01 \text{ second}$$

6.23 Time Estimates for FORTRAN Programs

As explained in Chapter V, a common way of preparing a program for a scientific calculation is to write a source program for use with a compiler such as FORTRAN. When this is done, the machine will eventually execute a machine language program. The input and print operations, as well as the multiply and divide operations and the main loops in this machine language program, can readily be predicted by looking at the FORTRAN program itself. Thus, the time rules given above can be applied to make time estimates for execution of FORTRAN programs. Prior to executing the program, however, the machine must compile an object program from the source program. This operation also consumes computer time; for relatively short calculations, the operation can require as much or even more time than the calculation itself. It is difficult to give general rules for estimating this time, and such estimates are best made on the basis of experience with the particular compiler and computer to be used. We will not consider compilation time further in this text, but will leave the subject with the admonition that compilation time can sometimes be significant.

6.24   Time Estimates from Equations

Even before the program is written, it is possible to make a rough estimate of the running time of a problem simply by estimating the number of additions (or subtractions), multiplications (or divisions), and inputs and outputs. Unless the calculation will involve unusually complicated loops, the control or logical intructions required in the program can usually be ignored without too great an error.

Example 1.   Estimate the time required to compute and print, off-line, the value of $y = 1 + 2x + 3x^2 + 4x^3 + 5x^4$ for 5000 different values of x.

The 5000 inputs require $5000 \times 10t_m = 50,000t_m$. (This ignores the five inputs of the constants, 1, 2, 3, 4, 5; since these need only be entered once, the time for these can be neglected in making a rough estimate.) While there appear to be many multiplications in the above calculation, the number can be reduced considerably by doing the operations in the best order. If one merely computes term by term, there is one multiplication for the second term, two for the third, three for the fourth, and four for the fifth, for a total of 10 multiplications (the additions can be neglected). If the terms are grouped as:

$$1 + x(2 + x(3 + x(4 + 5x)))$$

only four multiplications are required. With this latter method, the calculation for 5000 values of x will require roughly $5000 \times 4t_m = 20,000t_m$. The off-line printing will require $5000 \times 10t_m$. The total time, then, is $120,000t_m$. If $t_m = 10$ milliseconds, the total time is 1200 seconds, or 20 minutes. If $t_m = 10$ microseconds, the total time is 1.2 seconds. Note that largest proportion of the time is input and output time. If on-line printing had been used, the output time would have been $500,000t_m$, and the total time $570,000t_m$, almost five times as long.

Example 2.   Estimate the time for Problem 1 if the 5,000 values of x are equally spaced, each being larger than the preceding one by a fixed amount Δx.

In this case we do not need to read each x value into the machine, but only the first value of x and the value Δx. Then we can obtain succeeding values of x by repeated additions of Δx. Thus only 7 inputs are required; the numbers 1, 2, 3, 4, 5, the first value of x, and the value of Δx. The generation of a new value of x requires only three commands, of the form:

Bring x
Add Δx
Clear to the storage location reserved for x

These instructions require only an addition time each and, compared to the time $4t_m$ required for computation, can safely be ignored. Thus the total time for the problem is effectively only calculation time plus output time. From the previous example, these are $20,000t_m$ and $50,000t_m$, giving a total of $70,000t_m$. For a slow machine, $t_m = 10$ milliseconds, and the total time is 700 seconds, or about 12 minutes.

6.25   *Influence of Time Factors on Programming*

Since the major basic asset of the digital computer is its speed, it follows that programming should not be done in such a way as to waste the computer's time.   There are many ways in which the programmer can write his program in order to conserve computer time.   Although this text is not intended as a vehicle for training in the finer points of programming, some of the influences of time factors on programming do merit discussion.

It has been mentioned that input and output are by far the slowest operations for most computers.   The programmer should be careful, then, not to include unneeded inputs and outputs in his program.   Examples 1 and 2 of the preceding section illustrate this point.   Example 1 puts in each value of x as needed, and requires 20 minutes on a slow machine.   Example 2 generates the values of x internally, and requires only 12 minutes.   The problem in Example 2 is identical to that in Example 1, except that the values of x are equally spaced in Example 2.   The same program could be used for both problems, but an appreciable saving in time results from avoiding unnecessary inputs.   Another illustration is contained in Example 3 of Section 4.32.   In the first program for that example, there are 14 constants, plus three values x_1, x_2, and x_3 needed as inputs.   The program is written so as to have two separate loops, one putting in the 14 constants, the other putting in the values of x_1, x_2, x_3.   It would have been easier to write the program including all the inputs in one loop.   However, this would have required that all constants be read into the machine each time a new set x_1, x_2, x_3 is read in, a process that would probably quadruple the running time of the problem if many sets of x values are to be used.

Another way in which time can be conserved in calculations is by proper grouping of terms in algebraic expressions. Since the "multiply" and "divide" commands take the longest time for execution, expressions should ordinarily be grouped to minimize the number of these operations. Example 1 of Section 6.24 illustrates how proper grouping cuts the calculational effort from ten to four multiplications. In that particular example, if the wrong grouping of terms had been used, the calculational time would have been roughly $5000 \times 10t_m$ or $50{,}000t_m$. The total problem time on a slow machine with off-line printing would have been $150{,}000t_m$, or 25 minutes, as opposed to 20 minutes when terms are properly grouped.

When loops are used in a program, care should be taken to include only required calculations in the loop. The two solutions given for Example 1, below, illustrate how the total number of multiplications performed in a program is sometimes drastically affected by the way in which a loop is constructed.

Example 1. Write a FORTRAN program that will input values of constants a, b, and c, and compute and print $y = a^2 + b^2 + 2cx$ for $x = 1, 2, \ldots, 1000$.

One program is:

```
      READ 101,A,B,C
      X=0.
      DX=1.
      DO 2 I=1,1000
      X=X+DX
      Y=A*A+B*B+2.*C*X
    2 PRINT 101,X,Y
      STOP
  101 FORMAT (3E12.4)
      END
```

In this program, the products A∗A, B∗B, and 2.∗C are each formed 1000 times, instead of just once, because they occur inside a DO loop. Nearly 3000 unneeded multiplications are performed by the program. These unneeded multiplications are avoided if the program is written as follows:

```
      READ 101,A,B,C
      SQ=A*A+B*B
      TWOC=2.*C
      X=0.
      DX=1.
      DO 2 I=1,1000
      X=X+DX
```

```
       Y = SQ + TWOC*X
   2 PRINT 101,XY
       STOP
 101 FORMAT (3E12.4)
       END
```

6.3   CORRECTNESS OF THE PROGRAM

It is obvious that a program containing an erroneous command, or even an erroneous digit in the address portion of some command, will probably produce incorrect results.   It might be thought that we should dispose of this problem with the simple statement that one must use great care in programming and must recheck the program very carefully.   However, the larger calculations usually involve such a long and complicated sequence of commands, and the human tendency to err in writing such a sequence is so great, that no amount of review of the program can be depended upon to ensure that the program actually does what it is supposed to do.   This is true even when the program is written in an abbreviated form, as in FOR-TRAN.   In nearly every case, it is advisable to check the program by comparing the results of a few cases with the results of hand calculations.   This does not mean that it is necessary to duplicate all of the machine's operations by hand—indeed, this would be impossible from the standpoint of time. Ordinarily, however, the program requires the machine to repeat the same sequence of instructions hundreds or thousands of times, and if they are performed correctly once they can ordinarily be presumed to be performed correctly thereafter.   Furthermore, if the program gives correct answers with one set of input numbers, it will generally give correct answers for other sets.   (This is not an infallible rule, as we shall see shortly.)   Thus a check calculation can usually be prepared which will utilize numbers that make for simple hand calculations, but which will serve to check that the machine is performing all the steps of the calculation properly.   In preparing such check calculations, it is desirable to choose numbers that make the hand calculation simple, but care must be taken lest the numbers chosen be so simple as to fail to check the entire operation.

No universally applicable set of steps can be given for the construction of check calculations, but the following examples will illustrate some of the considerations involved.

Example 1.   Prepare a check calculation for the problem:

$$y = \frac{1 + x}{1 + 2x}$$

This particular illustration is so simple as to be almost trivial, but it will serve to illustrate a few points.   The simplest check is to feed $x = 0$ into the machine as the input value for x; the computed result should be $y = 1$. However, the fact that the machine produces $y = 1$ for $x = 0$ is not very much of a check on the correctness of the program. In fact, the machine may be performing a completely wrong operation with the term $+x$ in the numerator and the $+2x$ term in the denominator, but because the test value $x = 0$ eliminates these terms, we do not see the indications of such errors. The program might be doing:

$$y = \frac{1}{1} \qquad \text{or} \qquad y = \frac{1 + x^2}{1 + 4x}$$

or any number of other calculations instead of the desired ones and our check calculation would not indicate anything amiss. Thus it is dangerous to use $x = 0$ as a check value in this case; and in general it is dangerous to use numbers that will cause part of the terms to vanish, unless separate checks are arranged to make sure these terms are computed correctly.

In the present example, one might try $x = 1$ for a check value. This should give the result $y = 2/3$. If this value of y is obtained, we have some confidence in the program. Yet there are some relatively simple mistakes in programming that would produce the correct value of y for this case even with an erroneous program. For example, in terms of the hypothetical computer described in Chapter II, suppose the number 1 is stored in 3151 and the number x is stored in 3152. Then the machine language commands which are to compute the numerator might be:

B 3151
A 3152

which gives $1 + x$, or for the case $x = 1$ gives $1 + 1 = 2$. If the program is accidentally written:

B 3151
A 3151

this part of the calculation will still give 2 for the numerator, and the machine will be computing:

$$y = \frac{2}{1 + 2x}$$

A slightly different mistake would be:

B 3152
A 3152

which would again produce 2 for the numerator, and the machine would be computing:

$$y = \frac{2x}{1 + 2x}$$

In either of these cases the machine will still produce $y = 2/3$ for $x = 1$. Thus it appears that the check calculation using $x = 1$ is not a very safe one, primarily because there are ones appearing elsewhere in the problem, and this test value will not disclose errors in which one is used in the place of x, or vice versa.   It appears, then, that it is not advisable to use test inputs identical to any of the constants in the problem.

Other values of x, such as $x = 4$, which gives $y = 5/9$, are generally much less likely to give a false check on the calculation.   Still, the check is not absolute, and the use of two or more check values is frequently advisable.   A value that is clearly a poor choice is $x = -1/2$.   This choice makes the denominator 0, and would cause the machine to stop.

Example 2.   A machine language program has been prepared which will calculate $(1 + x)/(1 + 2x)$ for 1000 values of x that are stored in memory locations 1001 to 2000.   Prepare a check calculation for this program.

Let us assume that the actual program is:

0000	I	0000
0001	C	0980 (inputs 1 into 980)
0002	I	0000
0003	C	0981 (inputs 2 into 981)
0004	B	1001
0005	B	0004 (initializes register 0007)
0006	C	0007
0007	B	[1001] (brings next value of x)
0008	C	0982 (clears x into 0982, working storage)
0009	B	0982 (x to accumulator)
0010	M	0981 ($2x$ formed in accumulator)
0011	A	0980 ($1 + 2x$ formed in accumulator)
0012	C	0983 ($1 + 2x$ cleared to 0983, working storage)
0013	B	0982 (x to accumulator)
0014	A	0980 ($1 + x$ formed in accumulator)
0015	D	0983 ($(1 + x)/(1 + 2x)$ formed in accumulator)
0016	P	0000
0017	B	0007 (bring B command to be modified)
0018	L	2000 (skip if B 2000 has already been executed)
0019	U	0021
0020	Z	0000
0021	N	0001 (increment address of B command)
0022	C	0007
0023	U	0007

The arithmetic calculation for this problem is identical to that of Example 1 above. The same considerations apply for choosing test values for x. The values $x = 0$, $x = 1$, or $x = -1/2$ would be poor choices, but most other choices would be satisfactory. Apart from the problem of checking the arithmetic calculations involved in the above program, however, there is the problem of checking what might be termed the bookkeeping activities. Does the program indeed cause the quantity $(1 + x)/(1 + 2x)$ to be computed for each x stored in the locations from 1001 to 2000? Nearly as many of the commands in the program are for the purpose of assisting in obtaining the next consecutive value of x from memory as are concerned with calculating the desired quantity once a value for x is available. If one of these commands is wrong, the machine may use wrong values for x and give incorrect results even though it is performing the correct arithmetic. A good check calculation will test the bookkeeping part of the program as well as the arithmetic. One might think, for example, that one could obtain an adequate check of the above program by preparing a program and an input tape which will store $x = 4$ in memory locations 1001, 1002, 1003, etc. and seeing if the problem run with this set of x values will print $y = 5/9$ several times in a row. This is a partial check, but not a very good one. If the command in 0022 were to happen to read C 0077 by mistake, then the machine would indeed print out $y = 5/9$ over and over, regardless of what might be the value of x in any location after the first, for the command B 1001 stored in 0007 would never be altered. In this case, if the machine were allowed to run through all 1000 of its assigned calculations, it would be discovered that it would not stop after 1000 times, since the address in 0007 would never become 2000. However, because of the machine time involved, the programmer may be required to check the calculation only through a few cycles rather than through all 1000 cycles. In this case the failure of the program to take consecutive values of x would not be noted by merely using one value of x over and over. A more reliable check could be obtained by utilizing for the check calculation alternating values of x: $x = 4$, then $x = 5$, then $x = 4$, then $x = 5$, etc. This tape should produce alternating answers: $y = 5/9$, $y = 6/11$, $y = 5/9$, $y = 6/11$, etc. While it is possible that the program could perform these calculations correctly and still contain errors, the probability is rather low.

The principles demonstrated above for machine language programs apply as well to FORTRAN programs.

Example 3. The following program is designed to input values of a quantity u and calculate y from the formulas:

$$y = \frac{1 + u}{1 + 2u} \text{ if } u > 0$$

$$y = 1 + 4u + u^2 \text{ if } u \leqslant 0$$

Write input data for a check calculation for this program:

```
  1 READ 101,U
    IF(U — 1.E30)2,2,3
  2 IF(U)4,4,5
  4 Y = 1.+U*(4.+U)
    GO TO 6
  5 Y = (1.+U)/(1.+2.*U)
  6 PRINT 101,Y
    GO TO 1
  3 STOP
101 FORMAT(E12.4)
    END
```

In this program there are two arithmetic statements, the statements 4 and 5. Statement 5 is the same equation discussed in Example 1 above, in which it was seen that there are a few test values that would be poor choices. A value mentioned as a satisfactory one for checking that calculation was 4. Thus, $U = 4$ would be a good test value for the program. At least one other test value should be used also, a negative value of U. This is required for two purposes: first, to check the arithmetic statement 4; and second, to check statement 2. Note that statement 2 decides which equation will be used to compute Y. Even if both statements 4 and 6 are correct, we can obtain a wrong result if statement 2 picks the wrong equation. For example, it happens that, on the standard key punch keyboard, the character U and the numeral 1 are on the same key, U being the lower case symbol and 1 being the upper case symbol. Thus, it would be quite easy accidentally to print statement 2 as:

```
  2 IF(1)4,4,5
```

If this were done, the program would run, but would use the formula in statement 5 for both positive and negative U. The use of both a positive and a negative value of U as check values, say $U = 4$ and $U = -2$, would provide reasonable assurance that the program is correct. These inputs should cause the machine to give the results $Y = 5/9$ and $Y = -3$.

The above examples demonstrate that a good check calculation should check control statements as well as arithmetic statements. In many problems the checking of control statements is a much more imposing task than the checking of arithmetic statements, but is one that cannot safely be ignored.

6.31   *Programming Aids to Check Calculations*

It is frequently advisable to include extra instructions (or FORTRAN statements) within a program for the sole purpose of assisting in the checking of the program for correctness. These instructions most often take the form

of extra print instructions which will cause the machine to print out intermediate results that can be used for check purposes, or extra stop instructions
so that the machine will halt at some intermediate points in the program.
Such aids not only assist in determination of whether the program is right or
wrong, but also assist in determining in what section of the program the
faulty command or commands may be. For lengthy programs this can be a
most valuable aid. When the program is finally checked, these extra commands are removed, or in some other fashion ignored, for the "production
run," the final calculation using the real problem input data.

In FORTRAN, many checks are built into the compiler itself. For
example, the compiler will ordinarily refuse to compile a program in which
there are expressions mixing fixed and floating point expressions, or one
having improperly nested DO loops, or IF statements referring to non-
existent statement numbers, etc. In fact, a good compiler is so efficient in
finding programming errors that it is a temptation to assume that a program
which compiles successfully must be correct. This is not a safe assumption,
and the experienced programmer has usually learned by sad experience that
a program should not be trusted until checked and rechecked in every
reasonable way.

EXERCISE XIII

1. Using the timing information given in Section 6.22 for a fast machine, estimate
the machine time requirement for the following problems, including input,
calculation, and output, both on-line and off-line:

    a. $y = 1 + 3x^2 + 5x^4$, for 5000 unequally spaced values of x.

    b. $y = x_1 + 2x^3 + 7x^5 + 4x^7$, for 10,000 equally spaced values of x.

    c. $y = \dfrac{1 + 6x + 9x^3 + x^6}{2 + 4x^2 + 5x^5}$ for 10,000 equally spaced values of x.

    d. $y = x_1 + 4x_1x_2 + 3x_1^2x_2^2 + 5x_2^3$ for 5000 different *pairs* of values, x_1, x_2.

    e. $y = x_1^2 + x_2^2 + x_3^2 + x_4^2 + x_5^2$ for 1000 different *sets* of values,
       x_1, x_2, x_3, x_4, x_5.

2. Write a FORTRAN program for each of the calculations indicated in Problem 1.

3. Write a set of input data that will check both the arithmetic and the bookkeeping portions of the calculation for each of the programs in Problem 2.
Indicate two errors that could exist in your program and not be discovered by
your check calculation.

CHAPTER VII *Evaluation of Functions by Series Approximation*

7.1 INTRODUCTION

So far the computer programs discussed have been restricted to those involving only addition, subtraction, multiplication, and division. Since many of the calculations of higher mathematics require the use of sines, cosines, logarithms, exponentials, or even more sophisticated functions, it might appear that computer use would be restricted only to problems of a very elementary nature. A little reflection will make it clear, however, that wherever numbers are involved there are indeed only the four basic arithmetic operations for determining specific values. If the sine of an angle is required during a hand calculation, one ordinarily looks in a table of sines to obtain the value, and then uses it in the calculation. The person who prepared the table, however, must either have obtained the value from another table or have computed the value, possibly by using terms in a power series expansion, and performing a sequence of multiplications, divisions, additions, and subtractions, to determine the final value. It is possible to make the sines of angles, or the values of any of a large number of functions, available to a digital computer by either of the above methods: by storing a table of values within the memory of the machine and writing a program which will cause the machine to choose the correct value from this table, or by writing a program which will compute the required value directly from the series expansion or some other approximate relation. The computer performs arithmetic so rapidly that direct calculation is usually preferred to table look-up; however, both methods are used. This chapter will deal with the problem of computing of values of sines, cosines, and other functions directly by series or polynomial approximations.

148

7.2 TAYLOR'S FORMULA

In the calculus it was learned that any function of a single, real variable x, which behaved certain rather general rules, could be expanded into a power series by means of Taylor's formula.   Two standard forms of this formula are:

$$f(x) = f(a) + (x - a)f'(a) + \frac{(x - a)^2}{2!}f''(a) + \dots + \frac{(x - a)^{(n-1)}}{(n - 1)!}f^{(n-1)}(a)$$

$$+ \frac{(x - a)^n}{n!}f^{(n)}[a + \theta(x - a)], \qquad 0 < \theta < 1 \qquad \text{(7-1)}$$

$$f(x + h) = f(x) + hf'(x) + \frac{h^2}{2!}f''(x) + \dots + \frac{h^{n-1}}{(n - 1)!}f^{(n-1)}(x)$$

$$+ \frac{h^n}{n!}f^{(n)}(x + \theta h), \qquad 0 < \theta < 1 \qquad \text{(7-2)}$$

On putting $a = 0$ in (7-1) we obtain Maclaurin's formula:

$$f(x) = f(0) + xf'(0) + \frac{x^2}{2!}f''(0) + \dots + \frac{x^{n-1}}{(n - 1)!}f^{(n-1)}(0)$$

$$+ \frac{x^n}{n}f^{(n)}(\theta x), \qquad 0 < \theta < 1 \qquad \text{(7-3)}$$

The last term in these expressions may not look quite familiar to the survivor of a course in elementary calculus.   Frequently the significance of that term, or even its existence, is not stressed at that level of mathematical training. It is called the remainder term.   If one wishes to generate an infinite series for $f(x)$, one keeps making n larger and larger so that the remainder term moves farther and farther out in the series.   If the remainder term tends to zero as n tends to infinity, then the series converges, and gives an exact representation of the function $f(x)$.   If we wish to approximate $f(x)$ for some particular value of x, we compute several of the terms of the series and sum these terms to get the approximation.   The question then arises: how large is the error introduced by taking only a finite number of terms for the sum? That question is answered in each of the expressions (7-1), (7-2), (7-3) above. Directing our attention to expression (7-1), we see that the first n terms, which involve the zero'th derivative through the $n - 1$st derivative, are just the first n terms of a standard Taylor's series, and the remaining term, which has a somewhat different appearance, is the term we have called the remainder term.   We see that expression (7-1) states that $f(x)$ is not just approximately equal to the sum of these terms, but that $f(x)$ is *precisely* equal to the sum of these terms. This is why we refer to expression (7-1) as "Taylor's Formula" rather than "Taylor's Series." It is an exact relation between two quantities, both of which are expressed in quite finite form, without any infinite series being involved. If we wish to approximate $f(x)$ by the first n terms of the right hand side of expression (7-1), the error we make in so doing is given exactly by the remainder term. There is one catch. The quantity θ in this remainder term is some number we do not know, and usually cannot even calculate. All we do know about it is that it is some number between zero and one. Hence we cannot usually say what the exact value of the error is. This is not a great concern, however, if we can somehow estimate the maximum possible size of the remainder term. Then, by proper choice of n, the number of terms, we may be able to make the maximum possible error sufficiently small that it can be tolerated.

7.21   *Examples of the Use of Taylor's Formula*

As a review in the use of Taylor's Formula we will develop a few functions according to the expressions (7-1), (7-2), and (7-3).

Example 1.   Write the Maclaurin expansion for e^x.

SOLUTION: Here:

$$f(x) = e^x \qquad\qquad f(0) = 1$$
$$f'(x) = e^x \qquad\qquad f'(0) = 1$$
$$f''(x) = e^x \qquad\qquad f''(0) = 1$$
$$f'''(x) = e^x \qquad\qquad f'''(0) = 1$$
$$f^{iv}(x) = e^x \qquad\qquad f^{iv}(0) = 1$$

etc.

$$f^{(n-1)}(x) = e^x \qquad f^{(n-1)}(0) = 1$$
$$f^{(n)}(x) = e^x \qquad f^{(n)}(\theta x) = e^{\theta x}$$

Substituting these quantities in expression (7-3), we obtain:

$$e^x = 1 + x + \frac{x^2}{2!} + \frac{x^3}{3!} + \dots + \frac{x^{n-1}}{(n-1)!} + \frac{x^n}{n!} e^{\theta x}, \qquad 0 < \theta < 1$$

Example 2.   Write the Taylor expansion for $\ln x$ about the point $x = 1$.

SOLUTION: Here:

$$f(x) = \ln x \qquad\qquad\qquad f(1) = 0$$

$$f'(x) = 1/x \qquad\qquad\qquad f'(1) = 1$$

$$f''(x) = -1/x^2 \qquad\qquad\qquad f''(1) = -1$$

$$f'''(x) = +2/x^3 \qquad\qquad\qquad f'''(1) = 2$$

$$f^{iv}(x) = -2 \times \frac{3}{x^4} \qquad\qquad\qquad f^{iv}(1) = -2 \times 3$$

$$\cdot \qquad\qquad\qquad\qquad \cdot$$
$$\cdot \qquad\qquad\qquad\qquad \cdot$$
$$\cdot \qquad\qquad\qquad\qquad \cdot$$

$$f^{(n-1)}(x) = (-1)^n(n-2)!/x^{n-1} \qquad f^{(n-1)}(1) = (-1)^n(n-2)!$$

$$f^{(n)}(x) = (-1)^{n+1}(n-1)!/x^n \qquad f^{(n)}[1 + \theta(x-1)]$$

$$= (-1)^{n+1}(n-1)!/[1 + \theta(x-1)]^n$$

Substituting these values in expression (7-1), remembering that $a = 1$ in this case, we obtain:

$$\ln x = (x-1) - \frac{1}{2!}(x-1)^2 + \frac{2}{3!}(x-1)^3 - \frac{2 \times 3}{4!}(x-1)^4$$

$$+ \cdots + \frac{(-1)^n(n-2)!(x-1)^{n-1}}{(n-1)!} + \frac{(-1)^{n+1}(n-1)!(x-1)^n}{n![1 + \theta(x-1)]^n}, \qquad 0 < \theta < 1$$

or, simplifying the expression:

$$\ln x = (x-1) - \frac{(x-1)^2}{2} + \frac{(x-1)^3}{3} - \frac{(x-1)^4}{4}$$

$$+ \cdots + \frac{(-1)^n(x-1)^{n-1}}{n-1} + \frac{(-1)^{n+1}(x-1)^n}{n(1 - \theta + \theta x)^n}, \qquad 0 < \theta < 1$$

Example 3. Write the Maclaurin expansion for $\sin x$.

SOLUTION: Here:

$$f(x) = \sin x \qquad f(0) = 0$$

$$f'(x) = \cos x \qquad f'(0) = 1$$

$$f''(x) = -\sin x \qquad f''(0) = 0$$

$$f'''(x) = -\cos x \qquad f'''(0) = -1$$

$$f^{iv}(x) = \sin x \qquad f^{iv}(0) = 0$$

etc.

$$f^n(x) = ?$$

Here the pattern of the derivatives is quite clear—the sequence $\sin x$, $\cos x$, $-\sin x$, $-\cos x$, is repeated over and over. However, since the value of $\sin 0$ is zero, there is no particular point in stopping the series when the next term is a sine term, since no calculational effort is saved by doing so. Let us agree for now, then, that n will be an odd number, $n = 2p + 1$, where p is an integer. Then, we can write:

$$f^{(n)}(x) = (-1)^{(n-1)/2} \cos x = (-1)^p \cos x$$

Now, utilizing expression (7-3), we can write:

$$\sin x = x - \frac{x^3}{3!} + \frac{x^5}{5!} + \cdots + \frac{(-1)^p x^{2p+1} \cos \theta x}{(2p+1)!}, \qquad 0 < \theta < 1$$

7.22   A Program for the Exponential Function

In order to determine the error involved in approximating a function by its Taylor expansion, it is necessary to establish the maximum value of the remainder term. For the exponential function of the preceding section, this remainder was $x^n e^{\theta x}/n!$, where θ is some number between 0 and 1. If we are to establish an upper limit on the value of this quantity without further knowledge of the value of θ, we must choose that value of θ which will maximize the expression. For this expression the value $\theta = 1$ is the proper choice. It we use n terms of the Taylor expansion to approximate e^x, the error will certainly not be greater than $x^n e^x/n!$. If we are interested in writing a computer routine which will compute e^x to eight significant figures, then, by Corollary 3 of Chapter III, we should insist on a relative error of less than

$1/(2 \times 10^8)$.   Thus, we wish to have:

$$\frac{\dfrac{x^n}{n!}e^x}{e^x} < \frac{1}{2 \times 10^8}$$

or

$$\frac{x^n}{n!} < \frac{1}{2 \times 10^8}$$

It is clear that the value of n required depends on how big a value of x we desire to be able to handle.   For example, if $x = 1$ is the largest value required, we must have:

$$\frac{1}{n!} < \frac{1}{2 \times 10^8}$$

or $n! > 2 \times 10^8$.   This is satisfied by $n = 12$.   If we desired to have a series expansion suitable for values of x up to $x = 10$, we would need:

$$\frac{10^n}{n!} < \frac{1}{2 \times 10^8}$$

which will require $n = 41$, or 41 terms.   This would be a much longer calculation.   On the other hand, it is not necessary to use this many terms if we simply apply the laws of exponents.   For example, $e^{5.632} = e^5 \times e^{.632}$. The factor e^5 can be computed by multiplying e by itself five times.   The factor $e^{.632}$ can be computed to sufficient accuracy with twelve terms of a Maclaurin expansion.   To the accuracy required:

$$e^x = 1 + x + \frac{x^2}{2!} + \frac{x^3}{3!} + \frac{x^4}{4!} + \frac{x^5}{5!} + \frac{x^6}{6!} + \frac{x^7}{7!} + \frac{x^8}{8!} + \frac{x^9}{9!} + \frac{x^{10}}{10!} + \frac{x^{11}}{11!}$$

or, in a form requiring a smaller number of multiplications to compute:

$$e^x = 1 + x\left(1 + x\left(\frac{1}{2!} + x\left(\frac{1}{3!} + x\left(\frac{1}{4!} + x\left(\frac{1}{5!} + x\left(\frac{1}{6!} + x\left(\frac{1}{7!} + x\left(\frac{1}{8!} + x\left(\frac{1}{9!}\right.\right.\right.\right.\right.\right.\right.\right.\right.$$
$$\left.\left.\left.\left.\left.\left.\left.\left.\left. + x\left(\frac{1}{10!} + \frac{x}{11!}\right)\right)\right)\right)\right)\right)\right)\right)\right)$$

In FORTRAN, the constants for this expression could be determined by the statements:

```
DIMENSION A(11)
A(1)=1.
DO 2 J=2,11
FJ=J
2 A(J)=A(J-1)/FJ
```

With these coefficients, e^x could be calculated by the loop:

```
Y=X*A(11)+A(10)
DO 4 I=1,9
J=10-I
4 Y=Y*X+A(J)
Y=Y*X+1.
```

or by the single lengthy statement:

```
Y=((((((((((X+A(11))+A(10))*X+A(9))*X+A(8))*X+A(7))*X+A(6))*X
  +A(5))*X+A(4))*X+A(3))*X+A(2))*X+A(1))*X+1.
```

7.23   A Program for the Sine Function

The remainder term in the Maclaurin expansion of the sine function, from Section 7.21, was $(-1)^p x^{2p+1} \cos \theta x / (2p + 1)!$. If we desire the relative error to be less than $1/(2 \times 10^8)$, we note that $\cos \theta x < 1$, so that we require:

$$\frac{1}{\sin x} \frac{x^{2p+1}}{(2p + 1)!} < \frac{1}{2 \times 10^8}$$

Again the value of p, the number of terms required, depends on how large a value of x must be accommodated. Because of the periodicity of the sine function, it is certainly sufficient to consider only $x < 2\pi$. Also, since $\sin(\pi + x) = -\sin x$, values of x between π and 2π can be replaced by values between 0 and π. Further, since $\sin(\pi - x) = \sin x$, angles between $\pi/2$ and π can be replaced by angles between 0 and $\pi/2$. For values of x between 0 and $\pi/2$, the sin x in the denominator is no problem, since $1 \leqslant x/(\sin x) \leqslant \pi/2$ for x in this range. The largest value of the left hand side of the inequality occurs when $x = \pi/2$. For this value of x, the inequality is satisfied by $2p + 1 = 15$, or $p = 7$. Thus the value of the sine function will be given to eight significant figures by the expression:

$$\sin x = x - \frac{x^3}{3!} + \frac{x^5}{5!} - \frac{x^7}{7!} + \frac{x^9}{9!} - \frac{x^{11}}{11!} + \frac{x^{13}}{13!}$$

or, in a form which can be evaluated with a minimum of multiplication:

$$\sin x = x\left(1 - x^2\left(\frac{1}{3!} - x^2\left(\frac{1}{5!} - x^2\left(\frac{1}{7!} - x^2\left(\frac{1}{9!} - x^2\left(\frac{1}{11!} - \frac{x^2}{13!}\right)\right)\right)\right)\right)\right)$$

A pair of FORTRAN statements which will perform this calculation is:

```
U=X*X
Y=-((((((U*A(13)-A(11))*U-A(9))*U-A(7))*U-A(5))*U
   -A(3))*U-A(1))*X
```

provided the constants A(J) have already been calculated and stored, as in Section 7.22. This set of statements requires about 10 multiplication times, (8 actual multiplications, plus the time required for the other commands) or roughly .1 second on a slow machine or .0001 second on a fast one.

7.24   Forms for the Taylor and Maclaurin Remainder Terms

It is seen that an important part of preparing a program for the calculation of a function by a Taylor or Maclaurin expansion is the determination of the maximum size of the remainder.   It is possible to give the remainder in forms different from those given in expressions (7-1), (7-2), and (7-3). Denoting by $R_n(x)$ the remainder after n terms, we have the following useful forms:

1.   For Taylor's Formula (expression 7-1)

(a) $R_n(x) = \dfrac{(x-a)^n}{n!} f^{(n)}[a + \theta(x-a)], \qquad 0 < \theta < 1$

(b) $R_n(x) = \dfrac{1}{(n-1)!} \displaystyle\int_0^{x-a} f^{(n)}(x-t)t^{n-1}\, dt$

2.   For Taylor's Formula (expression 7-2)

(a) $R_n(x) = \dfrac{h^n}{n!} f^{(n)}(x + \theta h), \qquad 0 < \theta < 1$

(b) $R_n(x) = \dfrac{1}{(n-1)!} \displaystyle\int_0^h f^{(n)}(x + h - t)t^{n-1}\, dt$

3.   For Maclaurin's Formula (expression 7-3)

(a) $R_n(x) = \dfrac{x^n}{n!} f^{(n)}(\theta x), \qquad 0 < \theta < 1$

(b) $$R_n(x) = \frac{1}{(n-1)!} \int_0^x f^{(n)}(x-t)t^{n-1}\, dt$$

In each case the second form for $R_n(x)$ gives the remainder in terms of a definite integral. Since this form is not usually discussed in elementary calculus, we shall apply it in an example.

Example 1. In the Taylor expansion of ln x about $x = a$, where a is some positive number, find an upper limit on the remainder, using the integral form.

From Example 2, Section 7.21, the nth derivative is:

$$f''(x) = (-1)^{n-1}(n-1)!/x^n$$

so that in integral form the remainder is:

$$R_n(x) = \frac{1}{(n-1)!} \int_0^{x-a} \frac{(-1)^{n-1}(n-1)!}{(x-t)^n} t^{n-1}\, dt = (-1)^{n-1} \int_0^{x-a} \frac{t^{n-1}}{(x-t)^n}\, dt$$

In the integral, t is to vary from 0 to $x - a$. Let us consider only the case $x > a$. Since integration is basically a process of summation of the integrand for all values of t in this interval and since this integrand is positive throughout the interval, we can overestimate the value of the integral by replacing the integrand by a larger quantity. We can do this by replacing the denominator in the integrand by a quantity which is always as small as or smaller than $(x-t)^n$. If we replace t by its largest possible value, we have $(x - x + a)^n < (x-t)^n$, or $a^n < (x-t)^n$. Thus, replacing the denominator by a^n and omitting the factor $(-1)^{n-1}$, which is always equal to 1 in absolute value, we have:

$$R_n(x) < \int_0^{x-a} \frac{t^{n-1}}{a^n}\, dt = \frac{1}{a} \int_0^{x-a} t^{n-1}\, dt = \frac{(x-a)^n}{na^n}$$

This estimate can now be applied as in the preceding sections to determine the required number of terms to obtain the required accuracy. For example, if we require a calculation accurate to eight significant figures, we require:

$$\frac{R_n(x)}{\ln x} < \frac{1}{2 \times 10^8}$$

which will be satisfied if:

$$\frac{(x-a)^n}{na^n \ln x} < \frac{1}{2 \times 10^8}$$

Let us consider the case of an expansion about $a = 1$. This particular error estimate is somewhat difficult to deal with, since $\ln x \to 0$ as $x \to 1$, but by careful analysis which we shall not attempt to describe here it can be shown that $(x - 1)/\ln x \to 1$ as $x \to 1$ and that the value increases with increasing x. If we are interested in using the series for values of x between 1 and 1.1, we must have:

$$\frac{(.1)^n}{n \ln 1.1} < \frac{1}{2 \times 10^8}$$

By trial and error we can determine that $n = 9$ is the smallest value which will satisfy the inequality. If we desire to use the series for all values of x between 1 and 2, we must have:

$$\frac{1^n}{n \ln 2} < \frac{1}{2 \times 10^8}$$

which requires a value of n greater than 10^8, or well over 100 million terms! Clearly the Taylor expansion of $\ln x$ about $x = 1$ is not very practical for use in computing the logarithm for x very different from 1.

EXERCISE XIV

1. Write the Maclaurin expansion with remainder for the following functions:

    a. $\tan^{-1} x$ d. $1/\sqrt{1 + x}$

    b. $\cos x$ e. $\sqrt{1 + x}$

    c. $\ln (1 + x)$

2. Write the Taylor expansion with remainder for the following functions about the value indicated:

    a. $\sin x$ about $x = \pi/2$ c. $\sqrt{x}$ about $x = 10$

    b. $\tan x$ about $x = \pi/4$ d. e^x about $x = 1$

3. Determine how many terms are required to evaluate each of the following functions to eight significant figures for the indicated range of values of x:

    a. $\cos x$ by Maclaurin expansion for $0 \leqslant x \leqslant \pi/4$

    b. $\sin x$ by Maclaurin expansion for $0 \leqslant x \leqslant \pi/4$

    c. $\tan x$ by Maclaurin expansion for $0 \leqslant x \leqslant \pi/4$

    d. $\tan^{-1} x$ by Maclaurin expansion for $0 \leqslant x \leqslant 1$

    e. $\tan^{-1} x$ by Maclaurin expansion for $0 \leqslant x \leqslant 10$

    f. $\sqrt{x}$ by Taylor expansion about $x = 1$ for $1 \leqslant x \leqslant 1.1$

    g. $\sqrt{x}$ by Taylor expansion about $x = 1$ for $1 \leqslant x \leqslant 10$

    h. $\sqrt{1 + \cos x}$ by Taylor expansion about $x = \pi/2$ for $\pi/2 \leqslant x \leqslant 3\pi/4$

7.3 FORTRAN FUNCTIONS

It has been seen that there are ways of calculating such quantities as $\sin x$ or e^x to a sufficient degree of accuracy for practical purposes by a combination of simple arithmetic operations. For example, when one needs the value of e^x in a calculation, one can use a FORTRAN statement such as the one developed in Section 7.22. There are several disadvantages to this procedure, however. Some of them are:

(*1*) The statement is a lengthy one, and frequent repetition in the program would be cumbersome.

(*2*) Since the statement is in FORTRAN, when the program is compiled the machine must construct a whole machine language program to compute e^x each time the statement appears.

(*3*) The statement is limited to values of x between zero and one. For values of x greater than one its accuracy is insufficient.

It is possible to circumvent these difficulties by preparing, just once, a carefully constructed set of commands, or subroutines, in machine language, and then by having the compiler insert this set of commands in the object program if the source program requires them. This has been done for all the common functions as a part of the FORTRAN compiler. Functions such as sine, cosine, arctangent, square root, logarithm, and absolute value are available in the FORTRAN systems for most computers. For the larger machines, much more elaborate lists of functions are frequently available. Each function is assigned a name, which is usually a set of five or less letters ending with F. The argument of the functions is placed in parentheses immediately after the function name. For example, the FORTRAN statement

$$Y = EXPF(X)$$

will cause $y = e^x$ to be computed. Table I lists the common functions which are ordinarily available in all FORTRAN compilers and lists the names we will use for them.

TABLE I

Mathematical Function	FORTRAN Name
Square root	SQRTF
Exponential	EXPF
Sine of angle in radians	SINF
Cosine of angle in radians	COSF
Arctangent in radians	ATANF
Natural logarithm	LOGF
Absolute value	ABSF

The argument of a function does not have to be a single variable. It may be any floating point expression. The function value is computed in floating point form. For example, the equation:

$$Y = \sqrt{1 + X^2} + \sqrt{1 - X^2}$$

can be represented by a FORTRAN statement:

Y = SQRTF(1. + X*X) + SQRTF(1. - X*X)

An additional function or operation that is available in all FORTRAN systems is raising to a power. The FORTRAN expression for the function X^A is:

X**A

This function is usually described in programming manuals along with the arithmetic operations but strictly speaking it belongs in the same class as the functions just described. If A is not an integer, $y = x^A$ really means $y = e^{A \ln x}$, and it is this latter quantity which is really calculated when the FORTRAN expression X**A is used. This particular type of expression is an exception to the rule that fixed and floating point quantities cannot be mixed. When the argument is floating point, the exponent can be either fixed or floating. The expression X**2. would be calculated as $e^{2 \ln x}$, while X**2 without a decimal point would be calculated as X*X.

Example 1. Write a FORTRAN program that will compute and print the value of $y = \sqrt{a + b \sin x}$ for 100 equally spaced values of x from zero to $\pi/2$. The constants a and b are to be read from a card.

A suitable program is:

```
      READ 101,A,B
      X=0.
      DX= .015707963
      DO 2 I=1,100
      X=X+DX
    1 Y=SQRTF(A+B*SINF(X))
    2 PRINT 102,X,Y
  101 FORMAT(2E10.4)
  102 FORMAT(F10.5,E10.4)
      END
```

Note that in this program the argument of the square root function contains another function, the sine. This is permissible in most versions of

FORTRAN. If desired, that statement could be replaced by two simpler ones:

$$U = A + B*SINF(X)$$
$$Y = SQRTF(U)$$

7.31   Time Requirements for the Common Functions

The examples of Taylor Series for calculation of e^x and sin x in Sections 7.22 and 7.23 require on the order of ten multiplication times to compute. For other functions, such as the logarithm, it was seen that computation by Taylor Series can require a prohibitive amount of time. For such functions other approximation methods are available. Some of these are discussed in later chapters and others may be found in more advanced works on numerical analysis. Generally speaking, the best available programs for the common functions are based not on Taylor Series but instead on some more sophisticated approximation method, and are usually a little faster than the above estimates for sine and e^x would indicate. As a convenient rule of thumb, however, in making time estimates for programs involving such functions, we will assume that ten multiplication times are required for the square root, exponential, sine, cosine, arctangent, logarithm and power functions and that one multiplication time is required for the absolute value function.

Example 1.   Estimate the time required for the calculation of Example 1, Section 7.3 for a fast machine with on-line printing.

Since there is only one input, we will ignore it. The only statements requiring appreciable amounts of time are statements 1 and 2. Statement 1 takes 10 multiplication times for the sine, one to multiply by B, and 10 more for the square root, for a total of 21. Statement 2 requires 100 for on-line printing. The total is 121 multiplication times. The loop is repeated 100 times for a total of $12,100t_m$. The time is on the order of .1 second.

EXERCISE XV

1. Write FORTRAN programs to compute and print y for 500 equally spaced values of x for each of the following expressions. Estimate the time requirement for a slow machine with on-line printing and on a fast machine with off-line printing.

    a. $y = e^x \sin x$
    b. $y = e^x + 3e^{4x} + 2e^{5x}$
    c. $y = x \cos x + \tan x$
    d. $y = 1/2 \sin x + 4 \sin 2x + 5 \sin 3x$
    e. $y = \ln (1 + \cos x)$
    f. $y = 1 + \tan^4 x \, e^2 + \cos^2 x$

2. The transformation from polar to rectangular coordinates is given by:

$$x = r \cos \theta$$
$$y = r \sin \theta$$

Using the above subroutines

   a. Write a program that will print x and y, given r and θ.
   b. Write a program that will print r and θ, given x and y. (*Note*: be sure that θ is given in the correct quadrant.)

3. By the law of cosines, when two sides and the included angle of a triangle are known, the third side is given by:

$$a^2 = b^2 + c^2 - 2bc \cos A$$

Using the above subroutines, write a program to compute a, given b, c, and A. Under what circumstances do you think this program might give results with large errors?

4. Using the above subroutines, write a program to determine the area of a triangle, given the sides a, b, and c.

7.4 ADDITIONAL FORTRAN FUNCTIONS

It sometimes happens that repeated use must be made of some complicated expression or function which is not one of the standard functions included in the FORTRAN system. To provide for such cases the FORTRAN system allows a function to be defined within the program itself. The programmer gives the function a name, which must be four to seven characters in length, and the last character must be the letter F. The name of the function is followed by parentheses enclosing the argument or arguments, which are separated by commas if there is more than one. The function is defined in the program by writing a FORTRAN statement $a = b$. The right hand side is the name given to the function, and the left hand side is the arithmetic expression which describes the calculation that must be done to obtain the value of the function. For example, if the quantity $\sqrt{1 + x} + \sqrt{1 - x}$ were to be needed frequently during a calculation, one could put the FORTRAN statement:

SUSQF(X)=SQRTF(1.+X)+SQRTF(1.−X)

at the beginning of the program, and then use the symbol SUSQF(X) whenever this quantity is desired thereafter. The above statement merely defines the function. It does not cause computation to take place. It must appear in the program before any executable statement.

Example 1. The quantities $y = (x/2)(\sqrt{1+x} + \sqrt{1-x})$, $z = (y/2)(\sqrt{1+y} + \sqrt{1-y})$, and $w = (z/2)(\sqrt{1+z} + \sqrt{1-z})$ are to be computed for a series of values of x between zero and one. Write a program that will compute y, z, and w for each given x.

A suitable program is:

```
  1 GIVF(X)=X*(SQRTF(1.+X)+SQRTF(1.-X))/2.
  2 READ 101,X
    IF(X)4,3,3
  3 Y=GIVF(X)
    Z=GIVF(Y)
    W=GIVF(Z)
    PRINT 101,X,Y,Z,W
    GO TO 2
  4 STOP
101 FORMAT(4E12.4)
    END
```

Statement 1 merely defines the function GIVF(X). The X is a dummy variable which stands for the argument of the function. In statement 3 and the two succeeding statements, the function is actually calculated for the arguments X, Y, and Z. A negative number input for X will stop the problem.

7.5 FORTRAN SUBROUTINES

Useful as the FORTRAN function statement is, it has some rather significant limitations. First, the function must be something which can be defined by a single FORTRAN statement. Second, it can only compute a single value as output. These limitations are removed in another device included in the FORTRAN system, the subroutine—which is actually a separate program, identified by a name. The name is any combination of four to seven characters. It is followed by parentheses containing all the inputs and outputs of the subprogram, separated by commas. When it is desired that this subroutine be executed, a statement is put in the main program which consists of the word "CALL" followed by the name of the subroutine and the arguments to be used in the subroutine.

Example 1. Write a FORTRAN program that will compute the value of $w = \sqrt{y} + \sin y$, where y is the larger of the following:

$$y = \cos 1.2x^2 - \cos 1.1x$$

and

$$y = \cos 1.3x^3 - \cos 1.05x$$

for

$$x = 1, 2, \ldots, 100.$$

We will do this by first writing a subroutine that will compute *y*, and then using this in a main program that will compute *w*.

A suitable subroutine is:

```
SUBROUTINE COMP(A,B)
Z1=COSF(1.2*A*A)−COSF(1.1*A)
Z2=COSF(1.3*A*A*A)−COSF(1.05*A)
IF(Z1−Z2)2,2,3
2 B=Z2
GO TO 4
3 B=Z1
4 RETURN
END
```

This routine has been given the name COMP. Its arguments are A and B It is used in the main program as follows:

```
1 DO 5 I=1,100
X=I
2 CALL COMP(X,Y)
W=SQRTF(Y+SINF(Y))
5 PRINT 101,X,W
STOP
101 FORMAT (2E12.4)
END
```

Statement 2 causes the subroutine COMP to be executed. Note that before COMP can be called the first argument must be specified, since the subroutine needs this value. The subroutine is complete when statement 4 is executed. The statement "RETURN" causes the computer to return to the main routine after statement 2 of the main routine. Note that the variables A and B in the subroutine are dummy variables. When the calculation is actually called for in the main routine, X is used for A and Y for B.

If this program were to be used on a computer, the main program and subroutine would be compiled together.

Example 2. Write a program that will compute the function $w = r + 2r \sin^2 \theta + r^3\sqrt{1 - \cos^3 \theta}$ where r, θ, are polar coordinates of a point, for given sets of points (X, Y) given in cartesian coordinates.

We can use a subroutine to make the coordinate transformation. A suitable subroutine is:

```
SUBROUTINE TRANS(R,THET,X,Y)
R=SQRTF(X*X+Y*Y)
```

```
    THET=ATANF(Y/X)
    IF(X)2,3,3
  2 THET=THET+3.1415927
  3 RETURN
    END
```

Since the arctangent routine gives a principal value, between $-\pi/2$ and $\pi/2$, it was necessary to test to determine the quadrant which θ really belongs in and place it in that quadrant.

The main program which uses the above subroutine might appear as follows:

```
    READ 101,X,Y
    CALL TRANS(R,THET,X,Y)
    W=R+2.*R*(SINF(THET))**2
    W=W+R**3*SQRTF(1.-(COSF(THET))**3)
    PRINT 101,X,Y,W
    STOP
101 FORMAT(3E12.4)
    END
```

In this program the subroutine had several arguments. The values of X and Y are needed by the subroutine and must be made available before the subroutine is called. The values of R and THET are determined by the subroutine.

1. Write a FORTRAN statement to define each of the following functions:

    a. $y = e^x \cos 2\pi x$
    b. $y = 1 + 2 \cos x + 3 \cos 2x + 4 \cos 3x$
    c. $y = \ln (1 + \sqrt{1 + x^2})$
    d. $z = \sqrt{2x^2 + 3y^2} - x + 1$

2. Write a program that will define the function $x + \ln (1 + 3x + x^2)$ and use it to compute the quantities:

    $$y = x + \ln (1 + 3x + x^2)$$
    $$z = y + \ln (1 + 3y + y^2)$$
    $$w = z - \sin x - \ln (1 + 3 \sin x + \sin^2 x)$$

3. Write a FORTRAN subroutine that will convert a point (r, θ, ϕ) in spherical polar coordinates to rectangular coordinates (x, y, z).
4. Write a FORTRAN subroutine that will convert a point (x, y, z) in rectangular coordinate to spherical polar coordinates.

5. Write a FORTRAN subroutine that will convert a pair of values (x, y) to another pair (u, v) given by:

    a. $u = \cos x \sin y$
         $v = \sin x - \sin y$

    b. $u = e^x \cos y$
         $v = e^x \sin y$

    c. $u = \ln (y + \sqrt{y^2 + x^2})$
         $v = \ln (x + \sqrt{x^2 + y^2})$

CHAPTER VIII *Further Accuracy Considerations*

8.1 INTRODUCTION

The chapter just preceding has been concerned with causing a digital computer to evaluate various algebraic, trigonometric, or exponential expressions. We have found that by the use of Taylor Series or other approximating functions we can generate subroutines which can be used to evaluate e^x, $\sin x$, or similar functions to about the eight significant digit accuracy of which our idealized computer is capable. With these subroutines, we can quite easily cause the computer to perform a wide range of calculations. The ease with which this can be done, and the speed with which the computer can provide answers can be quite deceptive. There are still accuracy problems which must be investigated with care before the computer answers can be accepted as valid. As was pointed out in Chapter III, the input numbers in any calculation are usually only of limited accuracy, and when arithmetic operations are performed with approximate numbers, the results will be approximate. In Chapter III we learned what happens to the absolute error and relative error when two approximate numbers are added, subtracted, multiplied, or divided. Now we must consider what happens when approximate numbers are combined in more complex fashions.

8.2 A GENERAL RELATION FOR ERROR ACCUMULATION

The expressions given in Chapter III for error accumulation in the elementary arithmetic operations can be derived from a single, general relation from the calculus. Suppose the numbers u_1, u_2, u_3, ... , u_n, are to be combined in some way to give a resulting number which we will call N. The value of N then depends in some particular way on the values of u_1, u_2, etc. We can indicate this relationship by writing N as a function of u_1, u_2, etc., or:

$$N = f(u_1, u_2, u_3, \ldots , u_n)$$

166

Now if small changes are made in u_1, u_2, etc., by amounts Δu_1, Δu_2, etc., we can calculate a quantity called the differential of N, by the relation:

$$dN = \frac{\partial f}{\partial u_1} \Delta u_1 + \frac{\partial f}{\partial u_2} \Delta u_2 + \frac{\partial f}{\partial u_3} \Delta u_3 + \cdots + \frac{\partial f}{\partial u_n} \Delta u_n \qquad \text{(8-1)}$$

This quantity dN is approximately equal to ΔN, the error in N when u_1 is replaced by $u_1 + \Delta u_1$, u_2 by $u_2 + \Delta u_2$, etc. In order to demonstrate the meaning of this formula, we will use it to rederive the error rules for addition, subtraction, multiplication, and division given in Chapter III.

For addition, we have:

$$N = u_1 + u_2 + u_3 + \cdots + u_n$$

so:

$$dN = \Delta u_1 + \Delta u_2 + \Delta u_3 + \cdots + \Delta u_n$$

the situation expressed by Theorem III of Chapter III.

For subtraction, we have:

$$N = u_1 - u_2$$

so that

$$dN = \Delta u_1 - \Delta u_2$$

We must remember that Δu_1 and Δu_2 can be either positive or negative, so if we are interested in the maximum error, it is $|\Delta u_1| + |\Delta u_2|$.

For multiplication:

$$N = u_1 u_2 u_3 \ldots u_n$$

or, if we take logarithms, we can write:

$$\ln N = \ln u_1 + \ln u_2 + \cdots + \ln u_n$$

If now we take the total differential, we have:

$$dN/N = \Delta u_1/u_1 + \Delta u_2/u_2 + \cdots + \Delta u_n/u_n$$

This rule corresponds to the statement in Theorem V of Chapter III concerning relative errors.

For division, if:

$$N = u_1/u_2$$

then:

$$\ln N = \ln u_1 - \ln u_2$$

and:

$$dN/N = \Delta u_1/u_1 - \Delta u_2/u_2$$

As in subtraction, to obtain an estimate of the maximum possible error, we must allow for the case where Δu_1 and Δu_2 are of opposite sign, so we must consider:

$$|\Delta u_1/u_1| + |\Delta u_2/u_2|$$

as the correct expression for estimating the error.

For more complicated expressions, the equation (8-1) can be applied directly to give an expression for the error, remembering that in each case signs of the individual errors Δu_1, Δu_2, etc., should be chosen in such a way as to give the maximum result.

8.21   *Error Accumulation for the Exponential Function*

As a demonstration of the problem of error accumulation, let us apply the relation (8-1) of Section 8.2 for the function:

$$y = e^x$$

Applying the relation (8-1) with $f(x) = e^x$, we have:

$$dy = e^x \Delta x$$

where dy is the absolute error in y.   The relative error is:

$$dy/y = \Delta x$$

Hence the *relative* error in the computed value of e^x is eqal to the *absolute* error in x itself.   The disturbing feature of this result can be seen from the following example:

Example 1.   Suppose $x = 100$, to three correct significant figures.   What is the relative error in $y = e^x$?

The limit of the absolute error in x is:

$$\Delta x = .5$$

Hence the relative error in y is .5 or 50%. The value of y has *no* significant figures!

The above example demonstrates that, even though our subroutines may be designed to compute numbers to eight correct significant digits, the problem of error accumulation is still with us when we use these subroutines.

8.22   Error Estimate by Formula

The example of Section 8.21 was indicative of the problem associated with the evaluation of any function of one or more independent quantities or approximate numbers. No calculation of this sort can be considered complete until some sort of assessment of the error has been made. For functions which are not too complex, the relation of Section 8.2 can be used for this purpose. Further examples will be given to illustrate its use.

Example 1. The function $y = a \sin b$ is to be calculated, where $a = 30.0$ and $b = .45$, the numbers being correct to the number of significant digits shown. Find the absolute and relative errors in y.

By the formula of Section 8.2:

$$dy = \frac{\partial y}{\partial a} \Delta a + \frac{\partial y}{\partial b} \Delta b$$

$$= \sin b \Delta a + a \cos b \Delta b$$

$$= (.435)(.05) + (30.0)(.900)(.005)$$

$$= .022 + .14 = .16$$

or the absolute error is .16.

Since $y = (30.0)(.435) = 13.05$, the relative error is about .16/13 or roughly 1%.

Example 2. The function $y = a \sin b$ is to be calculated, where $a = 30.0$ and $b = \pi/6$, the number a being correct to three significant digits, and the number b being exact. Find the absolute and relative errors in y.

As before, we may write:

$$dy = \frac{\partial y}{\partial a} \Delta a + \frac{\partial y}{\partial b} \Delta b$$

but since b is exact, $\Delta b = 0$, so the term $(\partial y/\partial b)\Delta b$ will drop out. This points up the fact that, whenever the function under consideration involves *exact* numbers, they can be treated as constants throughout, and the expression need not be differentiated with respect to them. All quantities which may be in error, whether constants or variables, must be treated as variables in applying the error formula of Section 8.2. (In our computer, no number can be blindly presumed to be exact, since no number is represented to more than eight significant digits. In the present case, and in many cases, the truncation error involved in roundoff to eight digits is so small compared to other sources of error that it can safely be ignored.)

For the present problem, then:

$$dy = \frac{dy}{da} \Delta a$$

$$= \sin b \, \Delta a$$

$$= (.5)(.05)$$

$$\approx .025$$

The absolute error is .025 and the relative error is .025/15, or about 0.2%.

Example 3. The function $y = 2.0 \sin x + 3 \ln x$ is to be evaluated for $x = 1.26$. The constant 2.0 and the value of x are correct only to the number of significant digits shown. The constant 3 is exact. Find the absolute and relative errors in y.

Since the number 2.0 may be in error, it is best to replace it by a symbol before applying the error formula. Thus:

$$y = a \sin x + 3 \ln x$$

$$dy = \Delta a \sin x + (a \cos x + 3/x)\Delta x$$

$$= (.05)(.952) + [(2.0)(.306) + 3/1.26](.005)$$

$$= .048 + [.612 + 2.38](.005)$$

$$= .048 + .015 = .063$$

The absolute error is .063.
Since:

$$y = (2.0)(.952) + 3(.231)$$

$$= 1.90 + .69 = 2.59$$

the relative error is .063/2.59 or about .2%.

Example 4. Perform the calculation of Example 3 for $x = .65$.

Substituting in the formula of the previous exercise, we have:

$$dy = (.05)(.605) + [(2.0)(.796) + 3/.65](.005)$$

$$= .030 + [1.59 + 4.62](.005)$$

$$= .030 + .031 = .062$$

Again, the absolute error is about .062.
  However, since:

$$y = (2.0)(.605) + (3)(-.431)$$

$$1.21 - 1.29 = -.08$$

the relative error is about $.06/.08 = .75$!

Although all the numbers used in this case were accurate to 2% or better, the final result had a 75% error! Closer inspection shows that this error came from the operation remarked as dangerous in Chapter III, the subtraction of two nearly equal quantities. For $x = .65$, ln x is negative and the quantities 2 sin x and 3 ln x are very nearly equal in absolute value. The subtraction involved in finding y above resulted in loss of the two leading significant figures.

Example 5. The function $y = ke^{-\mu x}/x^2$ is to be evaluated for 100 values of x, ranging from 100 to 5000, and subject to an experimental error of one unit. The constants are $\mu = 3.0 \times 10^{-3}$ and $k = 1.3 \times 10^7$, each accurate to the number of significant digits indicated. Find the absolute and relative errors in y for a low, medium and high value of x (use $x = 100$, 700, and 5000).

For functions such as this, where only multiplications, divisions, and powers are involved, it is convenient to take logarithms and then differentiate, thus obtaining relative error directly. Thus:

$$\ln y = \ln k - \mu x - 2 \ln x$$

$$dy/y = \Delta k/k - \mu \Delta x - x \Delta \mu - 2\Delta x/x$$

For $x = 100$:

relative error

$$= \frac{dy}{y} = \frac{.05 \times 10^7}{1.3 \times 10^7} - (3.0 \times 10^{-3})(-1) - (100)(-.05 \times 10^{-3}) - \frac{2(-1)}{100}$$

(signs of Δk, Δu, and Δx were chosen to maximize the error)

$$= .038 + .003 + .005 + .02$$

$$= .066 \quad \text{or} \quad 7\%$$

Since:

$$y = 1.3 \times 10^7 \, e^{-(3.0 \times 10^{-3})(100)}/(100)^2$$
$$= 9.6 \times 10^2 \quad \text{or} \quad 960$$

the absolute error is:

$$(.07)(9.6 \times 10^2) = .7 \times 10^2 \quad \text{or} \quad 70$$

For $x = 700$:

relative error

$$= \frac{dy}{y} = \frac{.05 \times 10^7}{1.3 \times 10^7} - (3.0 \times 10^{-3})(-1) - (700)(-.05 \times 10^{-3}) - \frac{2(-1)}{700}$$

$$= .038 + .003 + .035 + .003 = .079 \quad \text{or} \quad 8\%$$

$$y = 1.3 \times 10^7 \, e^{-(3.0 \times 10^{-3})(700)}/(700)^2 = 3.3$$

so the absolute error is:

$$(.08)(3.3) \approx .3$$

For $x = 5000$:

relative error

$$= \frac{dy}{y} = \frac{.05 \times 10^7}{1.3 \times 10^7} - (3.0 \times 10^{-3})(-1) - (5000)(-.05 \times 10^{-3}) - \frac{2(-1)}{5000}$$

$$= .038 + .003 + .25 + .0004$$

$$= .29 \quad \text{or} \quad 29\%$$

$$y = 1.3 \times 10^7 \, e^{-(3.0 \times 10^{-3})(5000)}/(5000)^2$$
$$= 1.6 \times 10^{-7}$$

so the absolute error is about:

$$(.29)(1.6 \times 10^{-7}) = .5 \times 10^{-7}$$

Comparing the values of the errors for the three different values of x gives us some feel for the errors throughout the range of values of x.   The error is between 5 and 10% for the smaller values of x, and increases to about 30%

at the extremely large values of x. We cannot be sure that the percentage error remains in the ranges indicated for all values of x, since we have studied only three particular values. If we wish a surer picture of the behavior of the error throughout the entire range of x, we can look at the expression for the relative error with numerical values substituted for all quantities except x:

$$\frac{dy}{y} = \frac{.05 \times 10^7}{1.3 \times 10^7} - (3.0 \times 10^{-3})(-1) - x(-.05 \times 10^{-3}) - 2(-1)/x$$

$$= .038 + .003 + .00005x + 2/x$$

$$= .041 + .00005x + 2/x$$

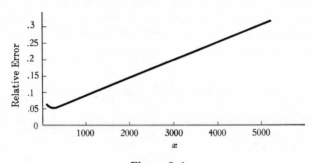

Figure 8–1

We can now study this expression as a function of x, making a plot of it if desired, and thus obtain a more complete picture of the relative error throughout the range of values of x. Figure 8–1 indicates this behavior. The relative error is .066 for $x = 100$, decreases to .061 at $x = 200$, then increases continuously to .29 at $x = 5000$.

8.23 *Error Estimate by Computer Trial*

The application of the error formula (8-1) of Section 8.2 is straightforward so long as the functions involved are simple enough to be differentiated easily. For extremely complex functions, however, the process may be impracticable because of the difficulties involved in finding the derivatives or in evaluating the derivatives once found. In such cases the process of estimating the errors is often ignored completely. This is indeed unfortunate, since these are just the cases in which error accumulation is most likely to have some unexpected effect on the accuracy of the final answer. Instead of neglecting the problem, one should attempt to estimate the error by other methods. One method, quite adaptable for computer use, is to perform the calculation several times, each time varying one or more of the quantities which may be in error, and observing the effect on the final answer. Used properly, this method can give a more valid index of the error than does the error formula of Section 8.2. Again, as in that section, assume that the quantities u_1, u_2, u_3, ... , u_n are to be combined to form some resulting number N, where:

$$N = f(u_1, u_2, ... , u_n) \qquad (8\text{-}2)$$

Suppose now that small changes Δu_1, Δu_2, ... , Δu_n are made in the quantities $u_1, u_2, ... , u_n$. Then N will be changed to a new value $N + \Delta N$, given by:

$$N + \Delta N = f(u_1 + \Delta u_1, u_2 + \Delta u_2, ... , u_n + \Delta u_n) \qquad (8\text{-}3)$$

The Taylor expansion for a function of one variable given in Section 7.2 has its analogue for functions of several variables, the chief difference being that the ordinary derivatives are replaced by partial derivatives. This expansion applied to expression (8-2) above gives:

$$N + \Delta N = f(u_1, u_2, ... , u_n) + \Delta u_1 \frac{\partial f}{\partial u_1} + \Delta u_2 \frac{\partial f}{\partial u_2} + \cdots + \Delta u_n \frac{\partial f}{\partial u_n}$$

$$+ \frac{1}{2} \left[(\Delta u_1)^2 \frac{\partial^2 f}{\partial u_1^{\,2}} + \cdots + (\Delta u_n)^2 \frac{\partial^2 f}{\partial u_n^{\,2}} + 2\Delta u_1 \Delta u_2 \frac{\partial^2 f}{\partial u_1 \partial u_2} + \cdots \right]$$

$$+ \frac{1}{3!} \left[(\Delta u_1)^3 \frac{\partial^3 f}{\partial u_1^{\,3}} + \cdots \right] + \cdots \qquad (8\text{-}4)$$

If the errors Δu_1, Δu_2, ... , Δu_n are so small that we can neglect their squares, products, and higher powers, we can write (8-4) as:

$$N + \Delta N \approx f(u_1, u_2, ... , u_n) + \Delta u_1 \frac{\partial f}{\partial u_1} + \Delta u_2 \frac{\partial f}{\partial u_2} + \cdots + \Delta u_n \frac{\partial f}{\partial u_n} \qquad (8\text{-}5)$$

or, subtracting (8-1) from (8-5):

$$\Delta N \approx \Delta u_1 \frac{\partial f}{\partial u_1} + \Delta u_2 \frac{\partial f}{\partial u_2} + \cdots + \Delta u_n \frac{\partial f}{\partial u_n} \qquad (8\text{-}6)$$

This is just the error formula (8-1) of Section 8.2. Thus that error formula is merely an approximation to the value of ΔN defined by the relation (8-3) above. Direct application of the relation (8-3) should give a better estimate of the error, since it does not neglect squares or products of errors. The task, once the computer program for evaluating the function f is prepared, is quite straightforward in concept. We merely run the calculation twice, once with input values $u_1, u_2, ... , u_n$, and once with input values $u_1 + \Delta u_1$,

$u_2 + \Delta u_2, \ldots, u_n + \Delta u_n$. The difference in the results is then the absolute error. There is one difficulty, however. In order to obtain the maximum error, we must choose the signs of the errors $\Delta u_1, \Delta u_2, \ldots, \Delta u_n$ so as to combine in the worst possible way. It is not usually possible to do this by inspection. Consequently it is necessary first to change each one separately and observe how much N is increased or decreased. In a sense, this procedure is somewhat analogous to applying the relation (8-6). Since by the definition of a partial derivative:

$$\frac{\partial f}{\partial u_1} = \lim_{u_1 \to 0} \frac{f(u_1 + \Delta u_1, u_2, u_3, \ldots, u_n) - f(u_1, u_2, \ldots, u_n)}{\Delta u_1}$$

then, for well behaved functions:

$$\frac{\partial f}{\partial u_1} \Delta u_1 \approx f(u_1 + \Delta u_1, u_2, u_3, \ldots, u_n) - f(u_1, u_2, \ldots, u_n)$$

Hence the difference between the value of N when $u_1 + \Delta u_1, u_2, u_3, \ldots, u_n$ are used in the calculation and that when $u_1, u_2, \ldots, u_n$ are used is roughly $(\partial f / \partial u_1)\Delta u_1$. If we do this for each variable and then add the absolute values of the resulting errors in N from all the calculations, we have an error estimate of the same type as is given by the relation (8-6). In order to determine if the higher order terms contained in relation (8-4) but ignored in relation (8-6) are important, it is usually wise to make a final calculation changing all the variables simultaneously. In each of the calculations in which only one variable has been changed, we observe whether N is increased or decreased, and then make a final calculation in which all variables are changed in directions chosen to produce the same direction change in N. The following set of steps outline the procedure:

1. Calculate $N = f(u_1, u_2, \ldots, u_n)$.
2. Calculate $N_i = f(u_1, u_2, \ldots, u_i + \Delta u_i, \ldots, u_n)$ for $i = 1$ to n.
3. Calculate $N + \Delta N = f(u_1 + a_1 \Delta u_1, u_2 + a_2 \Delta u_2, \ldots, u_n + a_n \Delta u_n)$, where $a_i = +1$ if $N_i > N$ and $a_i = -1$ if $N_i < N$.

Example 1. Use the method just described to estimate the error for Example 3 of Section 8.22.

In order to make the procedure clearer, the problem will be rewritten in the notation used in the description above. We wish to find:

$$N = f(u_1, u_2)$$

where:

$$f(u_1, u_2) = u_1 \sin u_2 + 3 \ln u_2$$

and:

$$u_1 = 2.0 \qquad u_2 = 1.26$$

$$\Delta u_1 = .05 \qquad \Delta u_2 = .005$$

Following the steps above, we calculate:
1. $N = f(u_1, u_2) = 2.0 \sin 1.26 + 3 \ln 1.26 = 2.59$
2. $N_1 = f(u_1 + \Delta u_1, u_2) = 2.05 \sin 1.26 + 3 \ln 1.26 = 2.64$
   $N_2 = f(u_1, u_2 + \Delta u_2) = 2.0 \sin 1.265 + 3 \ln 1.265 = 2.61$
3. Since $N_1 > N$, $a_1 = +1$. Since $N_2 > N$, $a_2 = +1$. Hence:
$N + \Delta N = f(u_1 + a_1 \Delta u_1, u_2 + a_2 \Delta u_2) = 2.05 \sin 1.265 + 3 \ln 1.265 = 2.66$
so that $\Delta N = 2.66 - 2.59 = .07$.

Example 2. The expression $y = \ln(a + \sqrt{b + e^{c \tan^{-1} x}})$ is to be calculated for values of x from 0 to 10 in order to make a graph. The values of the constants are $a = 2.0 \pm .1$, $b = 3.5 \pm .2$, $c = 1.0 \pm .1$. Draw a flow chart for the calculation, which includes an error estimate for each value of x.

Since in this problem we are allowed to choose the values of x, we may assume them to be precise, so that no error in x need be considered. The quantities a, b, and c are subject to errors $\Delta a = .1$, $\Delta b = .2$, and $\Delta c = .1$. Figure 8–2 shows the flow chart only for a single value of x. Additions to the chart to cause the calculation to be performed for a sequence of values of x are left to the reader.

In the discussion of flow charts it was pointed out that the charts could be made detailed or crude as the occasion required. In the example just given, the calculation of the very complex function y was relegated to a single box. Most of the chart is devoted to outlining the selection of the values of k_1, k_2, and k_3 to be used in the calculation. The variable connector symbol was used to good advantage in this chart to indicate the re-use of the basic formula for y several times with different values for k_1, k_2, and k_3.

The FORTRAN program given below follows the flow chart rather closely, but does include using a sequence of values of x:

```
        READ 101,A,B,C,DA,DB,DC,DX
        X=0.
        L=10./DX
        DO 14 I=1,L
        FK1=A
        FK2=B
        FK3=C
        J=1
    1   Z=LOGF(FK1+SQRTF(FK2+EXPF(FK3*ATANF(X))))
        GO TO (2,3,6,9,13),J
```

```
  2 J=2
    Y=Z
    FK1=A+DA
    GO TO 1
  3 J=3
    FK1=A
    FK2=B+DB
    IF(Z-Y)4,4,5
  4 FL1=A-DA
    GO TO 1
  5 FL1=A+DA
    GO TO 1
  6 J=4
    FK2=B
    FK3=C+DC
    IF(Z-Y)7,7,8
  7 FL2=B-DB
    GO TO 1
  8 FL2=B+DB
    GO TO 1
  9 J=5
    IF(Z-Y)10,10,11
 10 FL3=C-DC
    GO TO 12
 11 FL3=C+DC
 12 FK1=FL1
    FK2=FL2
    FK3=FL3
    GO TO 1
 13 PRINT 101,Y,Z
 14 X=X+DX
    STOP
101 FORMAT(7E10.4)
    END
```

8.24 Limitations on Validity of the Error Estimate

It might seem that the procedure outlined above and illustrated in the example would provide an absolutely certain means of obtaining an upper estimate on the error. Surprisingly enough, such is *not* the case. It is possible, although unusual, for the error to be much larger than indicated by the error estimate. If the function f happens to behave in a sufficiently erratic fashion, it may be that the quantities:

$$N = f(u_1, u_2, \ldots , u_n)$$

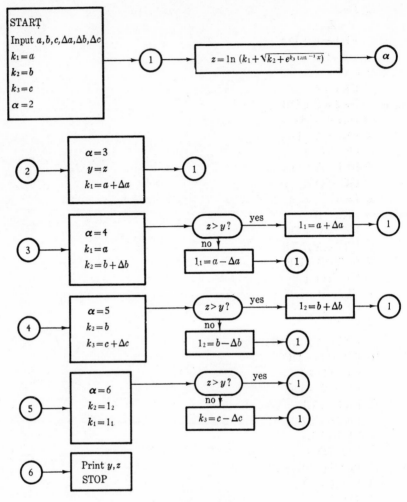

Figure 8–2

and:

$$N + \Delta N = f(u_1 + \Delta u_1, u_2 + \Delta u_2, \ldots, u_n + \Delta u_n)$$

may be nearly equal, but that for some set of values of the u's intermediate between $u_1, u_2, \ldots, u_n$ and $u_1 + \Delta u_1, u_2 + \Delta u_2, \ldots, u_n + \Delta u_n$, the function f has a very different value.   More advanced studies show that the estimate of ΔN given above can be depended upon, i.e., N will change only slowly as the u's change, if the following conditions are satisfied:

(*1*)   All of the partial derivatives $\partial f / \partial u_i$ exist and are continuous at the point $(u_1, u_2, \ldots, u_n)$.

(2) The errors $\Delta u_1, \Delta u_2, \ldots, \Delta u_n$ are sufficiently small. (We shall not try to define what is meant by "sufficiently." This is properly a subject for an advanced calculus course.)

An example will illustrate what may happen when these conditions are not satisfied.

Example 1. Compute $y = (1/16) \ln [\tan \sqrt{1 + x^2}]^2$ for $x = 1.211$, and estimate the error, where the constants in the expression are exact, and x is accurate to the number of digits shown.

Let us attempt to estimate the error by computing y for the value x and for the value $x + \Delta x$, where $\Delta x = .0005$. For $x = 1.211$, $y = 1.02$. For $x + \Delta x = 1.2115$, $y + \Delta y = 1.14$. Hence we would be led to believe that the maximum error is $\Delta y = .12$. However, if we believe this, we are badly

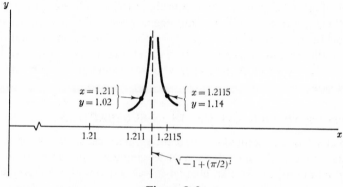

Figure 8–3

misled. For example, if the true value of x were 1.2113633, the value of y would be 1.39, a value differing from our original value by $.37$. Hence the maximum error is clearly more than $.12$. As a matter of fact, there is a value of x between 1.211 and 1.2115 for which y is infinite, so the error in y may be infinite! We can see this as follows: since $\tan \pi/2 = \infty$, y is infinite when $\sqrt{1 + x^2} = \pi/2$. This is true when $x = \sqrt{-1 + (\pi/2)^2}$. The exact value of of this number is between the two approximate numbers 1.2113633 and 1.2113634. The peculiar nature of this function in the region of interest is apparent from its graph, Figure 8–3. It has a vertical asymptote at the value $x = \sqrt{-1 + (\pi/2)^2}$, and the two values of x, 1.211 and 1.2115, happen to give nearly equal values of y on opposite sides of this asymptote. In this example the difficulty arises from the fact that the derivative dy/dx becomes infinite within the interval x to $x + \Delta x$. This gives some idea as to what is meant by errors "sufficiently small" in the condition (2) above. Δx must be small enough that the derivative dy/dx does not become inordinately large in the interval x to $x + \Delta x$.

The above example was included to demonstrate that calculation of an error estimate is no sure defense against the accidental acceptance of an answer grossly in error. The only sure protection is a detailed knowledge of the behavior of the function involved. This is no excuse, however, for failure to attempt to evaluate the effects of errors in the constants and variables involved in a calculation, both theoretically and experimentally by additional computer runs varying the values of any uncertain quantities. Stated another way, *part of the performance of any calculation is the testing of the sensitivity of the results to variations in the parameters involved in the problem.* In some cases, as in the preceding example, this testing of the sensitivity may be misleading, but such cases are fortunately rare. (They do however, tend to follow Gumperson's Law, which, stated roughly, is "those events which have a low probability of occurrence tend to occur at the least opportune time." This law has been cited as the reason for the ringing of the telephone when one is in the bathtub, or failure of the car to start when one is about to drive to an important engagement. Gumperson reportedly met his death by being struck by an automobile. He was walking down the left side of the road in order to face traffic, but was struck down from behind by a car driven by a visiting foreigner who was accustomed to driving on the left hand side.)

8.3 LOSS OF SIGNIFICANT DIGITS IN SUBTRACTION

In Chapter III it was pointed out that the primary cause of loss of accuracy in calculations was the introduction of leading zeros in subtraction of two nearly equal numbers. In that chapter it was stated that, whenever such an event might occur, special programming precautions must be taken to avoid the difficulty or at least to make the programmer aware that a dangerous point in the calculation has arisen. In very involved calculations it is not always possible to anticipate danger points of this sort, so that there is no guaranteed way of avoiding such trouble. There are techniques, however, which are applicable in certain special cases. Some of these will be discussed.

8.31 Programmed Warning of Accuracy Loss

The first problem in protecting against accuracy loss in subtraction is to recognize when such an error may occur in a program. Any subtraction command (or addition command, since the machine adds algebraically) may be guilty if the numbers being handled happen to be of the right size. A program may work beautifully for certain sets of input and yet produce worthless answers for other sets because of loss of leading digits in subtractions. Sometimes it is possible to recognize during programming that such a danger exists, and in other cases it may be virtually impossible to recognize a danger spot. When a potential danger spot in the program can be recognized, programming to provide warning of accuracy loss may be advisable.

Suppose, for example, that a part of our program contains the statement:

$$Y = A - B$$

Suppose further that we know that this part of the program will work satisfactorily for most sets of input numbers, but we suspect that in some cases the values of A and B at this point may be nearly equal. We fear that if as many as four leading zeros are produced by the subtraction our final answer will not be trustworthy. We would like the machine to warn us if four figures are lost at this point in the calculation. It is an easy matter to write a section for the program which will accomplish this. We note first that, if four digits are lost, then the difference obtained as the result of the subtraction is roughly 10^{-4} times the minuend or subtrahend. The following statements will test for this occurrence and print out a warning if it does happen:

```
    Y = A − B
    IF(ABSF(Y) − .0001*ABSF(A))9,10,10
  9 PRINT 101
101 FORMAT(26H ACCURACY LOSS,STATEMENT 9)
 10 (continuation of program)
```

After the calculation of $A - B$, a test is inserted which will determine if the difference is less than 10^{-4} times A. If it is, the print command is executed. If there is no excessive accuracy loss, the program continues without the print-out. A section of flow chart which describes this operation might appear as in Figure 8–4.

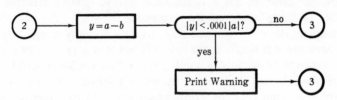

Figure 8–4

Example 1. The program given below will compute the third side a of a triangle, given sides b and c and the included angle A, the angle being denoted by the FORTRAN variable AA. The formula used is the law of cosines. Rewrite this program to give warning when subtraction results in the loss of two or more digits.

```
    READ 101,B,C,AA
    A = SQRTF(B*B + C*C − 2.*B*C*COSF(AA))
    PRINT 101,A
101 FORMAT(3E12.4)
    STOP
    END
```

A program which will give warning is:

```
      READ  101,B,C,AA
      U = B*B + C*C
      V = 2.*B*C*COSF(AA)
      IF(ABSF(U − V) − .01*ABSF(U))2,2,3
    2 PRINT  102
      STOP
    3 A = SQRTF(U − V)
      PRINT  101,A
      STOP
  101 FORMAT(3E12.4)
  102 FORMAT(29H ACCURACY LOSS IN COMPUTING A)
      END
```

In this example we arbitrarily settled on the loss of two leading digits as the danger point, the point at which we desire warning. It is fair to ask how such a requirement might come about. In a practical problem the loss of digits we could tolerate would be determined by accuracy of our knowledge of the input numbers b, c, and A and the required accuracy of the result. A careful error analysis using the general error formula of Section 8.2 would be quite difficult, but a loose line of reasoning following the accuracy theorems of Chapter III is sufficient to indicate how the error in the final result will depend on that of the input numbers. For example, suppose b, c, and A are each known to 1%. Then b^2, c^2, and bc have a relative error of about 2%. The absolute error in $\cos A$ is $\sin A \Delta A$, so the relative error in $\cos A$ is $\tan A \Delta A$. A little study of the expression $b^2 + c^2 - 2bc \cos A$ discloses that the quantities $(b^2 + c^2)$ and $(2bc \cos A)$ are nearly equal only when A is near zero and b is nearly equal to c. When A is near zero, $\tan A$ is small, so the relative error in $\cos A$ is small. Hence the term $2bc \cos A$ has a relative error of about 2%. From these values of relative error, we see that the terms $(b^2 + c^2)$ and $(2bc \cos A)$ each have about two significant figures. If one is lost in the subtraction, a^2 has one significant figure, or is accurate to about 10% (which means a is accurate to about 5%). If two significant digits are lost, a^2 may have no significant digits.

An error analysis of the type just given, while not at all precise, is usually sufficient to give guidance as to the acceptability of loss of leading significant digits in subtraction.

8.32 *Programming to Avoid Accuracy Loss in Subtraction*

In the preceding section it was demonstrated that it is sometimes possible to program a machine to give automatic warning in the event of serious accuracy loss in subtraction. It would be desirable to have the machine take automatic corrective action instead of merely issuing a warning. This can be done in many cases. Let us first consider the case in which we have only one uncertain input number, x. Suppose we are evlauating the expression:

$$y = f_1(x) - f_2(x)$$

where f_1 and f_2 are functions calculable to a high degree of accuracy by standard computer subroutines. Then by formula (8-1) of Section 8.2, the absolute error in y is:

$$dy \leqslant |f_1'(x)\Delta x| + |f_2'(x)\Delta x|$$

and the relative error is:

$$\frac{dy}{y} \leqslant \frac{|f_1'(x)| + |f_2'(x)|}{|f_1(x) - f_2(x)|} \Delta x$$

The relative error will be large due to loss of leading significant digits in subtraction when $f_1(x)$ and $f_2(x)$ are nearly equal. This will ordinarily occur near some value of x for which $f_1(x)$ and $f_2(x)$ are exactly equal. For example, suppose that for $x = a$:

$$f_1(a) = f_2(a)$$

Then for values of x near $x = a$, say for example $x = a + h$ where h is small:

$$f_1(a + h) \approx f_2(a + h)$$

and for small values of h we have subtraction problems. Now by Taylor's formula:

$$f_1(a + h) = f_1(a) + hf_1'(a) + \text{terms involving higher powers of } h$$

and:

$$f_2(a + h) = f_2(a) + hf_2'(a) + \text{terms involving higher powers of } h$$

Since h is small, we do not ordinarily need to carry these expansions past the first power in h to achieve sufficient accuracy. Thus, for h small, that is to say, for x near a, we have:

$$y = f_1(x) - f_2(x) \approx h[f_1'(a) - f_2'(a)]$$

If the first order terms were equal, $f_1'(a) = f_2'(a)$, it would be necessary to take the terms involving second powers of h in order to have a useful approximation for y. In cases in which a painstaking error analysis is warranted, the complete Taylor formula with remainder as given in Section 7.2 should be used.

Example 1. The function $y = 1 - e^{x-1}$ is to be calculated for values of x very near 1. Write an approximation which will have good accuracy for x sufficiently near 1.

Let us consider:

$$y = f_1(x) - f_2(x)$$

where:

$$f_1(x) = 1$$

$$f_2(x) = e^{x-1}$$

Let:

$$x - 1 = h$$

Then:

$$h[f_1'(1) - f_2'(1)] = h[0 - 1] = -h$$

so that the approximation is:

$$y = 1 - x$$

Example 2. If an observer takes horizontal sighting over a smooth sea level surface, how high is the line of sight at a distance of x miles from the observer? (The distance x is to be measured along the curved surface.) Write a program which will perform this calculation.

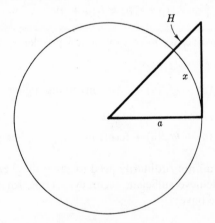

Figure 8–5

It can be seen from Figure 8–5 that the correct formula is:

$$H = a \sec x/a - a$$

where a is the radius of the earth. In order to use the standard functions of Chapter VII, we could write this as:

$$H = \frac{a}{\cos x/a} - a$$

This formula appears quite straightforward, yet in using it we are apt to have accuracy difficulties. For example, using 4,000 miles for the radius of the earth, consider the case where $x = 4$ miles. Then to eight correct significant digits:

$$\cos x/a = .99999950$$

The values of the various quantities involved then, as they would be carried inside the computer, are:

Quantity	Value in Floating Point	
a	40000000	54
$\dfrac{a}{\cos x/a}$	40000020	54
$\dfrac{a}{\cos x/a} - a$	20??????	48

The six leading digits are lost in the subtraction, leaving at most two correct significant digits. For $x = 1$ mile, we cannot even be sure of having one correct significant digit.

Note that in this case the accuracy problem results from the fact that the computer has only eight significant digits available, and not necessarily from inaccurate input data. It would not be at all unreasonable to ask for a program that would produce better accuracy for values of x on the order of a few miles, and this can easily be arranged if we use the method described above: taking:

$$f_1(x) = a \sec x/a, \qquad f_2(x) = a$$

When $x = 0$, we have $f_1 = f_2$, so we use the first nonzero term of a Taylor expansion about $x = 0$. We have:

$$f_1(x) = a + a(x/a)^2/2$$

$$f_2(x) = a$$

$$\therefore H_1 = f_1(x) - f_2(x) = x^2/2a$$

A use of the remainder term to calculate the error would show that we obtain a more accurate value for H with this formula than with the original formula when $x < .01a$, or when $x < 40$ miles. Figure 8–6, then, indicates a good way of setting up the problem to work for all reasonable values of x.

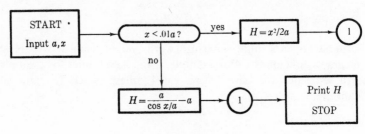

Figure 8–6

A FORTRAN program for this calculation is:

```
    A=4000.
  1 READ  101,X
    IF(ABSF(X)− .01*ABSF(A))2,3,3
  2 FH=X*X/(2.*A)
    GO TO 4
  3 FH=A/COSF(X/A)−A
  4 PRINT  102,X,FH
101 FORMAT(E12.4)
102 FORMAT(2E12.4)
    STOP
    END
```

An analogous procedure can be followed when several variables are involved. For Example 1 of Section 8.31 we can derive an approximate relation for use when subtraction error is a problem as follows:

We need the approximation when A is nearly zero and b and c are nearly equal. Let us write:

$$A = 0 + \Delta A$$
$$b = d + \Delta b$$
$$c = d + \Delta c$$

and assume henceforth that ΔA, Δb, and Δc are small. Then:

$$a^2 = (d + \Delta b)^2 + (d + \Delta c)^2 - 2(d + \Delta b)(d + \Delta c) \cos \Delta A$$

Expanding, and discarding all terms having powers higher than the *second* in small quantities (all first order terms drop out in this case, so we must keep the second order terms):

$$a^2 \approx d^2 + 2d\Delta b + \Delta b^2 + d^2 + 2d\Delta c + \Delta c^2$$

$$-2(d^2 + d\Delta b + d\Delta c + \Delta b \Delta c)\left(1 - \frac{\Delta A^2}{2}\right)$$

$$\approx \Delta b^2 + \Delta c^2 - 2\Delta b \Delta c + d^2 \Delta A^2$$

$$= (\Delta b - \Delta c)^2 + d^2 \Delta A^2$$

or, adding and subtracting d within the parentheses, and using $A = \Delta A$:

$$a^2 = (b - c)^2 + d^2 A^2$$

This relation says that, when b and c are nearly equal and A is small, we can determine a by considering it to be the hypotenuse of a right triangle, one of whose legs is $b - c$ and the other of whose legs is dA (or, to the same order of accuracy, bA or cA). Figure 8–7 illustrates this approximation.

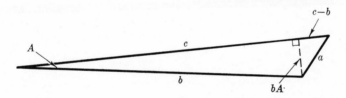

Figure 8–7

EXERCISE XVII

1. Find the absolute and relative error in y for the following functions. The constants are accurate to the number of digits shown.

   a. $y = 1.00 + \ln x$ $x = 2.71 \pm .01$
   b. $y = 2.00 \cos x + 3.00 \, x^5$ $x = 4.00 \pm .005$ (the exponent is exact)
   c. $y = x^{-1.2}$ $x = 1, 10, 100, 1000$ (exact values)
   d. $y = e^x \sin x$ $x = 6.3 \pm .05$
   e. $y = 1.00 \cos x + .60 \cos 2x$ $x = 1.0 \pm .05$
          $+ .30 \cos 3x$ $1.5 \pm .05$
                                 $2.4 \pm .05$

2. In a circle of radius a, a chord is drawn which subtends a central angle θ. Write the expression for the distance from the center of the chord to the edge of the circle, x. Draw a flow chart for a program that will calculate to four significant digits for *all* values of θ less than $\pi/2$.

3. Draw a flow chart for a calculation that will find y accurate to four significant figures for *all* values of x between 0 and 1.   Write a FORTRAN program to calculate and print y for 1000 equally spaced values of x.

a. $y = x - \sin x$

b. $y = \tan x - \sin x$

c. $y = e^x - \cos x$

d. $y = \cos x - 2 \ln (1 + x)$

e. $y = \dfrac{\tan x - 2 \ln (1 + x)}{\sin x - \ln (1 + x)}$

f. $y = \dfrac{\cos \pi x/2 - 1}{x - 1}$

CHAPTER IX *Quadrature*

9.1 INTRODUCTION

The preceding chapters have been devoted largely to describing the digital computer and the types of operations it can perform. The remaining chapters are devoted to topics ordinarily treated in a numerical analysis course.

Strangely enough, it seems proper to make quadrature, or integration, the first such topic to be covered. There are two reasons for doing this. First, quadrature as ordinarily done on the computer is a very direct extension of the material of Chapters VII and VIII. Second, quadrature is one of the fields of applied mathematics most markedly affected by the advent of the computer.

In elementary calculus the methods for differentiation and integration of various functions are taught. Generally speaking, differentiation turns out to be the more easily performed of the two operations. Physicists and engineers, then, sometimes find it strange that mathematicians usually consider integration to the "nicer" process. In particular, the mathematician is inclined to regard a problem as solved once he presents the answer in terms of a quadrature, that is, a definite integral of a known function, between known limits. After all, such an integral merely represents a number. To the physicist or engineer, however, the numerical value of this number may be a matter of considerable concern. Before the advent of the computer, the task of evaluating any but the most simple definite integrals was imposing to say the least, and was insurmountable in many cases. The digital computer has produced a marked change in this situation. Numerical evaluation of large classes of definite integrals is a process well within the capabilities of even the slower computers. However, there are still problems involving quadrature in two or more dimensions which would require inordinate amounts of time on even the fastest of present-day computers.

9.2 REVIEW OF THE DEFINITE INTEGRAL

In elementary calculus the definite integral is defined as follows: Let $y = f(x)$ be a function defined (and reasonably well behaved) between $x = a$ and $x = b$. Now divide the interval $a \leqslant x \leqslant b$ into n subintervals by the points $a < x_1 < x_2 < \cdots < x_{i-1} < x_i < \cdots < x_{n-1} < b$. Now let:

$$\Delta x_i = x_i - x_{i-1} \tag{9-1}$$

and ξ_i be any point between x_{i-1} and x_i, and form the sum:

$$\sum_{i=1}^{n} f(\xi_i)\Delta x_i \tag{9-2}$$

Now let the number of intervals n approach infinity in such a manner that all the lengths of the intervals Δx_i approach zero. Then if the quantity given by expression (9-2) approaches a limit, that limit is called the definite integral of $f(x)$ from a to b and is denoted by the symbol:

$$\int_a^b f(x)dx \tag{9-3}$$

This is the definition of the definite integral. By a most extraordinary circumstance, it happens that there is a function $F(x)$, whose derivative $F'(x)$ is equal to $f(x)$, and the number represented by the definite integral (9-3), above, is the same number one obtains by computing $F(b) - F(a)$. The fact that:

$$\int_a^b f(x)dx = F(b) - F(a) \tag{9-4}$$

is one of the most remarkable and useful facts in all mathematics. It is called the "Fundamental Theorem of Integral Calculus." It can be used to find the value of the definite integral, provided that the function $f(x)$ is sufficiently simple that its antiderivative $F(x)$ (i.e., the function which, when differentiated, gives $f(x)$) can be determined. A major part of the usual integral calculus course is devoted to the evaluation of definite integrals in this manner. The hardest part of this problem is the determination of the antiderivative, $F(x)$, and many hours are usually devoted to this problem. When the antiderivative cannot be found, as is quite often the case, it is necessary to employ the trapezoidal rule or Simpson's Rule or some other numerical method of approximation. This amounts to computing the definite integral from its definition rather than making use of the fundamental theorem of integral calculus. Such methods, because of the large amounts of calculation involved, ordinarily appear to be undesirable as presented in the elementary calculus course, but are quite natural and useful when digital computers are available.

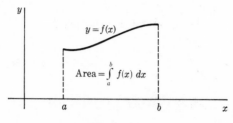

Figure 9–1

9.21 Geometrical Significance of the Definite Integral

As is well known, the definite integral of $f(x)$ between a and b can be considered to be the area lying between the curve $f(x)$ and the x axis, and between the lines $x = a$ and $x = b$, the area being considered positive if $f(x)$ is above the x axis and negative if it is below. The area marked in Figure 9–1 represents the situation. Because it is so difficult to give a rigorous definition of the geometrical concept of area, it is not uncommon to define area in terms of the definite integral rather than to regard the integral as being represented geometrically by the area. Be that as it may, most of the methods of numerical approximation to the definite integral are easily portrayed in terms of approximation of an area by another area, and will be presented from that viewpoint.

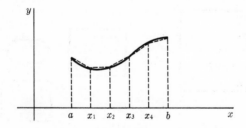

Figure 9–2

9.22 The Trapezoidal Rule

A very straightforward approximation to the definite integral is obtained by dividing the interval a to b into n *equal* parts, erecting an ordinate line to the curve at each of the points of division, and connecting the end points of these ordinate lines to form trapezoids, as in Figure 9–2. The sum of the areas of these trapezoids can be seen to approximate the area under the curve. The approximation can be made as close as desired by taking a sufficient number

of intervals.   Using the notation of Section 9.2, the areas of the trapezoids
are:

$$A_1 = 1/2\Delta x_1[f(x_1) + f(x_0)]$$

$$A_2 = 1/2\Delta x_2[f(x_2) + f(x_1)]$$

.

.

.

$$A_i = 1/2\Delta x_i[f(x_i) + f(x_{i-1})]$$

.

.

.

$$A_{n-1} = 1/2\Delta x_{n-1}[f(x_{n-1}) + f(x_{n-2})]$$

$$A_n = 1/2\Delta x_n[f(x_n) + f(x_{n-1})]$$

Since all the x's are equal:

$$\Delta x_1 = \Delta x_2 = \cdots = \Delta x_i = \cdots = \Delta x_n = \Delta x$$

we may sum up the above areas to obtain:

$$A = 1/2\Delta x[f(x_0) + 2f(x_1) + 2f(x_2) + \cdots + 2f(x_i) + \cdots + 2f(x_{n-1}) + f(x_n)]$$

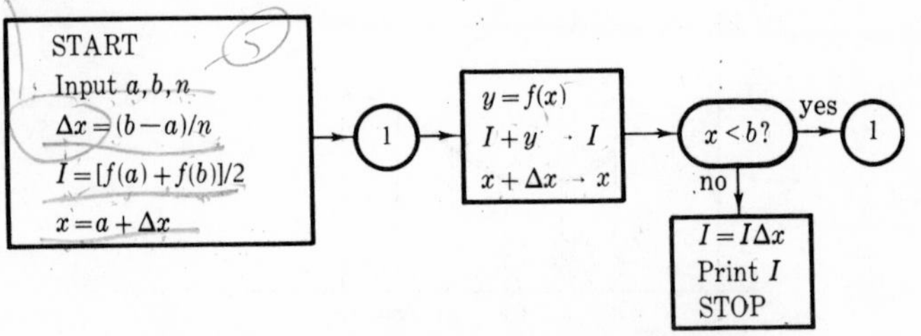

Figure 9–3: Integration by Trapezoidal Rule

To evaluate this quantity on a computer, one must calculate the function
$f(x)$ a total of $n + 1$ times, and then need do very little else.   It follows, then,
that the time required to perform the calculation will be roughly equal to
$n + 1$ times the computation time of the function $f(x)$.   Hence the time
required is roughly proportional to the number of subdivisions made, and
thus is closely tied to the question of accuracy.   The accuracy consideration
will be discussed in a later section.   The flow chart given in Figure 9–3 will
serve for the application of the trapezoidal rule for any value of $n \geqslant 2$.

The FORTRAN program given below will evaluate a definite integral, if statement 1 is completed to be the function which describes the integrand:

```
  1 GRANF(X)=   (insert correct expression for integrand)
    READ 101,A,B,N
    FN=N
    DX=(B−A)/FN
    FI=(GRANF(A)+GRANF(B))/2.
    X=A
    NN=N−1
    DO 3 I=1,NN
    X=X+DX
  3 FI=FI+GRANF(X)
    FI=DX*FI
    PRINT 101,FI
    STOP
101 FORMAT(2E12.4,I5)
    END
```

The first statement is a definition statement for the integrand function, as described in Section 7.5.

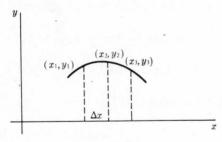

Figure 9–4

9.23 Simpson's Rule

The other method of numerical integration commonly taught in elementary calculus is that known as Simpson's Rule. It is slightly more sophisticated than the trapezoidal rule in that, instead of drawing a straight line between pairs of points, one passes a parabola through each three points, and the parabola is then expected to lie closer to the true curve than would simple line segments. The formula can be derived as follows: Suppose we have three points as shown in Figure 9–4 spaced equal distances Δx apart in the x direction. Suppose also that the parabola:

$$y = a_1x^2 + a_2x + a_3$$

passes through all three of the points. Then the area under the parabola from x_1 to x_3 is:

$$A = \int_{x_1}^{x_3} y\,dx = \int_{x_2-\Delta x}^{x_2+\Delta x} (a_1 x^2 + a_2 x + a_3)\,dx \qquad (9\text{-}6)$$

or

$$A = [a_1 x^3/3 + a_2 x^2/2 + a_3 x]_{x_2-\Delta x}^{x_2+\Delta x} \qquad (9\text{-}7)$$

Substituting the limits, we obtain:

$$A = 2a_1 x_2^2 \Delta x + (2/3)a_1 \Delta x^3 + 2a_2 x_2 \Delta x + 2a_3 \Delta x \qquad (9\text{-}8)$$

This relation can be reduced to a much nicer form. We note that since:

$$y_2 = a_1 x_2^2 + a_2 x_2 + a_3 \qquad (9\text{-}9)$$

we may write (9-8) as:

$$A = 2y_2 \Delta x + (2/3)a_1 \Delta x^3 \qquad (9\text{-}10)$$

Further, since the curve (9-5) passes through all three points, we have:

$$y_1 = a_1(x_2 - \Delta x)^2 + a_2(x_2 - \Delta x) + a_3$$

and:

$$y_3 = a_1(x_2 + \Delta x)^2 + a_2(x_2 + \Delta x) + a_3$$

Adding these last two relations, we find that:

$$y_1 + y_3 = 2a_1 x_2^2 + 2a_1 \Delta x^2 + 2a_2 x_2 + 2a_3$$

Using (9-9), we may write this as:

$$y_1 + y_3 = 2y_2 + 2a_1 \Delta x^2 \qquad (9\text{-}11)$$

This may be employed to eliminate the constant a_1 from the relation (9-10). Subtracting $2y_2$ from both sides in (9-11) and then multiplying by $\Delta x/3$, we find that:

$$\Delta x(y_1 - 2y_2 + y_3)/3 = 2a_1 \Delta x^3/3$$

Substituting this quantity into (9-10) we find that:

$$A = 2y_2 \Delta x + (\Delta x/3)(y_1 - 2y_2 + y_3)$$

or, regrouping terms:

$$A = (\Delta x/3)(y_1 + 4y_2 + y_3) \tag{9-12}$$

The relation (9-12), which gives the area under a parabola defined by three points equally spaced in the x-direction, can now be used to obtain an approximate relation for the area under any curve. As before, let the interval from a to b be divided into n equal parts. This time we require n to be even,

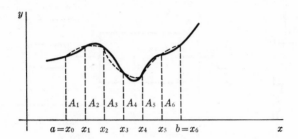

Figure 9–5

since our formula (9-12) computes the area of two parts at a time. Figure 9–5 shows the situation for $n = 6$. The first parabola determines the area $A_1 + A_2$, the second one $A_3 + A_4$, and the third one $A_5 + A_6$. In the general case we would have, using formula (9-12):

$$A_1 + A_2 = (\Delta x/3)[f(x_0) + 4f(x_1) + f(x_2)]$$
$$A_3 + A_4 = (\Delta x/3)(f(x_2) + 4f(x_3) + f(x_4)]$$

$$\cdot$$
$$\cdot$$
$$\cdot$$

$$A_{n-1} + A_n = (\Delta x/3)[f(x_{n-2}) + 4f(x_{n-1}) + f(x_n)]$$

Adding these subareas, we obtain for the total area:

$$A = (\Delta x/3)[f(x_0) + 4f(x_1) + 2f(x_2) + 4f(x_3)$$
$$+ 2f(x_4) + \cdots + 4f(x_{n-1}) + f(x_n)] \tag{9-13}$$

This formula has the same general appearance as that obtained for the trapezoidal rule. Again it involves computing $f(x)$ for $n + 1$ values of x and combining the results, the only difference being that in this case different coefficients are involved. The formula is easily remembered if certain of its features are noted. Inside the brackets, the first and last coefficients are one. The second and next to last are 4. In the middle, they alternate between 4 and 2.

The formula is slightly more complicated than the trapezoidal rule, but it will be shown later that, for the same value of *n*, the accuracy can be considerably better.

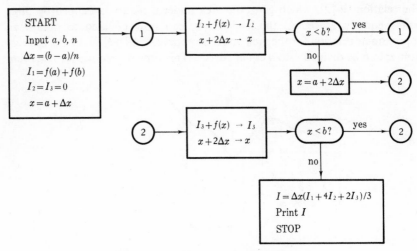

Figure 9–6: Integration by Simpson's rule

There are several possible ways of programming Simpson's Rule for a computer. The flow chart, Figure 9–6, is for using formula (9-13) rearranged as follows:

$$A = (\Delta x/3)\{[f(a) + f(b)] + 4[f(x_1) + \cdots + f(x_{n-1})]$$
$$+ 2[f(x_2) + \cdots + f(x_{n-2})]\} \quad \text{(9-14)}$$

It will work for *n* any even number.

The FORTRAN program given below will perform this calculation. Again statement 1 must be completed to describe the integrand completely:

```
1 GRANF(X)=   (insert correct expression for integrand)
  READ 101,A,B,N
  FN=N
  DX=(B−A)/FN
  TDX=2.*DX
2 FI=GRANF(B)+GRANF(A)
  AI=0.
  BI=0.
  X=A−DX
  NN=N/2
  DO 3 J=1,NN
```

```
    X=X+TDX
 3  AI=AI+GRANF(X)
    X=A
    NM=NN-1
    DO 4 J=1,NM
    X=X+TDX
 4  BI=BI+GRANF(X)
    FI=DX*(FI+4.*AI+2.*BI)/3.
    PRINT 101,FI
    STOP
101 FORMAT(2E12.4,I5)
    END
```

9.3 OTHER QUADRATURE FORMULAE

There are many other approximate formulae for the evaluation of definite integrals beyond the ones from elementary calculus just described. A few of the more important will be mentioned here. More complete description may be found in standard texts on numerical analysis.

9.31 Higher Degree Polynomial Approximations

The trapezoidal rule was based on passing straight lines through pairs of consecutive points on the graph of $y = f(x)$. Since the equation of a straight line is of the form $y = mx + b$, which is of first degree, or linear, in x, this is equivalent to fitting each pair of points with a first degree polynomial. In Simpson's Rule, a parabola, or second degree polynomial, is passed through each set of three consecutive points. It is possible to obtain other approximations by passing higher degree polynomials through consecutive points. In general, if the nth degree polynomial:

$$y = a_1 x^n + a_2 x^{n-1} + \ldots + a_n x + a_{n+1}$$

is passed through $n + 1$ points equally spaced in the x direction, the area under the curve can be expressed in the form:

$$\int_{x_0}^{x_n} y dx = \Delta x [c_0 y_0 + c_1 y_1 + \ldots + c_{n+1} y_{n+1}]$$

where the c's are constants which must be determined for the degree of polynomial used.

One can easily write FORTRAN programs similar to the ones given for the trapezoidal rule and Simpson's rule, for polynomials of any desired degree once the c's are known.   These higher order formulae have the advantage that they tend to give greater accuracy for a given number of subdivisions, but they require somewhat more effort to set up initially.   For a sixth degree polynomial passing through seven points, the formula becomes:

$$\int_{x_0}^{x_6} ydx = (\Delta x/140) [41y_0 + 216y_1 + 27y_2 + 272y_3 + 27y_4 + 216y_5 + 41y_6]$$

Weddle's Rule, a well known formula for hand computation, is a modification of this expression which sacrifices some accuracy to obtain simple coefficients.   It is:

$$\int_{x_0}^{x_6} ydx = (3\Delta x/10) [y_0 + 5y_1 + y_2 + 6y_3 + y_4 + 5y_5 + y_6]$$

This latter formula is no longer exact for a sixth degree polynomial, but it is for fifth or lower degree.   For hand computation the simplified coefficients are worth this sacrifice, but for computer use the more accurate formula can be applied with equal ease.

9.32   Gauss's Formula

In the quadrature formulae so far discussed, values of the function at equally spaced intervals are required.   Gauss investigated the possibility of obtaining greater accuracy with the same number of values of $f(x)$ by using a different spacing.   The problem which he undertook to solve is the following: If $\int_a^b f(x)dx$ is to be computed from a given number of values of $f(x)$, what selection of abscissas will in general give the most accurate result?   He found that the points of subdivision should not be equally spaced, but should be symmetrically placed with respect to the midpoint of the interval of integration.

Gauss's formula is usually expressed in the form:

$$\int_{-1/2}^{1/2} \phi(u)du = R_1\phi(u_1) + R_2\phi(u_2) + \cdots + R_n\phi(u_n)$$

i.e., for an integral over the interval from $-1/2$ to $1/2$.

The values of R_i and u_i to be used in this formula have been tabulated for various values of n.   For example, for $n = 2$, $R_1 = R_2 = 1/2$ and $-u_1 = u_2 = .2886751346$.   For this case. then, the formula is:

$$\int_{-1/2}^{1/2} \phi(u)dn = (1/2)\phi(-.2886751346) + (1/2)\phi(.2886751346)$$

For $n = 3$, the values for $R_1 = R_3 = 5/18$, $R_2 = 4/9$, and $-u_1 = u_3 = .3872983346$, $u_2 = 0$, so that the formula becomes:

$$\int_{-1/2}^{1/2} \phi(u)du = (5/18)\phi(-.3872983346) + (4/9)\phi(0) + (5/18)\phi(.3872983346)$$

Values for n up to 10 are available in many texts on numerical analysis.

While Gauss's formula is given in terms of integration over the interval from $-1/2$ to $1/2$, a change of variable can be employed to make it applicable to any interval. If we wish to evaluate:

$$I = \int_a^b f(x)dx \tag{9-15}$$

we make the substitution:

$$x = (b - a)u + \frac{a + b}{2}$$

Then when $u = -1/2$, $x = a$, and when $u = 1/2$, $x = b$. If we then write:

$$f(x) = f\left[(b - a)u + \frac{a + b}{2}\right] = \phi(u), \text{ say,}$$

then, since:

$$dx = (b - a)du$$

the integral (9-15) becomes:

$$I = (b - a)\int_{-1/2}^{1/2} \phi(u)du$$

and Gauss's formula can be applied. For computer applications, machine time saved in using a sophisticated formula such as this one is seldom worth the effort required.

9.33 Other Methods

The definite integral:

$$\int_a^b f(x)dx$$

can be regarded as the solution of the differential equation:

$$dy/dx = f(x)$$

subject to the initial condition $y = 0$ when $x = a$. If it is regarded in this light, numerical methods for the solution of differential equations can be applied to obtain its value. These are discussed in Chapter XVI.

9.4 ACCURACY OF QUADRATURE FORMULAE

It has been seen that the evaluation of an integral by the quadrature formulae involves computing of the integrand for a number of values of the independent variable, and the addition of the results, multiplied, perhaps, by certain coefficients, Hence the computer time required to evaluate an integral is just about proportional to the number of times the integrand must be computed, or the number of subdivisions made in the interval of integration. This in turn is determined by the accuracy required in the final answer. Thus a method is needed for estimating the accuracy to be obtained by subdivision into a given number of intervals. Methods are available for the several quadrature formulae discussed in this chapter.

9.41 *Inherent Error in the Trapezoidal Rule*

In the trapezoidal rule, the area under a segment of width Δx of the curve $y = f(x)$ is approximated by the area of a trapezoid:

$$A = (\Delta x/2)[f(x) + f(x + \Delta x)]$$

The true value of the area is:

$$I = \int_{x}^{x+\Delta x} f(x)dx$$

It can be shown that the difference between these two quantities is given by:

$$A - I = \frac{\Delta x^3}{12} f''(\xi) \tag{9-16}$$

where ξ is some value between x and $x + \Delta x$. This fact can be used to obtain an estimate of the error incurred in using the trapezoidal rule.

The relation (9-16) applies to a single interval. If we divide the range of integration into n intervals, then the total error will not be more than the sum of the errors for the separate subintervals. If we let M_2 stand for the maximum (absolute) value of the second derivative $f''(x)$ anywhere within the range $a < x < b$, then we can say that:

$$\text{Absolute error} \leqslant \frac{n\Delta x^3 M_2}{12} \tag{9-17}$$

This relation can be used to determine the number of subintervals required to attain a given accuracy and hence the time requirement for an integration by the trapezoidal rule. For this purpose it is convenient to write the relation in another form. If ΔI is the largest absolute error which can be tolerated, we must choose n so that:

$$\text{Absolute error} \leqslant \Delta I$$

This will certainly be true if n is chosen so that:

$$\frac{n\Delta x^3 M_2}{12} \leqslant \Delta I \tag{9-18}$$

When we use the trapezoidal rule, the value Δx is determined by n:

$$\Delta x = \frac{b - a}{n}$$

Using this relation in (9-18), we can write:

$$\frac{M_2(b - a)^3}{12n^2} \leqslant \Delta I \tag{9-19}$$

Solving for n, we must have:

$$n \geqslant \sqrt{\frac{M_2(b - a)^3}{12\Delta I}} \tag{9-20}$$

Example 1. The function $y = \cos \sqrt{x}$ is to be integrated from $x = .5$ to $x = 1$ by the trapezoidal rule. How many intervals should be taken to assure that the error in the answer is no worse than $.00001$?

SOLUTION: the second derivative is:

$$y'' = \frac{1}{4x}\left(\frac{\sin \sqrt{x}}{\sqrt{x}} - \cos \sqrt{x}\right)$$

We wish an upper limit for this quantity over the range .5 to 1. As a crude estimate, we note that sin u/u is never greater than 1. Hence in the range of interest both sin $\sqrt{x}/\sqrt{x}$ and cos $\sqrt{x}$ are between zero and 1. Hence the quantity in parentheses is certainly no greater than $1 - 0$, or 1. The quantity $1/4x$ has its maximum when $x = .5$. Its value is then .5. Hence we may certainly say that $y'' < .5$ in the range of interest. If we put $M_2 = .5$, $b = 1$, $a = .5$, and $\Delta I = .00001$ in formula (9-20), we obtain $n \geqslant 23$. Thus a subdivision into about 25 subintervals would be adequate. If the machine requires 10 multiplication times to extract a square root and 10 to compute a cosine, about 20 multiplication times would be required to compute the integrand once. Hence computation of the integral would require roughly $25 \times 20 = 500$ multiplication times, or about 5 seconds on a slow machine.

In this example a very crude estimate was made of the upper limit of the second derivative. By a more careful analysis it can be determined that the maximum value of y'' in the range of interest is $y'' < .25$. If this value is used in (9-20) it is found that $n \geqslant 17$ would be sufficient.

9.42 Inherent Error in Simpson's Rule

Just as for the trapezoidal rule, it is possible to determine the inherent error in Simpson's Rule. In this case the expression for the error is:

$$E \leqslant \left| \frac{(\Delta x)^5}{90} f^{iv}(\xi) \right| \tag{9-21}$$

where ξ is a value between x and $x + \Delta x$. It is seen that the error depends on the fourth derivative of the function being integrated. This is a surprising fact. It means that, for functions whose fourth derivative is zero, there is no error. Now a third degree polynomial has a zero fourth derivative. This means that Simpson's Rule, which is based on approximating by parabolas, which are second degree polynomials, is exact for third degree polynomials as well. This is a bonus in accuracy which accounts for the widespread use of Simpson's Rule.

As for the trapezoidal rule, the error relation can be converted into a form for the determination of the number of intervals required for a given maximum error. If ΔI is the maximum allowable error, and if M_4 is the maximum value of the fourth derivative of $f(x)$ in the range of integration, then the number of subdivisions n required to make the error less than ΔI is:

$$n \geqslant \sqrt[4]{\frac{M_4(b - a)^5}{90\Delta I}} \tag{9-22}$$

A comparison of this relation with that for the trapezoidal rule, relation (9-20), shows that, if the fourth derivative of a function is of the same order of magnitude as the second derivative, then Simpson's Rule will require many less steps than will the trapezoidal rule. In fact the number of steps required by Simpson's Rule will in this case be about equal to the square root of the number required in the trapezoidal rule. The chief difficulty in the application is the determination of M_4, the maximum value of the fourth derivative. For functions for which the fourth derivative cannot be found or estimated, it is necessary to estimate the error by some other means. One way, extremely simple on a computer, is to perform the calculations for two different values of n and note how much change takes place in the answer. This process can be somewhat risky and must be used with care, for it is possible that the answers obtained by the two calculations may be quite close to each other and

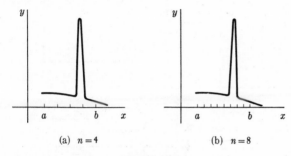

(a) $n = 4$ (b) $n = 8$

Figure 9–7

still be far form the correct answer. Figure 9–7 illustrates a case in which such an event occurs. In the figure, most of the area occurs inside of one of the smallest subintervals shown. Until the interval is divided into fine enough zones to sense the abrupt change of the function within that narrow region, an accurate estimate of the value of the integral cannot be obtained. If one were able to obtain an expression for the fourth derivative of $y = f(x)$ for the curve in Figure 9–7, one would find that the fourth derivative would be large in those regions where the curve undergoes an abrupt change in direction, so that one would find, on using this upper limit for the number M_4 of the relation (9-22), above, that a large number of terms would be required to achieve any appreciable accuracy. On the other hand, if one merely applies Simpson's Rule blindly to the problem, using $n = 4$ and $n = 8$, one would miss completely the fact that a sharp peak in the curve exists, and would obtain two estimates of the area with the peak ignored completely. These estimates might be very nearly equal, but both would underestimate the actual area by about a factor of two. Thus the estimation of accuracy based merely on using two different values of n can be trusted only if there is assurance that the curve has no abrupt changes of behavior.

9.43   *Automatic Selection of Interval Size*

It is easy to write a program, using either the trapezoidal rule or Simpson's Rule, which will automatically recompute an integral, using smaller and smaller subdivisions, until the accuracy in the answer is considered sufficient. If the subdivisions are cut exactly in half at each new trial, all the values of the integrand computed in one trial can be re-used in the next, so that total running time on the machine is only slightly longer than for a single evaluation of the integral using the number of subdivisions finally arrived at in the program.   The process is extremely simple for the trapezoidal rule, and only slightly more involved for Simpson's Rule.   The flow chart (Figure 9–8)

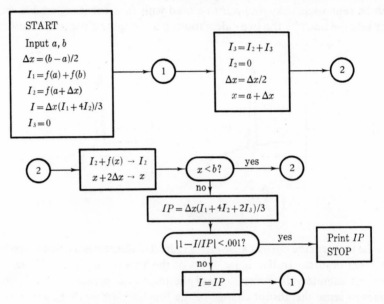

Figure 9–8: Integration by Simpson's rule with error control

and program below demonstrate the process for Simpson's Rule.   In the flow chart, the sum of the two end ordinates is denoted by I_1, the sum of all ordinates which must be multiplied by the coefficient 4 in Simpson's Rule is denoted by I_2, and the sum of all ordinates which must be multiplied by 2 is I_3.   The pattern of the coefficients in two successive applications of Simpson's Rule is:

1		4		2		4		2		4		1
1	4	2	4	2	4	2	4	2	4	2	4	1

so that except for the first and last ordinates, all ordinates computed at one trial will have the coefficient 2 at the next trial.   Hence, the I_3 for a new trial is simply the sum $I_2 + I_3$ for the preceding trial. As the flow chart is written, the process will stop when the change in the answer from one trial to the next is less than 0.1%. This suggests, but does not prove, that the relative error is on the order of .001. As was pointed out in the preceding section, and demonstrated in Figure 9–7, this sort of error estimate can be misleading; but it is often the best one available.

The process demonstrated below can sometimes become extremely long when the integrand is slowly varying over a large interval and widely varying over a relatively small interval. For such problems, it is possible to make additional improvements that will cause finer subdivisions to be used only in those regions where they are really needed. Such improvements will not be demonstrated here.

```
  1 GRANF(X)=   (insert correct expression for integrand)
    READ 101,A,B
    DX=(B−A)/2.
    FI1=GRANF(B)+GRANF(A)
    FI2=GRANF(A+DX)
    FI3=0.
    FI=DX*(FI1+4.*FI2)/3.
  2 FI3=FI2+FI3
    FI2=0.
    TDX=DX
    DX=.5*DX
    X=A+DX
  3 FI2=FI2+GRANF(X)
    X=X+TDX
    IF(X−B)3,3,4
  4 FIP=DX*(FI1+4.*FI2+2.*FI3)/3.
    IF(ABSF(FIP−FI)−.001*ABSF(FIP))6,6,5
  5 FI=FIP
    GO TO 2
  6 PRINT 101,FIP
    STOP
101 FORMAT(2E12.4)
    END
```

9.5 IMPROPER INTEGRALS

An integral is termed "improper" if either the integrand becomes infinite at some point in the interval of integration, or one or both of the limits of integration is infinite. The integral may or may not exist in these cases. When it does exist, machine calculation of its value requires some modification of the methods described earlier in this chapter.

9.51   Infinite Integrand

The function $y = 1/\sqrt{x}$ becomes infinite when x approaches zero, yet the integral from zero to one exists:

$$\int_0^1 \frac{1}{\sqrt{x}}\, dx = 2x^{1/2}\Big]_0^1 = 2$$

On the other hand, the function $y = 1/x$, whose graph is very similar in appearance, represents a different situation.   Here

$$\int_0^1 \frac{1}{x}\, dx = \ln x\Big]_0^1 = \infty$$

and the integral is infinite.   The graphs of the two functions are shown in Figure 9–9.   The area between zero and one is finite in Figure 9–9(a), but infinite in Figure 9–9(b).   The interpretation is that $1/\sqrt{x}$ approaches infinity so slowly that the area remains finite, while $1/x$ approaches infinity so rapidly that the area becomes infinite also.   For functions such as the one shown in Figure 9–9(b), we cannot expect to get a usable value for the integral by any method of numerical quadrature, since the integral does not have a value.   For functions such as the one shown in Figure 9–9(a), however, the integral does exist, and a method of numerical quadrature to such a case would be highly desirable.   Clearly, in the case of Figure 9–9(a), an attempt to apply Simpson's Rule or one of the similar rules in a form which includes the point $x = 0$ as one of the end points of a subdivision is doomed to failure, since the integrand is infinite at $x = 0$.   However, if the subdivision is started some small distance h to the right of $x = 0$, then Simpson's Rule can be applied, using a sufficient number of subintervals for proper accuracy in accordance with the rules already discussed.   Then the contribution of the part from $x = 0$ to $x = h$ must be computed by some other means and included in the final estimate of the integral.   *This part cannot be neglected.*   No matter how small h is chosen to be, the little region from zero to h may well include most of the area.   For example, in Figure 9–9(b), no matter how small

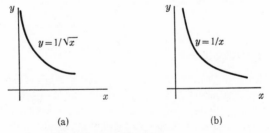

(a)   (b)

Figure 9–9

h is chosen to be, the contribution to the area of the subinterval from zero to h is infinite! A method that can frequently be used to estimate the contribution to the integral of a region near a singularity is illustrated below:

Example 1. Give a procedure for finding:

$$I = \int_0^1 \frac{dx}{\sqrt{1 - \cos \sqrt{x}}}$$

Simpson's Rule can be applied except in the neighborhood of $x = 0$. Thus we may split the integral into two parts:

$$I = \int_0^h \frac{dx}{\sqrt{1 - \cos \sqrt{x}}} + \int_h^1 \frac{dx}{\sqrt{1 - \cos \sqrt{x}}} = I_1 + I_2$$

The second integral can be evaluated by Simpson's Rule. The first requires some special technique. Usually the best procedure is to apply Taylor's Formula. We note that:

$$\cos \sqrt{x} = 1 - x/2! + x^2/4! - \cdots$$

so that:

$$1 - \cos \sqrt{x} = x/2 - x^2/4! + \cdots$$

and:

$$\sqrt{1 - \cos \sqrt{x}} = \sqrt{x/2 - x^2/4! + \cdots} = \sqrt{x/2}\sqrt{1 - x/4.3 + \cdots}$$

The square root of the power series under the second square root sign is again a power series:

$$1 - \frac{1}{2}\left(\frac{x}{4 \times 3}\right) + \text{terms involving higher powers of } x$$

Its reciprocal is again a power series:

$$1 + \frac{1}{2}\left(\frac{x}{4 \times 3}\right) + \text{terms involving higher powers of } x$$

Hence we may write:

$$I_1 = \int_0^h \frac{dx}{\sqrt{1 - \cos \sqrt{x}}}$$

$$= \int_0^h \sqrt{\frac{2}{x}}\left(1 + \frac{x}{4!} + \text{terms involving higher powers of } x\right)dx$$

Integrating term by term:

$$I_1 = \sqrt{2}\left[2x^{1/2} + (2/3)x^{3/2}/4! + \text{terms involving higher powers}\right]_0^h$$

If h is sufficiently small, we may neglect all but the first term, and obtain:

$$I_1 \approx 2\sqrt{2h} \tag{9-23}$$

Thus an easy method of evaluating I_1 is available. It is quite simple to write a FORTRAN program that will apply the formula to the subdivision next to the singularity and then apply Simpson's Rule to the rest of the integral.

A suitable FORTRAN program is:

```
  1 GRANF(X)=1./SQRTF(1.-COSF(SQRTF(X)))
    READ 101,P,N
    FN=N
    DX=(1.-P)/FN
    TDX=2.*DX
  2 FI=GRANF(1.)+GRANF(P)
    AI=0.
    BI=0.
    X=P-DX
    NN=N/2
    DO 3 J=1,NN
    X=X+TDX
  3 AI=AI+GRANF(X)
    X=P
    NM=NN-1
    DO 4 J=1,NM
    X=X+TDX
  4 BI=BI+GRANF(X)
  5 FI=DX*(FI+4.*AI+2.*BI)/3.+SQRTF(8.*P)
    PRINT 101,FI
    STOP
101 FORMAT(E12.4,I5)
    END
```

This program is almost identical to that of Section 9.23. The effect of the infinite integrand at $x = 0$ has been to require the use of another value, $x = P$, as the lower limit of integration and the addition in statement 5 of the term SQRTF(8.*P) to account for the integral from $x = 0$ to $x = P$.

In lieu of attempting a careful analysis of accuracy, one could run the program for several trial values of N and P. Generally speaking, increasing

N and decreasing P should tend to improve the accuracy. When P is very small, however, we are near the point where the integrand becomes infinite. In this region, the fourth derivative may be quite large, requiring that a very large value of N be used. Thus the choices of N and P are not really independent. A small P gives better accuracy for the contribution of the part near $x = 0$, but tends to diminish the accuracy for the remainder of the integral.

The procedure just illustrated is of sufficiently general applicability that it will be restated as a general step by step procedure: Suppose the function $f(x)$ is infinite at $x = a$, and the integral from a to b is to be computed. (The singularity is chosen here to be at one end point of the interval of integration. If it is at interior point, the integral can be broken in two at that point and this procedure applied to each part separately.) We expand all of those parts of $f(x)$ which are finite at $x = a$ as power series about $x = a$. The resulting series will simplify to give:

$$f(x) = k(x - a)^{-\alpha}(1 + a_1 x + a_2 x^2 + \cdots)$$

The value of the integral of this function from a to $a + h$ is approximately:

$$\int_a^{a+h} f(x)dx \approx \frac{kh^{1-\alpha}}{1 - \alpha}$$

Now let $h = (a - b)/n$, and choose n to be an *odd* number so that after this first subinterval is taken care of there will be an even number left for the application of Simpson's Rule. Then the entire integral is given by:

$$I = \frac{k}{1 - \alpha}\left(\frac{b - a}{n}\right)^{1-\alpha} + \frac{b - a}{3n}$$
$$[f(x_1) + 4f(x_2) + 2f(x_3) + \cdots + 4f(x_{n-1}) + f(x_n)] \quad \text{(9-24)}$$

The numbers k and α must be determined analytically from a study of the function $f(x)$ near the point $x = a$. Once this is done, these numbers merely become machine inputs in a program to perform the calculation indicated in equation (9-24).

9.52 Infinite Limits of Integration

The integral:

$$\int_1^\infty \frac{dx}{1 + x^3}$$

is convergent. This is easily seen from the following argument:

Since:

$$\frac{1}{1+x^3} < \frac{1}{x^3} \qquad \text{for positive } x$$

the curve:

$$y = \frac{1}{1+x^3}$$

lies below the curve $y = 1/x^3$ for positive x.   Hence:

$$\int_1^\infty \frac{dx}{1+x^3} < \int_1^\infty \frac{dx}{x^3} = -\frac{1}{2x^2}\bigg]_1^\infty = \frac{1}{2}$$

Figure 9–10 shows the areas represented by the above integrals.   The area under the upper curve is equal to 1/2, so the area under the lower curve is certainly less than this.

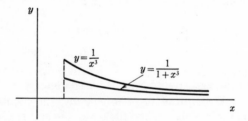

Figure 9–10

The actual value of the integral can be found by letting:

$$x = 1/z, \qquad dx = -1/z^2 dz$$

Then the integral becomes:

$$I = \int_1^0 \frac{-dz}{z^2 + 1/z} = \int_0^1 \frac{z\,dz}{z^3 + 1}$$

This integral is a proper integral, and can be evaluated by Simpson's Rule or the trapezoidal rule without further ado.

Although it happened in this particular case that the substitution $x = 1/z$ led to a proper integral, such a substitution will sometimes lead to an integral having a singularity in the integrand.   If this occurs, the method described in the preceding section can be used.   Alternatively, integrals of this type can be evaluated by making a change of variable only for large arguments of the variable of integration. The above problem will be redone to demonstrate this method. We write the integral as:

$$I = \int_1^R \frac{dx}{1+x^3} + \int_R^\infty \frac{dx}{1+x^3}$$

Let:

$$I_1 = \int_R^\infty \frac{dx}{1+x^3}$$

Let $x = 1/z$, $dx = -1/z^2 dz$. Then:

$$I_1 = \int_{1/R}^0 \frac{-dz}{z^2 + 1/z} = \int_0^{1/R} \frac{z\,dz}{z^3+1}$$

If we take R to be very large, then this integral can be approximated as in the preceding section:

$$I_1 = \int_0^{1/R} z(1 - z^3 + \cdots \text{ higher powers})dz \approx \int_0^{1/R} z\,dz = \frac{z^2}{2}\Big]_0^{1/R} = \frac{1}{2R^2}$$

Hence the integral can be written:

$$I \approx \int_1^R \frac{dx}{1+x^3} + \frac{1}{2R^2}$$

This can now be calculated using Simpson's Rule or any other suitable method for the first term. A suitable FORTRAN program is:

```
1 GRANF(X)=1./(1.+X**3)
  READ 101,R,N
  FN=N
  DX=(R-1.)/FN
  TDX=2.*DX
2 FI=GRANF(R)+GRANF(1.)
  AI=0.
  BI=0.
  X=1.-DX
  NN=N/2
  DO 3 J=1,NN
  X=X+TDX
3 AI=AI+GRANF(X)
  X=1.
```

```
      NM=NN-1
      DO 4 J=1,NM
      X=X+TDX
    4 BI=BI+GRANF(X)
    5 FI=DX*(FI+4.*AI+2.*BI)/3.+1./(2.*R*R)
      PRINT 101,FI
      STOP
  101 FORMAT(E12.4,I5)
      END
```

This program is again almost identical to those of Sections 9.23 and 9.51. The effect of the infinite limit of integration has been to require the use of $x = R$ as the upper limit of integration and the addition in statement 5 of the term $1./(2.*R*R)$ to account for the integral from R to infinity. Again, one may attempt to ascertain the accuracy by trying different values of R and N. Larger values of R and N should tend to improve accuracy. As R is increased, the range of integration increases, and N should be increased accordingly.

EXERCISE XVIII

1. In each of the following: (1) draw a flow chart; (2) write a FORTRAN program; (3) calculate the number of steps required to obtain an absolute error of not more than .001. Estimate the time required on a slow machine.

   a. $\int_0^2 \ln \sqrt{1 + x}\, dx$ by Simpson's Rule

   b. $\int_0^1 e^{\sin x}\, dx$ by trapezoidal rule

   c. $\int_0^{\pi/4} \dfrac{\sin^a x}{\sqrt{1 + \cos^2 x}}\, dx$ by trapezoidal rule, for $a = 1, 1.1, 1.2$, etc. up to 3

   d. $\int_0^c \ln \sqrt{1 + \sin x}\, dx$ by Simpson's rule, for $c = \pi/100, 2\pi/100, ..., \pi$

2. In each of the following: (1) evaluate the integral for the immediate vicinity of the singularity; (2) write a FORTRAN program for evaluation of the integral using this estimate near the singularity and Simpson's Rule elsewhere; (3) estimate the time required on a slow machine.

   a. $\int_0^1 \dfrac{dx}{\sqrt[3]{x} - \ln(1 + x)}$

   b. $\int_0^{\pi/2} \dfrac{\sin^b x}{\sqrt[4]{1 - \sin x}}\, dx,$ where $b = 1, 1.5, 2, ...$ up to 10

    c. $\displaystyle\int_0^a x^{1/2} \ln x \, dx,$ where $a = .1, .2, .3,$ etc. up to 10

3. In each of the following: (1) evaluate the contribution of large values of x; (2) write a FORTRAN program for evaluation of the integral using this estimate for large x and Simpson's Rule elsewhere; (3) estimate the time required on a fast machine.

    a. $\displaystyle\int_0^\infty \frac{dx}{1 + e^x}$

    b. $\displaystyle\int_1^\infty \tan^{-1} x \, \frac{\sqrt{1 + x^2}}{x^4} \, dx$

    c. $\displaystyle\int_1^\infty \frac{dx}{\sqrt{x^3 + \sin ax}}$ where $a = 0, .01, .02, \dots$ up to 1

CHAPTER X *Solution of Algebraic and Transcendental Equations*

10.1 INTRODUCTION

In the preceding chapters methods have been described by which functions of many different types can be evaluated; that is, given a value of x, we can find $y = f(x)$. The reverse problem is frequently of interest; that is, given a value of y, find x such that $f(x) = y$. Of particular interest are the values of x which make $y = 0$. These are called the zeros of the function $f(x)$, or the roots or solutions of the equation $f(x) = 0$. If $f(x)$ is a quadratic expression, the roots are given by the quadratic formula of algebra. Algebraic formulae are also available for the solution of cubic or biquadratic equations. For higher degree polynomials, however, formulae do not exist, and numerical methods must be employed to find the roots. For equations such as $ae^x + b \cos x = 0$ or $ax + b \tan x = 0$, algebraic methods are not available. These are transcendental equations, and there is no general method of stating their roots in terms of their coefficients. This means that the solutions to such equations are quite difficult to tabulate, and so, prior to the advent of computers, such solutions have been considered relatively inaccessible, and obtainable only by means of a considerable expenditure of effort. The capability for numerical calculations at high speed provided by the computer has changed this picture considerably. Although the problem of finding the roots of an equation on a computer is by no means trivial, it is a problem solvable in the majority of cases by straightforward application of simple procedures. The object of the present chapter is to set forth the most useful methods for performing this task.

214

10.2 GRAPHICAL APPROXIMATION

In order to understand thoroughly the methods of solution to be given for computer use, it is well first to consider some aspects of the problem from the graphical standpoint. An understanding of the graphical representation of functions and of the graphical analogues of the methods of solution will be quite helpful in following the methods themselves at a later stage. Let:

$$f(x) = 0 \qquad \text{(10-1)}$$

be the equation whose roots are to be found. Then if we take a set of rectangular coordinate axes and plot the graph of

$$y = f(x) \qquad \text{(10-2)}$$

it is evident that the abscissas of the points where the graph crosses the x-axis are the real roots of the given equation, for at these points y is zero and therefore (10-1) is satisfied. Thus a graph of the function $y = f(x)$ displays the roots of the equation $f(x) = 0$. One method, then, of determining the roots is to compute y for a sequence of values of x and plot the results, and use the graph to read the roots. The accuracy of the determination will depend upon the number of values of x for which y is computed and upon the care used in constructing the graph. The first attempt by this method ordinarily gives only rough values for the roots. It is possible to improve the accuracy by replotting the curve in the vicinity of the roots on a graph of larger scale, but such a procedure is not particularly adaptable to computer use, so it will not be considered here. The discussion of the graphical approach will be limited to two topics: obtaining a rough estimate of the roots, and clarification of the computer methods for obtaining precise values, which will be described later.

10.21 *Isolation of the Roots*

In many respects, the problem of obtaining a first rough estimate of the roots of an equation is the most difficult part of the problem of determination of these roots. Once a reasonably decent first estimate is available, the methods that will be described later will ordinarily furnish an accurate value of the root. An important first step will have been made when the roots of $f(x)$ have been isolated, i.e., when the range of possible values of x has been divided into intervals, each of which contains only one root of $f(x)$. This process is not an easy one, but is necessary for some of the methods of finding roots. Some theorems which are useful in this connection will be given without proof.

Theorem I. *If $f(x)$ is continuous from $x = a$ to $x = b$ and if $f(a)$ and $f(b)$ have opposite signs, then there is at least one real root of $f(x) = 0$ between a and b.*

Stated in terms of the graph, if $f(x)$ is on one side of the x axis at $x = a$ and the other side at $x = b$, and if $f(x)$ is continuous from $x = a$ to $x = b$, the graph must cross the x-axis at least once between a and b. Figure 10–1 shows some of the possible configurations for which this theorem applies.

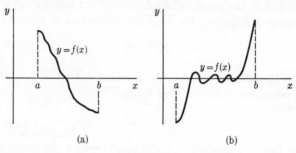

(a)   (b)

Figure 10–1

In Figure 10-1a, the root between a and b is isolated, i.e., it is the only root in the interval. In Figure 10–1b, on the other hand, there are several roots between a and b, so the roots have not yet been isolated. To complete the task of isolation, other values of x between a and b would have to be found for which the sign of $f(x)$ changes. Figure 10–2 shows a case in which the theorem does not apply because of a discontinuity between $x = a$ and $x = b$. $f(a)$ is positive and $f(b)$ is negative, yet there is no root between a and b.

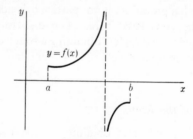

Figure 10–2

This theorem is of great value in isolating the roots of $f(x) = 0$, but it is not in itself sufficient. For example, in Figure 10–1b, there are many roots between a and b. On the other hand, Figure 10–3 illustrates a case in which $f(x)$ never crosses the x-axis, yet $f(x)$ is equal to zero at several points. The roots of a function such as this one can be quite difficult to locate. It may be difficult to determine that the function even has real zeros. The following theorem is of some assistance in this regard.

Theorem II.   *If $f(x)$ is continuous and strictly monotonic from $x = a$ to $x = b$, then $f(x) = 0$ has at most one discrete real root in the interval.*

By a strictly monotonic function is meant one which is either always in-creasing as x increases or always decreasing as x increases. It is characterized by a derivative which does not change sign or become zero. For example,

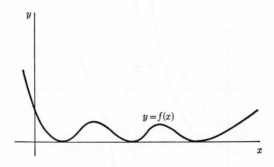

Figure 10–3

Figure 10–4 illustrates functions that are strictly monotonic for the range of values of x indicated. In Figure 10–4c, the interval is intended to be $-\infty$ to $+\infty$. Figure 10–5 represents a case in which the theorem does not apply because the function is discontinuous between a and b. Although it is strictly

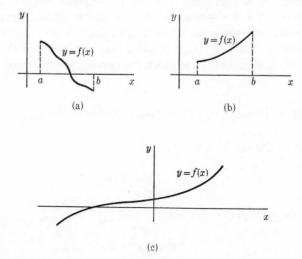

Figure 10–4

monotonic except at the point of discontinuity, it has two roots between a and b. Fortunately, in many cases of practical interest corresponding to physical problems, there is only one root. Knowledge of this fact sometimes simplifies the problem of finding the root.

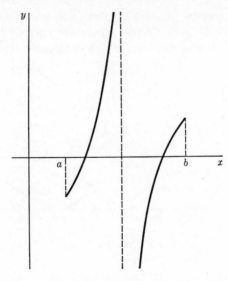

Figure 10–5

10.22   Graphical Representation as the Intersection of Two Curves

The representation of the roots of $f(x) = 0$ as points where the function $y = f(x)$ crosses the x-axis is not the only possible graphical representation, nor is it necessarily the most useful one in all cases.   If the equation $f(x) = 0$ can be written in the form $f_1(x) = f_2(x)$, then the roots of the equation $f(x) = 0$ are those values of x for which the curves $y_1 = f_1(x)$ and $y_2 = f_2(x)$ intersect.

Example 1.   Find approximate values of the real roots of $xe^x = 2$.

We first write the equation as:

$$xe^x - 2 = 0$$

It is now in the form $f(x) = 0$, where:

$$f(x) = xe^x - 2$$

Figure 10–6 shows a graph of $y = f(x)$, and the table of values used to plot the graph.   Since y is negative for $x = 0$ and positive for $x = 1$, there is at least one root between $x = 0$ and $x = 1$.   Further investigation shows that this is the only root.   The derivative of $f(x)$ is:

$$f'(x) = (x + 1)e^x$$

which is positive so long as x is greater than -1 and negative so long as x is less than -1. Hence $f(x)$ is monotonically decreasing in the interval from $-\infty$ to -1 and monotonically increasing in the interval from -1 to $+\infty$.

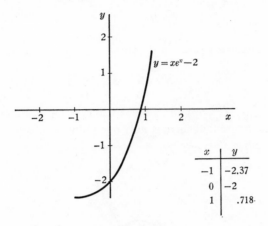

x	y
-1	-2.37
0	-2
1	$.718$

Figure 10–6

By Theorem II, then, it has at most one discrete root in each of these intervals. Now when x is negative, the quantity xe^x is also negative, so that $f(x)$ must be less than -2. Hence there can be no root in the interval $-\infty$ to -1, so that the root between $x = 0$ and $x = 1$ is the only real root.

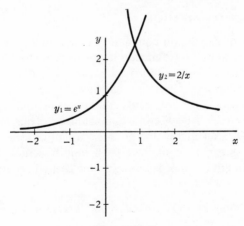

Figure 10–7

Figure 10–7 shows a different way in which the root can be displayed graphically. The equation can be written as $e^x = 2/x$ (this representation is not valid at $x = 0$, since division by zero is not defined in the laws of arithmetic). The root is then the abscissa of the point of intersection of the curves $y_1 = e^x$ and $y_2 = 2/x$.

Example 2. Find the approximate values of the real roots of:

$$2x - \cos x - 1 = 0.$$

This equation can be written in the form:

$$2x - 1 = \cos x$$

The two curves $y_1 = 2x - 1$ and $y_2 = \cos x$ are plotted in Figure 10–8. It is evident from the figure that there is only one point of intersection and hence only one real root.

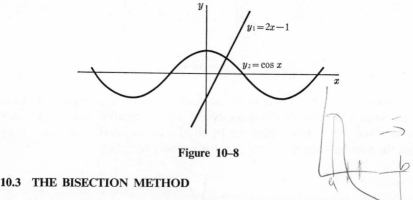

Figure 10–8

10.3 THE BISECTION METHOD

The first method of solving an equation is based on Theorem I of Section 10.21. Suppose a continuous function $f(x)$ is negative at $x = a$ and positive at $x = b$. Then there is at least one root between a and b. Let us calculate $f[(a + b)/2]$, the value of the function halfway between a and b. If this is zero, we have the root. If it is negative, the root is between that point and b. If it is positive, the root is between that point and a. Thus either we have the root or we have it bracketed within an interval half as large as the previous one. This process can be continued, each time bisecting the interval. It can be continued until the root is known to the desired accuracy.

10.31 Flow Chart and Program for the Bisection Method

A flow chart describing the process for finding a root by bisection when the function is known to be negative at $x = A$ and positive at $x = B$ is given in Figure 10–9. The symbol d is used in the chart to represent the prescribed error limit on x which will be accepted. A FORTRAN program generally following this flow chart is given below.

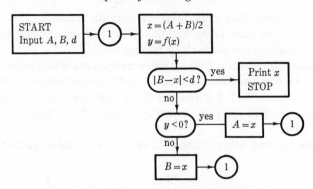

Figure 10–9: Bisection method for finding root

```
  1 GIVF(X) =   (insert given function of X)
    READ 101,A,B,D
  2 X=(A+B)/2.
    Y=GIVF(X)
    IF(ABSF(B−X)−D)3,3,4
  3 PRINT 101,X
    STOP
  4 IF(Y)5,3,6
  5 A=X
    GO TO 2
  6 B=X
    GO TO 2
101 FORMAT(3E12.4)
    END
```

10.32   Comments on the Bisection Method

The method described above for finding the value of the root is simple, but it does have several virtues.   As is seen, the program is rather easy to write. On a computer, the operation is fairly rapid.   The main calculation is the determination of GIVF(X), which must be done once each time the loop is repeated.   Each repetition reduces the maximum error by a factor of two, so three repetitions produce roughly an order of magnitude improvement. If the root were initially known to within about 10 units, it would be determined by the program to 10^{-4} unit, an improvement of 5 orders of magnitude, in about 15 iterations.

The greatest virtue of the bisection method is that it is virtually assured to converge to a root.   It can fail to do so under the unusual circumstance that an accumulation of errors would cause *y* at some step to be calculated, say, as a small negative value when actually it should have a small positive value. The machine could then be halving the wrong interval from then on.   If proper precautions have been taken concerning accuracy, this should not occur. It will be seen later that this assurance of convergence is not a property of many other methods of finding a root.

The greatest drawbacks of the bisection method are that it is slow compared to some of the other methods and that it can be applied only when the function is negative at one value of x and positive at another. It could not be used, for example, to find the root shown in Figure 10–10, since the function is never negative.

For these reasons, other methods of finding roots are frequently used.

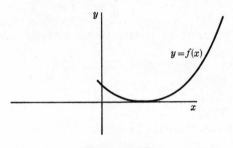

Figure 10–10

10.4 THE METHOD OF ITERATION

When an equation $f(x) = 0$ can be written in the form:

$$x = \phi(x) \tag{10-3}$$

accurate values for the real roots can usually be found by the process of iteration. The process is as follows: by some means we obtain a rough approximation x_0 of the desired root. We then substitute it into the right hand of (10-3) to obtain a better approximation $x^{(1)}$, given by:

$$x^{(1)} = \phi(x_0)$$

This new value is again substituted into the right hand side of (10-3) to obtain a still better approximation $x^{(2)}$, given by:

$$x^{(2)} = \phi(x^{(1)})$$

The process is then repeated (hence the name "iteration"), to give successive approximations:

$$x^{(3)} = \phi(x^{(2)})$$
$$x^{(4)} = \phi(x^{(3)})$$

etc.

until a sufficiently close approximation to the true root is obtained. This process is quite readily adaptable to computer use, since the program merely involves the repeated calculation of the same function $\phi(x)$. The flow chart, Figure 10–11, describes the process. In this chart, the number x_0 is the starting value for x, and the number a is a quantity used to cause the calculation to stop when the answer has been obtained with sufficient accuracy.

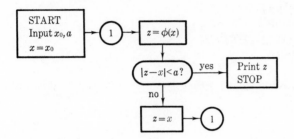

Figure 10–11: Iteration method for finding root

For example, if it is desired that the value of x should be accurate to .01, then $a = .01$ would be used. If a value of x accurate to .0001 is desired, then $a = .0001$ would be used. (This statement is not completely accurate, as will be seen later in Section 10.41.) Following through the steps of the flow chart, we find that the first value of x used is $x = x_0$. Hence the first value of z obtained in $z = \phi(x_0)$. This is the quantity denoted by $x^{(1)}$ in the description given above. Hence the first time through, the quantity called $|z - x|$ in the flow chart is actually $|x^{(1)} - x_0|$. In the test we determine if $x^{(1)}$ and x_0 are sufficiently close together that we are willing to accept the value $x^{(1)}$ as the true value x. If the answer is yes, we print $x^{(1)}$ and stop. If the answer is no, we replace x_0 by $x^{(1)}$ and again return to the assertion box $z = \phi(x)$, this time with $x = x^{(1)}$, and compute a new value of z. This time the value obtained for z will be the quantity denoted by $x^{(2)}$ in the previous discussion. This time, then, the quantity called $|z - x|$ in the flow chart will actually be $|x^{(2)} - x^{(1)}|$. If this quantity is small enough, the value of $x^{(2)}$ will be printed. If not, the process will be repeated (or iterated) with $x = x^{(2)}$. After n iterations, we will have $z = x^{(n)}$ and $x = x^{(n-1)}$. If $|x^{(n)} - x^{(n-1)}|$ is sufficiently small, the process will stop and $x^{(n)}$ will be printed.

Example 1. Write a FORTRAN program for finding the root of $xe^x = 1$ to an accuracy of .0001.

This equation can be written as $x = e^{-x}$, which is then in the form:

$$x = \phi(x), \qquad \text{with } \phi(x) = e^{-x}$$

A suitable FORTRAN program is:

```
    X=1.
  1 Z=EXPF(-X)
    IF(ABSF(Z-X)-.0001)3,3,2
  2 X=Z
    GO TO 1
  3 PRINT 101,Z
    STOP
101 FORMAT(E12.4)
    END
```

The successive values of x that would be obtained by this routine are:

$$
\begin{aligned}
x_0 &= 1.00000 \\
x^{(1)} &= .36788 \\
x^{(2)} &= .69215 \\
x^{(3)} &= .50042 \\
x^{(4)} &= .60620 \\
x^{(5)} &= .54534 \\
x^{(6)} &= .57959 \\
x^{(7)} &= .56005 \\
x^{(8)} &= .57111 \\
x^{(9)} &= .56484 \\
x^{(10)} &= .56839 \\
x^{(11)} &= .56637 \\
x^{(12)} &= .56751 \\
x^{(13)} &= .56686 \\
x^{(14)} &= .56720 \\
x^{(15)} &= .56704 \\
x^{(16)} &= .56712
\end{aligned}
$$

Sixteen iterations would be performed before $|x^{(n)} - x^{(n-1)}| < .0001$.

Example 2.   Write a program for finding the root of $2x - 1 - 2 \sin x = 0$ to an accuracy of .0001.

This equation can be written as $x = \sin x + .5$, which is then of the form:

$$x = \phi(x), \quad \text{with } \phi(x) = \sin x + .5$$

We can write a FORTRAN program as:

```
    X=1.
  1 Z=SINF(X)+.5
    IF(ABSF(Z-X)-.0001)3,3,2
```

```
 2 X=Z
   GO TO 1
 3 PRINT 101,Z
   STOP
101 FORMAT(E12.4)
   END
```

The successive values of x that would be obtained by this routine are:

$$x_0 = 1.00000$$
$$x^{(1)} = 1.34147$$
$$x^{(2)} = 1.47381$$
$$x^{(3)} = 1.49528$$
$$x^{(4)} = 1.49713$$
$$x^{(5)} = 1.49727$$
$$x^{(6)} = 1.49729$$

In this case only six iterations are required to obtain a four decimal digit accuracy.

Example 3. Write a program for finding the positive root of $x^2 = 3$ to an accuracy of .0001.

This equation can be written as $x = 3/x$, which is then of the form:

$$x = \phi(x), \qquad \text{with } \phi(x) = 3/x$$

Following the flow chart, a program can be written as in the two preceding examples:

```
   X=1.
 1 Z=3./X
   IF(ABSF(Z−X)−.0001)3,3,2
 2 X=Z
   GO TO 1
 3 PRINT 101,Z
   STOP
101 FORMAT(E12.4)
   END
```

If we attempt to utilize this program on a computer, we will find that it will never print an answer! It will never perform the transfer to statement 3, but instead will loop through statements 1 and 2 until the machine is stopped.

The reason for this is seen if the first few values for x are computed by hand. We have:

$$x_0 = 1$$
$$x^{(1)} = 3/x_0 = 3$$
$$x^{(2)} = 3/x^{(1)} = 1$$
$$x^{(3)} = 3/x^{(2)} = 3$$
$$x^{(4)} = 3/x^{(3)} = 1$$
$$\text{etc.}$$

The value of x alternates between the numbers 1 and 3, and never converges toward a limit. Thus $|z - x|$ will never be less than .0001.

Before considering the problem of convergence or lack of convergence, let us point out how, in a program such as the one above, we can prevent the machine from hanging up in a loop and wasting valuable time by performing it millions of times. The FORTRAN program below provides this kind of protection:

```
    X=1.
    I=1
  1 Z=3./X
    IF(ABSF(Z−X)− .0001)3,3,2
  2 X=Z
    I=I+1
    IF(I−100)1,4,4
  3 PRINT 101,Z
    STOP
  4 PRINT 102
    STOP
101 FORMAT(E12.4)
102 FORMAT(15H NOT CONVERGING)
    END
```

In this program we have included a counter, which only allows the loop to be performed a maximum 100 times, and then skips to statement 4 that prints out "NOT CONVERGING," as specified by the FORMAT statement 102, and stops the problem. If the answer had been obtained in less than 100 steps, it would have been printed out in the normal fashion.

10.41   Convergence of the Iteration Process

From the three examples of the preceding section we see that the iteration process may converge slowly as in the first example, or rapidly, as in the second example; or it may not converge at all, as in the third example. We shall look at the iteration process in more detail in order to determine the conditions under which it does converge. Let x stand for the true value of the root, which would exactly satisfy the equation:

$$x = \phi(x) \tag{10-4}$$

The first approximation in the iteration process is:

$$x^{(1)} = \phi(x_0) \tag{10-5}$$

Subtracting (10-5) from (10-4), we have:

$$x - x^{(1)} = \phi(x) - \phi(x_0) \tag{10-6}$$

By the mean value theorem of differential calculus, the right hand member of (10-6) can be written:

$$\phi(x) - \phi(x_0) = (x - x_0)\phi'(\xi_0) \tag{10-7}$$

where ξ_0 is a value between x_0 and x. Hence (10-6) can be written:

$$x - x^{(1)} = (x - x_0)\phi'(\xi_0) \tag{10-8}$$

In like manner, the second approximation is:

$$x^{(2)} = \phi(x^{(1)}) \tag{10-9}$$

Subtracting (10-9) from (10-4), we have:

$$x - x^{(2)} = \phi(x) - \phi(x^{(1)}) \tag{10-10}$$

Again by the mean value theorem:

$$\phi(x) - \phi(x^{(1)}) = (x - x^{(1)})\phi'(\xi_1) \tag{10-11}$$

where ξ_1 is a value between $x^{(1)}$ and x. Substituting in (10-10), we have:

$$x - x^{(2)} = (x - x^{(1)})\phi'(\xi_1) \tag{10-12}$$

A similar equation can be obtained for each of the approximations, so that:

$$x - x^{(3)} = (x - x^{(2)})\phi'(\xi_2)$$
$$x - x^{(4)} = (x - x^{(3)})\phi'(\xi_3)$$

$$\cdot$$

$$\cdot$$

$$\cdot$$

$$x - x^{(n)} = (x - x^{(n-1)})\phi'(\xi_{n-1})$$

Multiplying together all these equations:

$$(x - x^{(1)})(x - x^{(2)}) \cdots (x - x^{(n)})$$
$$= (x - x_0)(x - x^{(1)}) \cdots (x - x^{(n-1)})\phi'(\xi_0)\phi'(\xi_1) \cdots \phi'(\xi_{n-1}) \quad \text{(10-13)}$$

Dividing the result by the common factors:

$$x - x^{(1)}, x - x^{(2)}, \dots, x - x^{(n-1)}$$

we obtain:

$$x - x^{(n)} = (x - x_0)\phi'(\xi_0)\phi'(\xi_1) \cdots \phi'(\xi_{n-1}) \quad \text{(10-14)}$$

The iteration process converges if $x^{(n)}$ becomes close to x as n becomes large, i.e., $|x - x^{(n)}|$ becomes small. It can be seen that this will happen if the quantities $\phi'(\xi_1)$ are less than one, for in this case each iteration will multiply the right hand side of (10-14) by a number less than one, and thus reduce the error. Continuing the iteration another step reduces the error by the amount $\phi'(\xi_n)$, where ξ_n is some value of x between $x^{(n)}$ and x. If in equation (10-14) each of the quantities $\phi'(\xi_0)$, $\phi'(\xi_1)$, etc. is less than or equal to some number m less than one, then:

$$|x - x^{(n)}| \leqslant |x - x_0|m^n \quad \text{(10-15)}$$

The right hand member of (10-15) approaches zero as n becomes large, so that the absolute error $|x - x^{(n)}|$ can be made as small as we please by repeating the iteration process a sufficient number of times.

It can be seen from equations (10-14) and (10-15) that the number of iterations required to attain a given accuracy depends on two things: the value of $|x - x_0|$, and the value of $\phi'(x)$ in the neighborhood of the root. If the initial estimate x_0 is well chosen, so that $|x - x_0|$ is small, then fewer iterations will suffice to make $|x - x^{(n)}|$ sufficiently small. If $\phi'(x)$ is small, then the convergence will be rapid, so that few iterations will be required. In Example 1 of the preceding section, the initial estimate x_0 was 1 and the final value was .5671. Hence $|x - x_0|$ was about .43. The value of $\phi'(x) = -e^{-x}$ was, in this case, about $-e^{-.56}$ or $-.57$. Thus each iteration should have reduced the error by about .6. Hence, after 16 iterations, the error should have been about:

$$(.43)(.6)^{15} \approx 10^{-4}$$

This was found to be the case. (It might be noted that the bisection method, which reduces the error by a factor of .5 at each step, would have been a little faster in this case.) In Example 3, on the other hand, $\phi'(x) = -3/x^2$, which is equal to -1 at the root $x = \sqrt{3}$, and is greater than 1 in absolute value for $x < \sqrt{3}$. Hence the iteration process does not converge in this case.

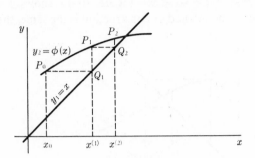

Figure 10–12

10.42 Geometry of the Iteration Process

It is instructive to look at a graphical representation of the iteration process. In Figure 10–12, two curves are drawn, one corresponding to $y_1 = x$ and the other $y_2 = \phi(x)$. The root of $x = \phi(x)$ is the abscissa of the point of intersection. The starting value x_0 is depicted as being to the left of that point. Since the absolute value of $\phi'(x)$ must be less than one for convergence, the inclination of the curve $y_2 = \phi(x)$ is depicted as being less than $45°$ in the vicinity of the root. The iteration process can be traced as follows: At the abscissa x_0, draw a vertical line intersecting the curve $y_2 = \phi(x)$ at P_0. The ordinate at P_0 is then $\phi(x_0)$. From this point draw a horizontal line intersecting the line $y_1 = x$ at the point Q_1. The ordinate at Q_1 is then $\phi(x_0)$, and so, since ordinate equals abscissa along this line, the abscissa is also equal to $\phi(x_0)$. Let us denote this abscissa by $x^{(1)}$. From the point Q_1, draw a vertical line, intersecting the curve $y_2 = \phi(x)$ at P_1. The ordinate at P_1 is then $\phi(x^{(1)})$. From P_1 draw a horizontal line intersecting the line $y_1 = x$ at Q_2. The ordinate at Q_2 is then $\phi(x^{(1)})$, so the abscissa is also. Denote this abscissa by $x^{(2)}$. So far we have:

$$\text{at } Q_1, \qquad x^{(1)} = \phi(x_0)$$

$$\text{at } Q_2, \qquad x^{(2)} = \phi(x^{(1)})$$

We can continue this process, obtaining:

$$Q_3, \qquad \text{where } x^{(3)} = \phi(x^{(2)})$$

$$\text{etc.}$$

$$Q_n, \qquad \text{where } x^{(n)} = \phi(x^{(n-1)})$$

The points Q_1, Q_2, etc. converge toward the intersection of the two curves.

In Figure 10–12, $\phi'(x)$ is positive, and the convergence is from one side, that is $x_0 < x^{(1)} < x^{(2)} < \cdots < x$. Figure 10–13 shows a case in which $\phi'(x)$ is negative. The method of construction is the same, that is, start at x_0

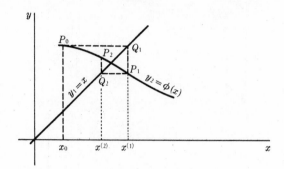

Figure 10–13

and go vertically to the curve, then horizontally to the straight line, then vertically to the curve, then horizontally to the straight line, etc. In this case, it is seen that the value oscillates, being alternately larger and then smaller than the true value of the root.

Figure 10–14 depicts a case in which the derivative $\phi'(x)$ is bigger than one in absolute value, so that the process diverges instead of converging.

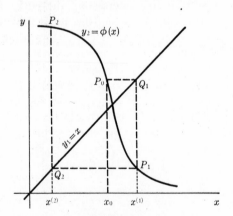

Figure 10–14

10.43   Methods of Inducing or Speeding Convergence

There are many possible ways of rewriting an equation $f(x) = 0$ in the form $x = \phi(x)$. It is necessary to choose one for which $\phi'(x)$ is less than one in absolute value, so that the iteration process will converge. It is highly desirable to choose one for which $\phi'(x)$ will be small, so that the convergence will be rapid and not many iterations will be required on the machine. (At the same time it is desirable that $\phi(x)$ itself be kept to a reasonably simple function, so that it may be computed without an inordinate amount of machine time or programming effort.)

Example 1. Write an iteration scheme for the solution of $2 \tan x - x - 1 = 0$.

If we write the equation as:

$$x = 2 \tan x - 1$$

then:

$$\phi(x) = 2 \, tan \, x - 1$$

and:

$$\phi'(x) = 2 \sec^2 x$$

which is greater than one for all values of x. Hence the iteration scheme for this system will diverge. The equation can also be written:

$$x = \tan^{-1}\left(\frac{x+1}{2}\right)$$

In this form:

$$\phi(x) = \tan^{-1}\left(\frac{x+1}{2}\right)$$

and:

$$\phi'(x) = \frac{1}{2}\frac{1}{1 + \left(\frac{x+1}{4}\right)^2}$$

which is less than one for all values of x. Hence the iteration scheme based on that formulation will converge. The graphs for the two cases are shown in Figures 10–15a and b. (There are actually an infinite number of solutions in this case, one on each of the branches of the tangent function. If a standard arctangent subroutine is used, it will give a value between $-\pi/2$ and $\pi/2$, so that the intersection indicated by the solid lines will be obtained from the iteration process.) Figure 10–15b was obtained by reflecting Figure 10–15a about the line $y = x$. This process changed the curve whose slope is greater than one into a curve whose slope is less than one, and hence produced a situation wherein the iteration process would be convergent.

There are other methods of producing a convergent iteration process, or of speeding the convergence of an already convergent process.   Consider the iteration scheme illustrated in Figure 10–16.   Suppose that, after n iterations,

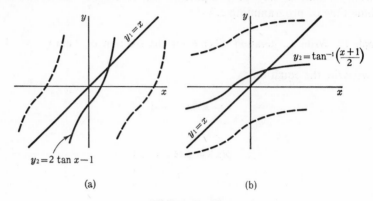

(a)   (b)

Figure 10–15

the value of x is that which is indicated by the point Q_n.   In accordance with the method as described in Section 10.42, the next iteration is performed by drawing a vertical line which intersects the curve $y = \phi(x)$ at the point P_n,

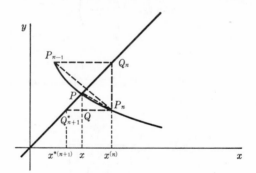

Figure 10–16

and then a horizontal line which intersects the line $y = x$ at the point Q_{n+1}^* whose coordinates are $(x^{*(n+1)}, x^{*(n+1)})$, where:

$$x^{*(n+1)} = \phi(x^{(n)})$$

(We will use the asterisk to indicate the value of x given by the standard iteration step and x without asterisk to indicate an improved value obtained by the method to be described below.   It will be most important in the argument to follow for the reader to remember the difference between quantities with an asterisk and those without.)

It is evident from the figure that instead of Q^*_{n+1}, we would like to choose the point Q between P_n and Q^*_{n+1}, so that the next vertical line would strike the true solution, point P.   Of course we have no way of knowing where the point Q is located.   We can make an estimate of its location, however.   If we denote its abscissa by x, then:

$$\frac{x - x^{*(n+1)}}{x^{(n)} - x} = \frac{\overline{Q^*_{n+1}Q}}{\overline{QP_n}} \tag{10-16}$$

Now $\overline{Q^*_{n+1}Q} = \overline{QP}$, so that:

$$\frac{\overline{Q^*_{n+1}Q}}{\overline{QP_n}} = \frac{\overline{QP}}{\overline{QP_n}} = -m$$

where m is the slope of the line $\overline{PP_n}$.   By Rolle's theorem there is some point ξ along the curve $y = \phi(x)$ between P and P_n at which the slope of the curve, $\phi'(\xi)$, is equal to m.   The best estimate we have available for this slope is obtained by an application of the theorem of the mean:

$$\phi(x^{(n)}) - \phi(x^{(n-1)}) = (x^{(n)} - x^{(n-1)})\phi'(\eta) \tag{10-17}$$

where η is a point between $x^{(n-1)}$ and $x^{(n)}$.   Since:

$$x^{*(n)} = \phi(x^{(n-1)}) \qquad \text{and} \qquad x^{*(n+1)} = \phi(x^{(n)}) \tag{10-18}$$

then (10-17) can be written:

$$x^{*(n+1)} - x^{*(n)} = (x^{(n)} - x^{(n-1)})\phi'(\eta) \tag{10-19}$$

or

$$\phi'(\eta) = \frac{x^{*(n+1)} - x^{*(n)}}{x^{(n)} - x^{(n-1)}} \tag{10-20}$$

Using this as an estimate of the slope m, we can rewrite (10-16) as:

$$\frac{x - x^{*(n+1)}}{x^{(n)} - x} \simeq -\frac{x^{*(n+1)} - x^{*(n)}}{x^{(n)} - x^{(n-1)}} \tag{10-21}$$

or, solving for x, we have:

$$x \simeq \frac{x^{*(n+1)}x^{(n-1)} - x^{(n)}x^{*(n)}}{x^{*(n+1)} - x^{*(n)} - x^{(n)} + x^{(n-1)}} \tag{10-22}$$

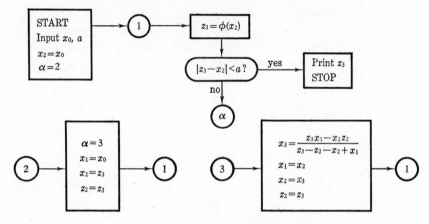

Figure 10–17: Improved iteration method for finding root

If we make the definition:

$$x^{(n+1)} = \frac{x^{*(n+1)}x^{(n-1)} - x^{(n)}x^{*(n)}}{x^{*(n+1)} - x^{*(n)} - x^{(n)} + x^{(n-1)}},\qquad (10\text{-}23)$$

the value of $x^{(n+1)}$ will ordinarily be a much better approximation to the root than is $x^{*(n+1)}$. A procedure for using this improved iteration process is shown in the flow chart, Figure 10–17. In this chart, the notation has been simplified by using:

$$x_1 \quad \text{for} \quad x^{(n-1)}$$

$$x_2 \quad \text{for} \quad x^{(n)} \qquad\qquad z_2 \quad \text{for} \quad x^{*(n)}$$

$$x_3 \quad \text{for} \quad x^{(n+1)} \qquad\qquad z_3 \quad \text{for} \quad x^{*(n+1)}$$

The method will be applied to examples from Section 10.4 in order to illustrate the improvement.

Example 2. Find the root of $xe^x = 1$ to an accuracy of .0001.

This is Example 1 of Section 10.4. The iteration is performed by writing the equation as $x = e^{-x}$. Then a program that will perform the operations outlined in the flow chart is:

```
   X2=1.
   J=1
 1 Z3=EXPF(-X2)
   IF(ABSF(Z3-X2)-.0001)6,6,3
```

```
  3 GO TO (4,5),J
  4 J=2
    X1=X2
    X2=Z3
    Z2=Z3
    GO TO 1
  5 X3=(Z3*X1−Z2*X2)/(Z3−Z2−X2+X1)
    X1=X2
    X2=X3
    Z2=Z3
    GO TO 1
  6 PRINT 101,Z3
    STOP
101 FORMAT(E12.4)
    END
```

The values that would be obtained by this program are:

Iteration	$x^{(n-1)}$	$x^{*(n)}$	$x^{(n)}$	$x^{*(n+1)}$	$x^{(n+1)}$
1			1	.36788	
2	1	.36788	.36788	.69220	.58223
3	.36788	.69220	.58223	.55865	.56770
4	.58223	.55865	.56770	.56683	.56714
5	.56770	.56683	.56714	.56714	

Whereas this problem required 16 iterations by the ordinary method, only 5 are required in this improved method. For Example 3 of Section 10.4, the iteration process diverged. By the present method, the following values would be obtained:

Iteration	$x^{(n-1)}$	$x^{*(n)}$	$x^{(n)}$	$x^{*(n+1)}$	$x^{(n+1)}$
1			1	3	
2	1	3	3	1	2
3	3	1	2	1.5	1.6
4	2	1.5	1.6	1.875	1.729
5	1.6	1.875	1.729	1.735	

Clearly the process converges, and rather rapidly. In Section 10.5, however, a superior method for this problem is given.

10.44 *Functions not Readily Expressible as* $x = \phi(x)$

Sometimes an equation $f(x) = 0$ is not easily placed in the form $x = \phi(x)$ by usual algebraic manipulations. In such cases a simple expedient is to write the equation as:

$$x = x + \theta f(x) \tag{10-24}$$

where θ is some suitably chosen nonzero constant.   Figure 10–18 shows the significance of this representation.   The curve $y = x + \theta f(x)$ is essentially a

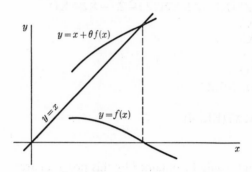

Figure 10–18

displacement of the curve $y = f(x)$ so that it runs along the line $y = x$ instead of along the x-axis.   The constant θ should be chosen to make the derivative of $x + \theta f(x)$ less than 1, near the root, in order to induce convergence.   In the graph, $\theta = 1$ was used.

10.5   THE NEWTON RAPHSON METHOD

When the derivative of $f(x)$ is a simple expression and easily found, the real roots of $f(x) = 0$ can sometimes be computed by the Newton-Raphson method.   Let x_0 denote an approximate value for the root, and h denote the correction that must be applied to give the true value of the root, which we shall denote by x.   Then:

$$x = x_0 + h$$

The equation $f(x) = 0$ then becomes:

$$f(x_0 + h) = 0$$

Expanding this by Taylor's Formula, we obtain:

$$f(x_0 + h) = f(x_0) + hf'(x_0) + (h^2/2)f''(x_0 + \theta h), \qquad \text{where } 0 < \theta < 1$$

Hence:

$$f(x_0) + hf'(x_0) + (h^2/2)f''(x_0 + \theta h) = 0$$

If h is sufficiently small, we may ignore the term containing h^2 and write:

$$f(x_0) + hf'(x_0) \simeq 0$$

or

$$h \simeq -\frac{f(x_0)}{f'(x_0)}$$

Denoting this approximate value of h by h_1, we have:

$$h_1 = -\frac{f(x_0)}{f'(x_0)}$$

and the quantity $x^{(1)}$ given by:

$$x^{(1)} = x_0 + h_1 = x_0 - \frac{f(x_0)}{f'(x_0)} \tag{10-25}$$

should be a better estimate of the root than was the quantity x_0. In like manner, better approximations can be obtained from continued application of the process, thus:

$$x^{(2)} = x^{(1)} - \frac{f(x^{(1)})}{f'(x^{(1)})}$$

$$x^{(3)} = x^{(2)} - \frac{f(x^{(2)})}{f'(x^{(2)})}$$

etc.

$$x^{(n)} = x^{(n-1)} - \frac{f(x^{(n-1)})}{f'(x^{(n-1)})} \tag{10-26}$$

Thus we have an iteration scheme which, like the one discussed in Section 10.4, can be continued until the root is known to the desired accuracy.

10.51 *The Square Root Subroutine*

One application of the Newton-Raphson method in computer programming is as a subroutine for computing the square root of a number. The Taylor Series is not very good for this purpose because of convergence problems. The Newton-Raphson method is applied as follows: finding the square root of a number A is equivalent to finding the positive root of the equation:

$$x^2 = A$$

or

$$x^2 - A = 0$$

Hence we take:

$$f(x) = x^2 - A$$

so that:

$$f'(x) = 2x$$

The formula (10-25) can then be written:

$$x^{(1)} = x_0 - \frac{x_0^2 - A}{2x_0} = \frac{1}{2}\left(x_0 + \frac{A}{x_0}\right)$$

or, for the nth iteration:

$$x^{(n)} = \frac{1}{2}\left(x^{(n-1)} + \frac{A}{x^{(n-1)}}\right)$$

Example 1.   Compute the square root of 10 to seven significant figures.

Taking $x_0 = 1$, we find:

$$x^{(1)} = \frac{1}{2}\left(1 + \frac{10}{1}\right) = 5.5$$

$$x^{(2)} = \frac{1}{2}\left(5.5 + \frac{10}{5.5}\right) = 3.66$$

$$x^{(3)} = \frac{1}{2}\left(3.66 + \frac{10}{3.66}\right) = 3.181$$

$$x^{(4)} = \frac{1}{2}\left(3.181 + \frac{10}{3.818}\right) = 3.1623$$

$$x^{(5)} = \frac{1}{2}\left(3.1623 + \frac{10}{3.1623}\right) = 3.162278$$

Five iterations are required to obtain the seven digit accuracy.

It is seen that this method furnishes a convenient and rapidly convergent method for finding the square root. For standard square root subroutines subject to repeated use, however, still more rapidly convergent processes using rational functions are ordinarily employed.

10.52   Graphical Representation of the Newton-Raphson Method

Figure 10–19 gives a graphical representation of the Newton-Raphson method. The graph of $y = f(x)$ near the root is shown. The steps of the process are as follows: At x_0 draw a vertical line intersecting the curve at P_0.

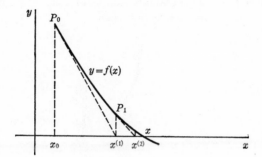

Figure 10–19

At P_0 draw the tangent line. This will intersect the x-axis at $x^{(1)}$. At $x^{(1)}$ draw a vertical line intersecting the curve at P_1. At P_1 draw the tangent line. This will intersect the x-axis at $x^{(2)}$, etc. The formula can be readily derived from the figure. The ordinate of P_0 is $f(x_0)$, and the slope of the tangent line is $f'(x_0)$. From the triangle $x_0 P_0 x^{(1)}$, we see that

$$f'(x_0) = -\frac{f(x_0)}{x^{(1)} - x_0}$$

or

$$x^{(1)} = x_0 - \frac{f(x_0)}{f'(x_0)}$$

In like manner the succeeding steps can be derived.

From the graph it is clear that each step of the process is performed by following the line tangent to the x-axis rather than the curve itself. If the derivative does not change too rapidly, or if the curve does not become nearly horizontal near the crossing point, convergence would be expected to be good.

10.53   Convergence of the Newton-Raphson Method

If we let:

$$\phi(x) = x - \frac{f(x)}{f'(x)} \tag{10-27}$$

then the expression (10-26), the nth iteration of the Newton-Raphson method, can be written:

$$x^{(n)} = \phi(x^{(n-1)})$$

which is the nth step in the general iteration method discussed in Section 10.4. We found that that method converged when:

$$|\phi'(x)| < 1$$

near the root.

From (10-27):

$$\phi'(x) = 1 - \frac{[f'(x)]^2 - f(x)f''(x)}{[f'(x)]^2} = \frac{f(x)f''(x)}{f'(x)^2}$$

Hence the method converges when:

$$\left| \frac{f(x)f''(x)}{[f'(x)]^2} \right| < 1$$

or

$$|f(x)f''(x)| < [f'(x)]^2$$

near the root.

10.6 SPEED OF CONVERGENCE

It was remarked in the discussion of convergence for the basic iteration process that each iteration tends to reduce the error by a fixed factor, that factor being the value of the derivative, $\phi'(x)$ at, the root.   A process which converges in this fashion is referred to as a first order process.   For the Newton-Raphson method, if the convergence criterion of Section 10.53 is satisfied, the speed of convergence tends to increase markedly as the error becomes small.   This can be seen as follows:

The basic convergence scheme is:

$$x^{(n+1)} = x^{(n)} - \frac{f(x^{(n)})}{f'(x^{(n)})} \tag{10-28}$$

Let the error at step n be denoted by e_n. Then:

$$e_n = x - x^{(n)}$$

and:

$$e_{n+1} = x - x^{(n+1)}$$

Subtracting both sides of (10-28) from x, we have:

$$x - x^{(n+1)} = x - x^{(n)} + \frac{f(x^{(n)})}{f'(x^{(n)})}$$

or, in terms of the errors:

$$e_{n+1} = e_n + \frac{f(x - e_n)}{f'(x - e_n)}$$

expanding in Taylor Series:

$$e_{n+1} = e_n + \frac{f(x) - e_n f'(x) + (e_n^2/2)f''(x) + \cdots}{f'(x) - e_n f''(x) + (e_n^2/2)f'''(x) + \cdots}$$

Making use of the fact that $f(x) = 0$, and dividing the denominator into the numerator, we obtain:

$$e_{n+1} = e_n - e_n - \frac{e_n^2}{2} \frac{f''(x)}{f'(x)} + \text{higher order terms}$$

or

$$e_{n+1} \approx -\frac{e_n^2}{2} \frac{f''(x)}{f'(x)}$$

This says that the absolute error at step $n + 1$ is proportional to the *square* of the absolute error at step n. Hence if we have an answer correct to one decimal place at one step, it should be accurate to two places at the next step, four at the next, eight at the next, and so forth. This behavior is seen in Example 1 of Section 10.51, where the tenths place was correct at step 3, the thousandths at step 4, and the millionths at step 5. This rapid convergence, where the error at one step is proportional to the square of the previous error, is called "second order" convergence. It is to be contrasted with the first order convergence exhibited in Example 1 of Section 10.4, where the error was reduced at each step by the constant factor .57, and also the first order convergence of the bisection method, where the error at each step is reduced by the factor .5. It can be proved that the iteration process described by the flow chart, Figure 10–17, and used in Example 2 of Section

10.43, is also a second order process. In computer programs which are to
be subject to repeated use, it is usually well to use a second order process.
In programs which will receive relatively little use, it is frequently wise to use
a first order scheme if convergence can be more fully assured by doing so,
accepting an assured but slow convergence rather than fast but uncertain
convergence.

10.7 IMPLICIT FUNCTIONS

There are occasions when a dependent variable, y, is given in terms of an
independent variable, x, but only in an implicit fashion. For example, the
expression:

$$ye^y = x$$

defines y in terms of x, but only in an implicit way. Given a value of x, we
can find y by means of the techniques discussed in this chapter. By a few
simple changes, the program of Example 1, Section 10.4, can be converted
into a subroutine to do this. The subroutine given below will suffice:

```
      SUBROUTINE XINV(X,Y)
      Y=1.
    1 Z=X*EXPF(-Y)
      IF(ABSF(Z-Y)-.0001)3,3,2
    2 Y=Z
      GO TO 1
    3 Y=Z
      RETURN
      END
```

The concerns about speed of convergence and assurance of convergence
expressed in the preceding pages must be considered in constructing and
utilizing a subroutine such as this one. We noted, for example, that for
$x = 1$ the method given in Example 2 of Section 10.43 produced more rapid
convergence than the above method. Also, we noted in Example 3 of Section 10.4 how the program can be modified to prevent the computer from
remaining in a loop if convergence does not occur in a reasonable number of
steps. It is usually advisable to include such a feature in a subroutine
designed to evaluate an implicit function.

10.71 Experimental Approach

Methods have been described that allow one to assess the convergence and
speed of convergence of a proposed scheme for evaluating an implicit
function. However, these methods are for the most part rather awkward

and cumbersome. On the other hand, it is quite easy to write the program itself, and is ordinarily a matter of seconds for the computer to attempt the program. In this circumstance it is frequently expedient, and even economical, to guess at a calculation method and try it out, and if it does not converge, try another.

Example 1. Write a subroutine to calculate y for x between zero and one, where:

$$y^2 + ye^{xy} = e^x$$

The following iteration schemes suggest themselves:

(1) $y = e^x/(y + e^{xy})$

(2) $y = \sqrt{e^x - ye^{xy}}$

(3) $y = \dfrac{1}{x} \ln \dfrac{e^x - y^2}{y}$

The following program can be used to test each of these, in order to select the best or eliminate all as possibilities:

```
      DO 1 J=1,100
      FJ=J
      X=.01*FJ
      CALL SQIZ(X,Y,I)
    1 PRINT 101,X,Y,I
      STOP
  101 FORMAT(2E12.4,I5)
      END
      SUBROUTINE SQIZ(X,Y,I)
    1 QUNF(R, S)=   (insert correct function)
      Y=1.
      I=1
    2 Z=QUNF(X,Y)
      IF(ABSF(Z-Y)-.0001)4,4,3
    3 Y=Z
      I=I+1
      IF(I-100)2,5,5
    4 Y=Z
      RETURN
    5 PRINT 201
      RETURN
  201 FORMAT (17H DID NOT CONVERGE)
      END
```

We would run this program three times, once with:

$$QUNF(R,S) = EXPF(R)/(S + EXPF(R*S))$$

once with:

$$QUNF(R,S) = SQRTF(EXPF(R) - S*EXPF(R*S))$$

and once with:

$$QUNF(R,S) = LOGF((EXPF(R) - S*S)/S)/R$$

corresponding to the expressions (1), (2), and (3), above.   Upon completion
we would have values of y for $x = .01$, $.02$, etc., up to 1, as computed by
each method, and also the number of iterations required to obtain each value,
as well as a printout indicating any cases that did not converge.   These
results should give a good idea of the relative value of the three iteration
schemes.

10.8 FUNCTIONS OF SEVERAL VARIABLES

The methods discussed in this Chapter can be applied with only minor
modification to functions of more than one variable.   For example, if we
wish to find a root of the system of equations:

$$f(x, y) = 0$$
$$g(x, y) = 0$$

(10-29)

We may rewrite the equations as:

$$x = \phi_1(x, y)$$
$$y = \phi_2(x, y)$$

and use the iteration scheme:

$$x^{(n+1)} = \phi_1(x^{(n)}, y^{(n)})$$
$$y^{(n+1)} = \phi_2(x^{(n)}, y^{(n)})$$

A procedure analogous to the Newton-Raphson method for the equations
(10-29) can be obtained by writing:

$$x = x^{(n)} + \Delta x$$
$$y = y^{(n)} + \Delta y$$

(10-30)

where (x, y) are the coordinates of the true root, and $x^{(n)}$, $y^{(n)}$ are the appropriate coordinates at the nth iteration. Then, using Taylor's theorem:

$$f(x^{(n)} + \Delta x, y^{(n)} + \Delta y) = 0 = f(x^{(n)}, y^{(n)})$$
$$+ \Delta x f_x(x^{(n)}, y^{(n)}) + \Delta y f_y(x^{(n)}, y^{(n)}) + \cdots$$

$$g(x^{(n)} + \Delta x, y^{(n)} + \Delta y) = 0 = g(x^{(n)}, y^{(n)})$$
$$+ \Delta x g_x(x^{(n)}, y^{(n)}) + \Delta y g_y(x^{(n)}, y^{(n)}) + \cdots$$

where f_x, f_y, etc., denote partial derivatives. Neglecting all terms involving terms higher than the first power in Δx and Δy, we have:

$$\Delta x f_x + \Delta y f_y \simeq -f$$
$$\Delta x g_x + \Delta y g_y \simeq -g$$

Solving for Δx and Δy we have:

$$\Delta x \simeq (g f_y - f g_y)/(f_x g_y - g_x f_y)$$
$$\Delta y \simeq (f g_x - g f_x)/(f_x g_y - g_x f_y)$$

If these approximate values for Δx and Δy are used in (10-30) we will (hopefully) obtain a better estimate for x and y. Denoting these new estimates by $x^{(n+1)}$ and $y^{(n+1)}$, we have:

$$x^{(n+1)} = x^{(n)} + [g(x^{(n)}, y^{(n)})f_y(x^{(n)}, y^{(n)}) - f(x^{(n)}, y^{(n)})g_y(x^{(n)}, y^{(n)})]/d$$

(10-31)

$$y^{(n+1)} = y^{(n)} + [f(x^{(n)}, y^{(n)})g_x(x^{(n)}, y^{(n)}) - g(x^{(n)}, y^{(n)})f_x(x^{(n)}, y^{(n)})]/d$$

where:

$$d = f_x(x^{(n)}, y^{(n)})g_y(x^{(n)}, y^{(n)}) - g_x(x^{(n)}, y^{(n)})f_y(x^{(n)}, y^{(n)})$$

This method is easily extended to three or more variables. Examples of its use are given in Sections 11.6 and 14.42.

The methods given above have the same convergence problems as do their single variable counterparts. Convergence criteria can be derived, but will not be given here.

EXERCISE XIX

1. In the following problems: (1) draw a graph and obtain a rough estimate of the roots; (2) draw a flow chart and write a FORTRAN program for the determination of the roots by one of the processes discussed in the text;

(3) calculate by hand rough values for the first three steps of the process; (4) estimate the computer time required for the solution to 4 significant figures:

a. $x^3 = e^{-x}$ c. $e^{\sin x} = e^x + e^{-3x}$

b. $x^3 + 3x - 1 = 0$ d. $x \ln x = e^x - 4$

2. In the following problems, y is defined implicitly as a function of x. In each case, write a FORTRAN subroutine that will compute y, given x. Include a feature that will print out "NON-CONVERGE" and continue if the iteration scheme does not converge in 100 steps. Estimate the maximum time for performing the subroutine on a fast machine.

a. $y \ln y = x$ c. $\sin (x + y) = y + \cos x$

b. $y \sin y = x$ d. $e^x \cos y + 2xy = 3$

3. Write a program that will employ the bisection method to find a root of $f(x) = 0$, given that $f(A)$ and $f(B)$ have opposite signs, but not given the information as to which one is positive.

4. Write a FORTRAN program to find the root of:

$$(x - 1)^{1/3} + 1 = 0$$

by the Newton-Raphson method. Test your program with the starting value $x_0 = -2.375$. Explain the result.

CHAPTER XI *Solution of Polynomial Equations*

11.1 INTRODUCTION

The preceding chapter treated the problem of finding roots of an equation $f(x) = 0$. Of frequent interest is the case in which $f(x)$ is a polynomial, $f(x) = a_1 x^n + a_2 x^{n-1} + \cdots + a_{n+1}$. This is a special case of the general problem studied in Chapter X, and superficially it appears to be a more simple one than those in which $f(x)$ involves trigonometric, exponential, or other transcendental functions. The case deserves special consideration for two reasons, however: first, the problem of obtaining roots to a polynomial equation appears frequently in many fields of science and engineering; second, the methods of the preceding chapter, while of some use for this particular problem, do not ordinarily give complete solutions. Other methods are frequently of greater use, although, unfortunately, there is no single method which is completely satisfactory for solving polynomial equations.

11.2 NATURE OF THE ROOTS OF A POLYNOMIAL EQUATION

A large amount of general information is available concerning roots of a polynomial equation. The first salient fact is the fundamental theorem of algebra:

Theorem I. *Every polynomial equation with arbitrarily given real or complex coefficients has at least one real or imaginary root.*

The second is a special case of the remainder theorem:

Theorem II. *If c is a root of the polynomial equation:*

$$f(x) = 0$$

then $f(x)$ is divisible by $x - c$, so that:

$$f(x) = (x - c)f_1(x)$$

where $f_1(x)$ is a polynomial of degree $n - 1$.

We say that c is a root of multiplicity n if $f(x)$ is divisible by $(x - c)^n$ but not by $(x - c)^{n+1}$. With this definition it follows from the above two theorems that a polynomial equation of degree n has precisely n roots, each root being counted according to its multiplicity. If the coefficients a_1, $a_2, \dots, a_{n+1}$ are real numbers (the case with which we shall concern ourselves), then these roots are either real or in complex conjugate pairs. The problem of solving a polynomial equation of degree n, then, involves isolating n different roots, some of which may be complex, and then utilizing some process for finding the value of each root to the required accuracy. Since our computer has no capability for handling complex numbers directly, we must treat real part and imaginary part separately. This can be done, although the process is usually quite involved.

11.21   Real Roots

Frequently it is not necessary to find all the roots of a polynomial equation, but instead to find only a root or roots satisfying a special property, such as the largest real root, or all real roots. A few facts concerning real roots are worth noting.

Theorem III.   *Every polynomial equation of odd degree with real coefficients has at least one real root.*

This fact follows directly from the fact that the complex roots occur in conjugate pairs, so that there must be an even number of these. Another useful theorem is the famous Descartes rule of signs:

Theorem IV.   *The number of positive real roots of an equation:*

$$f(x) = a_1x^n + a_2x^{n-1} + a_3x^{n-2} + \cdots + a_{n+1} = 0$$

with real coefficients is never greater than the number of variations of sign in the sequence of its coefficients:

$$a_1, a_2, \dots, a_{n+1}$$

and, if less, always by an even number.

Example 1. Determine the possible numbers of positive real roots for the equation:

$$x^4 - x^2 + 2x - 1 = 0$$

The equation has three variations of sign in the sequence of coefficients 1, -1, 2, -1 (terms with zero coefficients can be ignored). Hence it has at most three positive roots, and at least one. The theorem can be used to obtain information concerning negative roots. If we make the substitution $x_1 = -x$, we obtain:

$$x_1{}^4 - x_1{}^2 - 2x_1 - 1 = 0$$

There is only one variation, hence one positive real root for this equation. Thus the original equation had one negative real root.

The following theorem gives a quick, although somewhat crude, estimate of the maximum size of the roots.

Theorem V. *All roots are less than*

$$(|a_1| + |a_2| + \cdots + |a_{n+1}|)/|a_1|$$

in absolute value.

11.3   QUADRATIC EQUATIONS

For equations of degree less than five, formulae exist for the values of the roots. It is generally advisable to use such formulae rather than the methods discussed later in this chapter because all problems of isolation of roots and convergence of iteration processes are avoided thereby. A program for the quadratic equation only will be developed here. Analogous considerations apply to the cubic and biquadratic equations.

The general quadratic equation is usually written in the form:

$$ax^2 + bx + c = 0$$

so we shall discuss it in that form. The roots are given by the formula:

$$x = \frac{-b \pm \sqrt{b^2 - 4ac}}{2a}$$

If the quantity $b^2 - 4ac$ is zero or positive, there are two real roots. If it is negative, the roots are complex conjugates. Hence the program to perform this calculation must distinguish between these two cases. In the first case it computes the square root of $b^2 - 4ac$ and combines with the term $-b$ to obtain the roots. In the second, it must take the square root of $4ac - b^2$

and print out both a real and imaginary part for the roots. The flow chart, Figure 11–1, describes how this might be done. In the case in which the roots are complex, some printout with the numbers to indicate this fact would be advisable. Since the roots are conjugates, only two numbers are required to describe them, a real part $x(rl)$ and an imaginary part $x(im)$. The roots are then $x(rl) + ix(im)$ and $x(rl) - ix(im)$.

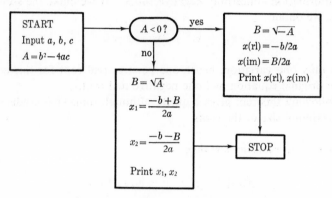

Figure 11–1: Roots of quadratic equation

A problem of accuracy can arise in using the quadratic formula if one of the roots is nearly equal to zero. For example, suppose b is positive. Then if the root:

$$\frac{-b + \sqrt{b^2 - 4ac}}{2a}$$

is nearly zero, the subtraction in the numerator may cause the loss of leading significant digits. This can be avoided by multiplying both numerator and denominator of the above expression by $b + \sqrt{b^2 - 4ac}$, giving:*

$$\frac{-b^2 + b^2 - 4ac}{2a(b + \sqrt{b^2 - 4ac})} = \frac{-2c}{b + \sqrt{b^2 - 4ac}}$$

If b is negative, then the other root is the one which may be inaccurate. A similar protective measure can be used in this case. The flow chart, Figure 11–2, includes protection against this type of accuracy loss. It might be noted that this method is equivalent to computing the larger root (in absolute value) by the quadratic formula, and then computing the smaller one from the fact that the product of the roots is c/a.

---

* This method was called to my attention by M. P. Shuler.

The following FORTRAN subroutine will find the roots of a quadratic equation roughly following the flow chart; Figure 11–2:

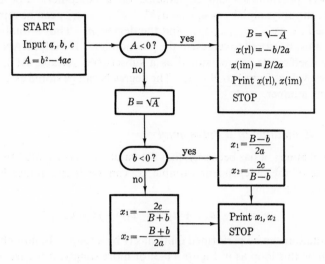

Figure 11–2: Roots of quadratic equation—improved method

```
SUBROUTINE QUADROO(A,B,C,I,X1,X2)
D=B*B-4.*A*C
IF(D)2,3,3
2 DS=SQRTF(-D)
X1=-B/(2.*A)
X2=DS/(2.*A)
I=2
RETURN
3 I=1
DS=SQRTF(D)
IF(B)4,5,5
4 X1=(DS-B)/(2.*A)
X2=2.*C/(DS-B)
RETURN
5 X1=-2.*C/(DS+B)
X2=-(DS+B)/(2.*A)
RETURN
END
```

In this subroutine, the output I serves to indicate whether the roots are real or imaginary. If $I = 1$, X1 and X2 are two real roots. If $I = 2$, they are real and imaginary parts of complex roots.

11.4 COMPUTER ARITHMETIC WITH POLYNOMIALS

Before proceeding to equations of higher degree, we require some background on the way polynomials can be handled on a computer. For use in a computer, the polynomial $y = a_1x^n + a_2x^{n-1} + \cdots + a_{n+1}$ can be represented by the coefficients $a_1, a_2, \ldots, a_{n+1}$ and the degree, n. Thus a total of $n + 2$ numbers must be stored to represent the polynomial. If FORTRAN is being used, the coefficients can be stored as a subscripted variable A(I), where I will take on values from 1 to N + 1. The degree N can be stored as a separate, fixed point number.

11.41 Evaluation of a Polynomial

In earlier chapters, it has been seen that the value of a polynomial for a particular value of the independent variable, x, can be found rather efficiently by grouping the terms:

$$y = ((\cdots (a_1x + a_2)x + a_3) \cdots)x + a_{n+1}$$

This calculation can be performed quite nicely by a loop. In flow chart form we can show this loop as in Figure 11–3, or more simply, if we are confident the coder knows how to program the evaluation of a polynomial, as a simple assertion box, as in Figure 11–4.

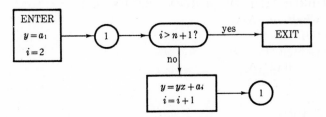

Figure 11–3: Evaluation of a polynomial

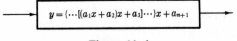

Figure 11–4

A set of FORTRAN statements that will perform the evaluation is:

```
    Y=A(1)
    DO 1 I=1,N
  1 Y=Y*X+A(I+1)
```

The number of multiplications required actually to find the value is equal to N, the degree of the polynomial.

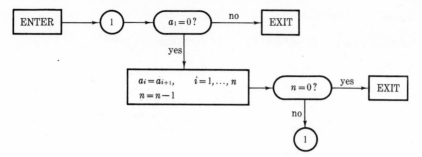

Figure 11–5: Rewriting a polynomial in normal form

11.42 Normal Form for a Polynomial

For a particular polynomial, some of the coefficients a_i may be zero. This is no problem unless the leading coefficient a_1 is zero. In this case, if n, the degree, is also zero, the polynomial is just the number zero. If n is different from zero then the polynomial is incorrectly written. It is not really of degree n at all, but of some lower degree. Steps must be taken to assure that the computer always has polynomials correctly represented, with leading coefficient a_1 different from zero. If we are providing the coefficients as inputs this is easy to do, but, if the computer obtains the polynomial as the result of some internal calculation, the machine itself must assure that the leading coefficient is not zero. Suppose the computer has performed a calculation which has resulted in the numbers $a_1, a_2, \ldots, a_{n+1}, n$, which are supposedly the coefficients and degree of a polynomial. The segment of flow chart shown in Figure 11–5 will assure that the representation is put in a form with leading coefficient different from zero, a form we might refer to as the "normal" form.

A program following this flow chart will redefine the coefficients so that a_1 is indeed the first nonzero coefficient, and will determine a new n which is the correct degree. A set of FORTRAN statements that will perform the same function is:

```
1 IF(A(1))5,2,5
2 DO 3 I=1,N
3 A(I)=A(I+1)
  N=N−1
4 IF(N)5,5,1
5 .........continuation of program
```

11.43 Division of One Polynomial by Another

When one polynomial is divided by another of equal or lower degree, the quotient is again a polynomial, and ordinarily there is a remainder which is also a polynomial.

Example 1. Divide $x^4 + 3x^3 + 6x + 5$ by $x^2 + 2x - 2$.

Performing the division in the normal manner we have:

$$
\begin{array}{r}
x^2 + x \\
x^2 + 2x - 2 \;\overline{)x^4 + 3x^3 + 0x^2 + 6x + 5} \\
\underline{x^4 + 2x^3 - 2x^2} \\
x^3 + 2x^2 + 6x \\
\underline{x^3 + 2x^2 - 2x} \\
8x + 5
\end{array}
$$

In this case the quotient is $x^2 + x$ and the remainder is $8x + 5$. Each step of the operation is a straightforward arithmetic operation, and clearly should be reducible to computer application. The powers of x that appear actually serve no useful purpose except to keep straight which terms are to be combined with which. The calculation can as well be done as follows:

$$
\begin{array}{ccccccccc}
 & & & 1 & & 1 & & & \\
 & & & \overline{} & & & & & \\
1 & 2 & -2 &)1 & 3 & 0 & 6 & 5 \\
 & & & 1 & 2 & -2 & & \\
\cline{4-6}
 & & & 1 & 2 & 6 & & \\
 & & & 1 & 2 & -2 & & \\
\cline{4-6}
 & & & & 8 & 5 & &
\end{array}
$$

All the numerical values are given by this procedure, and these can then be combined with the correct powers of x to give the quotient and remainder.

Example 2. Divide

$$a_1 x^n + a_2 x^{n-1} + \cdots + a_n x + a_{n+1} \quad \text{by} \quad b_1 x^m + b_2 x^{m-1} + \cdots + b_{m+1}.$$

We can, of course, only do this symbolically since we do not have numerical values for the coefficients and degrees of the terms, but the procedure used in Example 1 can be followed.

$$
\begin{array}{llllll}
 & & q_1 & q_2 \cdots\cdots & q_{n-m+1} & \\
b_1 & b_2 \cdots b_{m+1} &)a_1 & a_2 & a_3 \cdots\cdots\cdots\cdots\cdots & a_{n+1} \\
 & & b_1 q_1 & b_2 q_1 & b_3 q_1 \cdots b_{m+1}q_1 & \\
\hline
 & & a'_2 & a'_3 \cdots a'_{m+1} & a_{m+2} & \\
 & & b_1 q_2 & b_2 q_2 \cdots b_m q_2 & b_{m+1}q_2 & \\
\hline
 & & & a''_3 \cdots a''_{m+1} & a'_{m+2} & \\
 & & & \vdots & & \\
 & & & \vdots & & \\
 & & & a^*_{n-m+1} \cdots\cdots & a^*_n & a_{n+1} \\
 & & & b_1 q_{n-m+1} \cdots\cdots & b_m q_{n-m+1} & b_{m+1}q_{n-m+1} \\
\hline
 & & & r_1 \cdots\cdots & r_{m-1} & r_m
\end{array}
$$

In this symbolic representation of the division, q_1 represents a_1/b_1, so that $a_1 - b_1 q_1 = 0$. The symbol a_2' represents $a_2 - b_2 q_1$, a_3' represents $a_3 - b_2 q_1$, etc., q_2 represents a_2'/b_1, so that $a_2' - b_2 q_2 = 0$. The process is repeated as many times as necessary. The quotient will be of degree $n - m$, so $n - m + 1$ coefficients will be obtained in the quotient. The remainder is of degree $m - 1$, so m coefficients $r_1, r_2, \ldots, r_m$ will be obtained there. When we convert this operation to a computer program, the intermediate results a_2', a_3', a_3'' a_{n-m+1}^*, etc. are not needed; so in the flow chart, rather than use separate symbols for these, we can re-use the symbols a_2, a_3, etc., thus re-using the same memory cells over and over for these intermediate results. A section of flow chart describing the process outlined in the above symbolic division is shown in Figure 11–6.

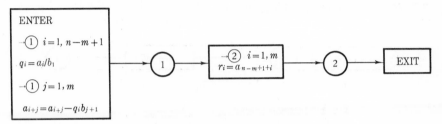

Figure 11–6: Polynomial division

In Figure 11–6 a new convention is introduced. This is the use of a remote connector inside an assertion box. The symbol:

$$\rightarrow \textcircled{1} \; i = 1, n - m + 1$$

means continue through the flow chart with $i = 1$ until remote connector 1 is reached, then return to this point and trace the same path with $i = 2$, then with $i = 3$, etc., up to and including $i = n - m + 1$. It is seen that this usage is analogous to the DO loop in a FORTRAN program, and greatly simplifies the structure of the flow chart.

The second symbol:

$$\rightarrow \textcircled{1} \; j = 1, m$$

indicates a second loop terminating on the same connector. This inner loop is to be performed m times, for $j = 1, 2, \ldots, m$ for each value of i. This new convention will be used where advantageous in the remainder of the text.

We enter this section of a flow chart with $n + 2$ numbers $a_1, \ldots, a_{n+1}, n$, representing a polynomial of degree n, and $m + 2$ numbers $b_1, \ldots, b_{m+1}, m$, representing a polynomial of degree m. We leave with $n - m + 1$ coefficients $q_1, q_2, \ldots, q_{m-n+1}$ representing a quotient of degree $n - m$, and m coefficients $r_1, r_2, \ldots, r_m$, representing a remainder of degree $m - 1$.

In Section 8.3 there was a discussion of accuracy loss associated with the subtraction of two nearly equal numbers. Such a situation is likely at one point in Figure 11–6 where the operation $a_{i+j} = a_{i+j} - q_i b_{j+1}$ is to be performed. The major problem occurs when this result is supposed to be zero. Ordinarily, roundoff error in the computer will keep it from being exactly zero, but will make it have some small value. This means, for example, that if the polynomial $a_1 x^n + \cdots + a_{n+1}$ is exactly divisible by $b_1 x^m + \cdots + b_{m+1}$, this result would not ordinarily appear on the computer following the above flow chart, since the remainder would be some polynomial with small but nonzero coefficients. The difficulty can be circumvented by checking for loss of significant figures as described in Section 8.31. For example, we might choose to set $a_{i+j} = 0$ every time the subtraction above introduces four leading zeros. This can be done by replacing that part of the flow chart in Figure 11–6 by Figure 11–7.

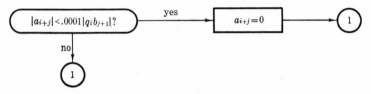

Figure 11–17: Error protection for polynomial division

The FORTRAN subroutine given below divides the polynomial:

$$A(1)x^N + A(2)x^{N-1} + \cdots + A(N + 1)$$

by:

$$B(1)x^M + B(2)x^{M-1} + \cdots + B(M + 1)$$

giving quotient:

$$Q(1)x^K + Q(2)x^{K-1} + \cdots + Q(K + 1)$$

and remainder:

$$R(1)x^L + R(2)x^{L-1} + \cdots + R(L + 1)$$

The dimension statement allows for 20 values of A(I), B(I), Q(I), and R(I) so that polynomials of degree 0 to degree 19 could be handled. The statements up to statement 6 put the divisor into normal form, so that B(1) will not be zero. If the divisor is identically zero, statement 3 prints that fact and the machine is stopped. Statement 6 computes the degree of the

quotient.   If the degree of the dividend is less than that of the divisor, statements 7 through 8 set the quotient equal to zero and the remainder equal to
the dividend.   Statement 30 checks to see if the divisor is of degree zero,
i.e., merely a constant.   If it is, statements 31 to 32 set the remainder equal
to zero and obtain the quotient by dividing the coefficients of the dividend
by the constant divisor.   Statements 9 through 12 do the computation as
outlined by the flow charts, Figures 11–6 and 11–7.   Statements 13 to 18
put the remainder in normal form:

```
    SUBROUTINE POLYDIV(A,N,B,M,Q,K,R,L)
    DIMENSION A(20),B(20),Q(20),R(20),F(20)
 1  IF(B(1))6,2,6
 2  IF(M)3,3,4
 3  PRINT 1001
    STOP
 4  DO 5 I=1,M
 5  B(I)=B(I+1)
    M=M-1
    GO TO 1
 6  K=N-M
    IF(K)7,30,30
 7  K=0
    L=N
    LL=N+1
    DO 8 I=1,LL
    Q(I)=0.
 8  R(I)=A(I)
    RETURN
30  IF(M)31,31,9
31  L=0
    R(1)=0.
    K=N
    LL=N+1
    DO 32 I=1,LL
32  Q(I)=A(I)/B(1)
    RETURN
 9  LL=N+1
    DO 40 I=1,LL
40  F(I)=A(I)
    LL=N-M+1
    DO 12 I=1,LL
    Q(I)=F(I)/B(1)
    DO 12 J=1,M
    W=Q(I)*B(J+1)
```

```
    10  F(I+J)=F(I+J)-W
        IF(ABSF(F(I+J))-.0001*ABSF(W))11,11,12
    11  F(I+J)=0.
    12  CONTINUE
        DO 13 I=1,M
    13  R(I)=F(N-M+I+1)
    14  L=M-1
    15  IF(R(1))19,16,19
    16  IF(L)19,19,17
    17  DO 18 I=1,L
    18  R(I)=R(I+1)
        L=L-1
        GO TO 15
    19  RETURN
  1001  FORMAT(16H DIVISOR IS ZERO)
        END
```

The operation of dividing one polynomial by another as outlined in this section involves $n - m + 1$ divisions and $(m + 1)(n - m + 1)$ multiplications or about $(m + 2)(n - m + 1)$ multiplication times. For division of a twentieth degree polynomial by a tenth degree polynomial, this is about $12 \times 11 = 132$ multiplication times or about 1.3 seconds on our hypothetical slow machine or $.001$ second on a fast machine.

11.44   Highest Common Factor

The highest common factor of two polynomials is a polynomial of highest degree which will divide both the polynomials exactly, leaving zero remainder. For example, the highest common factor of $x^2 - 2x + 1$ and $x^2 - 3x + 2$ is $x - 1$. The highest common factor of $f(x)$ and $g(x)$, where the degree of $g(x)$ is equal to or less than that of $f(x)$, is obtained as follows:

Divide $f(x)$ by $g(x)$, obtaining quotient $q_1(x)$ and remainder $f_1(x)$. Then:

$$f(x) = g(x)q_1(x) + f_1(x)$$

Now divide $g(x)$ by $f_1(x)$, obtaining quotient $q_2(x)$ and remainder $f_2(x)$. Then:

$$g(x) = f_1(x)q_2(x) + f_2(x)$$

Now divide $f_1(x)$ by $f_2(x)$, obtaining quotient $q_3(x)$ and remainder $f_3(x)$. Then:

$$f_1(x) = f_2(x)q_3(x) + f_3(x)$$

If this process is continued, at some point the remainder will finally become zero, and in the last step we have:

$$f_{r-2} = f_{r-1}q_r + f_r$$
$$f_{r-1} = f_r q_{r+1}$$

The last nonzero remainder, $f_r(x)$, is the highest common factor of $f(x)$ and $g(x)$.

Example 1. Find the highest common factor of $f(x) = x^3 - 4x^2 + 5x - 2$ and $g(x) = 3x^2 - 8x + 5$.

Dividing $f(x)$ by $g(x)$:

$$
\begin{array}{r}
(1/3)x - 4/9 \\
3x^2 - 8x + 5 \overline{)x^3 - 4x^2 + 5x - 2} \\
x^3 - (8/3)x^2 + (5/3)x \\
\hline
-(4/3)x^2 + (10/3)x - 2 \\
-(4/3)x^2 + (32/9)x - 20/9 \\
\hline
-(2/9)x + 2/9
\end{array}
$$

We have $q_1(x) = (1/3)x - 4/9$ and $f_1(x) = -(2/9)x + 2/9$. Dividing $g(x)$ by $f_1(x)$:

$$
\begin{array}{r}
-(27/2)x + 45/2 \\
-(2/9)x + 2/9 \overline{)3x^2 - 8x + 5} \\
3x^2 - 3x \\
\hline
-5x + 5 \\
-5x + 5 \\
\hline
0
\end{array}
$$

Since the remainder is zero, the highest common factor is the last nonzero remainder, $f_1(x) = -(2/9)x + 2/9$. The highest common factor is not uniquely defined. Any constant multiple of $f_1(x)$ could be regarded as the highest common factor. For example:

$$-(9/2)f_1(x) = x - 1$$

is a neater expression for the highest common factor. In the above example:

$$f(x) = (x - 1)(x^2 - 3x + 2) = (x - 1)^2(x - 2)$$

and:

$$g(x) = 3x^2 - 8x + 5 = (x - 1)(3x - 5)$$

Once we have a program for dividing one polynomial by another, the finding of the highest common factor merely requires repeated application of that program. The flow chart, Figure 11–8, illustrates the process. In this flow chart, the assertion box entered by connector 1 represents the entire division process described in the preceding section.

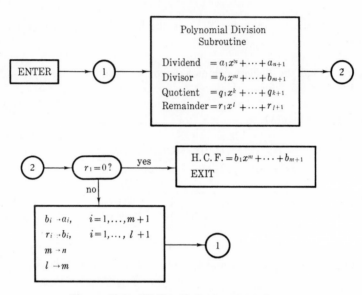

Figure 11–8: Finding highest common factor

The FORTRAN subroutine given below would perform the process by repeated application of the subroutine POLYDIV given in the preceding section:

```
SUBROUTINE HIFACT(A,N,B,M,F,K)
DIMENSION  A(20),B(20),Q(20),F(20),R(20),D(20)
NN=N
LL=N+1
DO  10  I=1,LL
10  D(I)=A(I)
K=M
LL=M+1
DO  1  I=1,LL
1  F(I)=B(I)
2  CALL  POLYDIV(D,NN,F,K,Q,KK,R,L)
IF(R(1))3,6,3
3  NN=K
LL=K+1
```

```
    DO 4 I=1,LL
  4 D(I)=F(I)
    K=L
    LL=L+1
    DO 5 I=1,LL
  5 F(I)=R(I)
    GO TO 2
  6 RETURN
    END
```

The number of multiplications required to find the highest common factor depends on how many times the division of two polynomials must be done. The longest time is required when $m = n - 1$ and the highest common factor turns out to be of degree zero. In that case, we must divide an nth degree polynomial by an $n - 1$st, then an $n - 1$st by an $n - 2$nd, etc. The total number of multiplication times in this case is:

$$(n + 1) (2) + n(2) + (n - 1) (2) + \cdots (1) (2) = (n + 1) (n + 2)$$

or roughly n^2 multiplications. For a 10th and a 9th degree polynomial, about 11×12, or 132 multiplication times may be required, or about 1.3 seconds on a slow machine or .001 second on a fast machine.

EXERCISE XX

1. By Descartes' Rule find the maximum number of positive roots for each of the following equations. Find the maximum number of negative roots.

    a. $x^5 + 3x - 1 = 0$
    b. $x^6 + x^4 + x^2 + 1 = 0$
    c. $x^7 - 2x^6 + x^4 - 3x^3 + 4 = 0$
    d. $3x^4 - 4x^3 + 2 = 0$

2. By Theorem V of Section 11.2, find an upper bound on the absolute values of the roots for each of the equations in Problem 1.

3. Following the second flow chart of Section 11.3, solve each of the following quadratic equations:

    a. $x^2 - 7x + 12 = 0$
    b. $2x^2 + 6x + 5 = 0$
    c. $1000x^2 - 1001x + 1 = 0$
    d. $500x^2 + 1001x + 2 = 0$

4. Following the flow chart, Figure 11–3, evaluate the following polynomials at the points indicated:

$$
\begin{array}{lll}
\text{a.} & y = 5x^3 + 3x^2 + 2x + 1, & x = .5 \\
\text{b.} & y = 3x^4 - 4x^3 - 2x + 6, & x = 2 \\
\text{c.} & y = x^6 - 1 & x = 2
\end{array}
$$

5. Following the flow chart, Figure 11–6, perform the following divisions, and count the number of multiplications required:

$$
\begin{array}{lll}
\text{a.} & x^3 + 3x^2 + 3x + 1 & \text{by} \quad x + 1 \\
\text{b.} & x^4 + 4x^2 + 4 \quad \text{by} \quad x^3 + 3x + 1 \\
\text{c.} & 2x^5 + 5x^4 - 3x^2 + 7 \quad \text{by} \quad x^4 - 2x^3 + x - 1
\end{array}
$$

6. Find the highest common factor of the following polynomials, and count the number of multiplications required:

$$
\begin{array}{lll}
\text{a.} & x^3 + 3x^2 + 3x + 1 & \text{and} \quad x + 1 \\
\text{b.} & x^3 + 3x^2 - 4x - 12 & \text{and} \quad x^2 - 4 \\
\text{c.} & x^3 + 4x^2 - x - 4 & \text{and} \quad 2x^3 + x^2 - 2x - 1
\end{array}
$$

7. Write a FORTRAN program that will input two polynomials, call subroutine POLYDIV, and print the quotient and remainder.

8. Write a FORTRAN program that will input two polynomials, call subroutine HIFACT, and print the highest common factor.

9. Estimate the time required, on a fast machine with on-line printing to:

   a. Divide a 15th degree polynomial by a 10th degree polynomial.
   b. Divide a 12th degree polynomial by a first degree polynomial.
   c. Find the highest common factor of a 20th degree polynomial and an 18th degree polynomial.
   d. Find the highest common factor of a 6th degree polynomial and a 5th degree polynomial.

11.5   REAL ROOTS

For equations of degree higher than four, there are no general formulae, which give the roots directly in terms of the coefficients. Such methods as the halving of the interval, the iteration method, or the Newton-Raphson method discussed in the preceding chapter are frequently useful for finding real roots.

11.51   *Real Root in a Known Interval*

If $f(x)$ is of opposite signs for two values of x, $x = x_1$ and $x = x_2$, then by Theorem I of Chapter X there is at least one real root between x_1 and x_2. The method of bisection, described in Section 10.3, could be used to obtain a real root in this case. The FORTRAN subroutine given below would serve to find a real root X of:

$$A(1)^N + A(2)X^{N-1} + \cdots + A(N+1)$$

known to lie between X1 and X2, to an accuracy specified by the number ACC:

```
    SUBROUTINE FINDROO(A,N,X1,X2,X,ACC)
    DIMENSION A(20)
    J=1
 1  X=X2
 2  Z=A(1)
    DO 3 I=1,N
 3  Z=Z*X+A(I+1)
    GO TO (4,5),J
 4  X=X1
    J=2
    Y=Z
    GO TO 2
 5  IF(ABSF(X2-X)-ACC)10,10,6
 6  IF(Y*Z)7,10,8
 7  X1=X
    GO TO 9
 8  X2=X
 9  X=(X1+X2)/2.
    GO TO 2
10  RETURN
    END
```

As mentioned in the preceding chapter, the method of bisection is somewhat slow compared to the Newton-Raphson process, which is a second order process, and converges extremely rapidly if the initial value is rather near the root. If one wishes to take advantage of this more rapid convergence (at some risk of having the process fail to converge at all), one could use a few steps of bisection to obtain a value fairly close to the root, and then switch to Newton-Raphson. Figure 11-9 illustrates the importance of obtaining a good initial estimate of the root before switching to the Newton-Raphson method. Remembering the geometry of the Newton-Raphson process from the preceding chapter, we see that an initial guess $x_0 = a$ will give a set of successive values that will oscillate about the minimum point at f, but will not converge. An initial guess $x_0 = b$ will give values that will oscillate about the maximum point at g, but will not converge. Convergence to the root c is assured only when the initial guess is in a rather narrow range about that

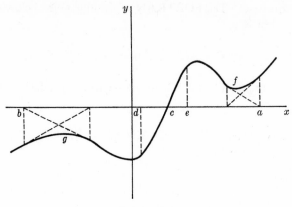

Figure 11-9

value, say, between *d* and *e*.   It is clear from this illustration that, if there are other maxima or minima in the curve quite near the root, it may be hard to choose an initial value near enough to ensure convergence.

11.52   Reducing the Degree of an Equation

Once a real root to a polynomial equation has been found, Theorem II of Section 11.2 can be used to obtain a new equation for the remaining roots, having degree reduced by one.   If the value of the root is *c*, then we must divide the polynomial $a_1 x^n + \cdots + a_{n+1}$ by the polynomial $x - c$, obtaining a new polynomial of degree $n - 1$.   The method for doing this has been discussed in Section 11.42.   If this new polynomial is of degree 4 or less, the remaining roots may be found by formula.   If it is of higher degree, other methods must still be used to find another root.

11.53   Isolation of the Roots

In Section 11.51 a method was described which will find a real root if it is known that $f(x)$ has opposite signs at the two ends of some interval.   This suggests that a way to find all the real roots of $f(x)$ is to try various values of *x* until a change in the sign of $f(x)$ is found, and then use the methods described in the two preceding sections to find the root and reduce the degree of the equation, and then repeat the process.   The difficulty with this approach is illustrated in Figure 11-10.   This equation has two real roots, but they are so close together that one might try a multitude of values of *x* and never obtain a negative value for $f(x)$.   What is needed is a procedure for determining precisely how many roots there are in an interval, so that a systematic scheme can be followed to isolate roots into separate intervals.   For equations which do not have multiple roots, such procedures exist, one of the best being

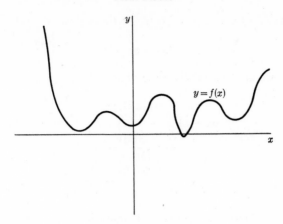

$y = f(x)$

Figure 11–10

that due to Sturm.   Consider the sequence of polynomials:

$$h_1(x), h_2(x), \ldots, h_{n+1}(x)$$

defined as follows:

$h_1(x) = f(x)$

$h_2(x) = f'(x)$

$h_3(x)$ = minus one times the remainder when $h_1(x)$ is divided by $h_2(x)$

$h_4(x)$ = minus one times remainder when $h_2(x)$ is divided by $h_3(x)$ etc.

Such a sequence is called a Sturm sequence for $f(x)$, the nature of which is illustrated by the following example:

Example 1.   Write a Sturm sequence for the polynomial $f(x) = x^3 - 6x^2 + 3x - 9$.

We have:

$$h_1(x) = f(x) = x^3 - 6x^2 + 3x - 9$$
$$h_2(x) = f'(x) = 3x^2 - 12x + 3$$

To find $h_3(x)$, we divide $h_1(x)$ by $h_2(x)$, thus:

$$
\require{enclose}
\begin{array}{r}
(1/3)x - 2/3 \\[-2pt]
3x^2 - 12x + 3 \enclose{longdiv}{x^3 - 6x^2 + 3x - 9} \\[-2pt]
\underline{x^3 - 4x^2 + x} \\[-2pt]
-2x^2 + 2x - 9 \\[-2pt]
\underline{-2x^2 + 8x - 2} \\[-2pt]
-6x - 7
\end{array}
$$

The remainder is $-6x - 7$, so $h_3(x)$ is -1 times this, or:

$$h_3(x) = 6x + 7$$

To find $h_4(x)$, we divide $h_2(x)$ by $h_3(x)$, thus:

$$
\begin{array}{r}
(1/2)x - 31/12 \\
\hline
6x+7\overline{)3x^2 - 12x + 3} \\
3x^2 + (7/2)x \\
\hline
-(31/2)x + 3 \\
-(31/2)x - 217/12 \\
\hline
253/12
\end{array}
$$

The remainder is $253/12$, so $h_4(x)$ is -1 times this, or:

$$h_4(x) = -253/12$$

Thus the complete Sturm sequence is:

$$h_1(x) = x^3 - 6x^2 + 3x - 9$$
$$h_2(x) = 3x^2 - 12x + 3$$
$$h_3(x) = 6x + 7$$
$$h_4(x) = -253/12$$

We see, then, that the Sturm sequence is a sequence of polynomials of decreasing degree, the lowest one being of zero degree, or a constant.

Now, if we substitute any real number a in each of the polynomials, we can obtain a sequence of numbers:

$$h_1(a), h_2(a), h_3(a), h_4(a)$$

Some of these may be positive, others negative. If one of the numbers differs in sign from the one next to it, we will say a "variation" in sign occurs. The theorem of Sturm has to do with the number of variations of sign in the Sturm sequence. Let $V(a)$ denote the number of variations in sign for $x = a$. Some examples will serve to illustrate how $V(a)$ is determined.

Example 2. Find $V(0)$ and $V(6)$ for the Sturm sequence of Example 1.

$$h_1(0) = -9$$
$$h_2(0) = 3$$
$$h_3(0) = 7$$
$$h_4(0) = -253/12$$

The sequence of signs is $-$, $+$, $+$, $-$. There are two variations in this sequence, so $V(0) = 2$.

For $x = 6$, we have:

$$h_1(6) = 9$$

$$h_2(6) = 39$$

$$h_3(6) = 43$$

$$h_4(6) = -253/12$$

The sequence of signs is $+$, $+$, $+$, $-$. There is one variation in the sequence, so $V(6) = 1$.

With this background we are now ready for the theorem of Sturm, which states:

Theorem. *The number of real roots of $f(x)$ between $x = a$ and $x = b$, where $b > a$, is exactly $V(a) - V(b)$.*

This theorem gives us a tool for isolating the real roots of a polynomial equation in a systematic fashion. In the above example, since $V(0) = 2$ and $V(6) = 1$, there is exactly one real root between $x = 0$ and $x = 6$. We can determine very quickly from the Sturm sequence in the above example that there are no other real roots. If x is very large, only the highest power term will matter, so we can see by inspection that $V(\infty) = 1$, $V(-\infty) = 2$, so there is only one real root. (On a computer, it will be more practical to use the fact, obtained from Theorem V of Section 11.2, that all the roots lie between -19 and 19, since $1 + |-6| + |3| + |-9| = 19$, and calculate $V(-19) = 2$, $V(19) = 1$.)

It is seen that computing a value $V(a)$ involves calculating the value of polynomials of degree n, $n - 1$, $n - 2$, ... 2, 1, 0. Since the evaluation of a polynomial of degree n ordinarily requires n multiplications, the computation of one value $V(a)$ involves:

$$1 + 2 + 3 + \cdots + n = \frac{n(n + 1)}{2}$$

multiplications, which means it is a somewhat slow process. However, it can be used to perform a systematic separation of the real roots.

11.54   *Flow Chart and Subroutine for Construction of a Sturm Sequence*

The process of constructing a Sturm sequence is almost identical to that of finding the highest common factor described in Section 11.43, except at each stage the negative of the remainder is taken.   The section of flow chart shown in Figure 11–11 illustrates the process.

The subroutine given below will form a Sturm sequence for a polynomial of 19th degree or less.   In this subroutine, the Sturm polynomial $h_j(x)$ is

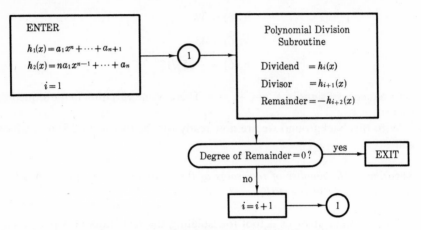

Figure 11–11: Generation of a sturm sequence

represented by the coefficients $S(J,1)$, $S(J,2)$, ... , $S(J,M(J)+1)$ and the constant $M(J)$ which specifies its degree.   As in finding the highest common factor, the process requires about $(n + 1)(n + 2)$ multiplications.

```
      SUBROUTINE STURM (A,N,S,M)
      DIMENSION  A(20),S(20,20),B(20),M(20),Q(20),R(20),F(20)
      LL=N+1
      DO 1 I=1,LL
      FN=N-I+1
      S(1,I)=A(I)
    1 S(2,I)=FN*A(I)
      M(1)=N
      M(2)=N-1
      J=0
    2 J=J+1
      LL=M(J)+1
      DO 3 I=1,LL
    3 F(I)=S(J,I)
      LL=M(J+1)+1
      DO 4 I=1,LL
    4 B(I)=S(J+1,I)
      M1=M(J)
      M2=M(J+1)
```

```
        CALL POLYDIV(F,M1,B,M2,Q,L,R,M3)
        M(J+2)=M3
        DO 5 I=1,LL
   5    S(J+2,I)=-R(I)
        IF(M3)6,6,2
   6    RETURN
        END
```

11.55   Flow Chart and Subroutine for Use of Sturm Sequence

In order to apply the theorem of Sturm to isolate roots, we must be able to take the Sturm sequence, once obtained, and compute the number of variations in sign, as illustrated in Example 2 of Section 11.53.   The section of flow chart, Figure 11–12, shows how this can be done on a computer, given the Sturm sequence:

$$h_1(x), h_2(x), \ldots, h_{n+1}(x)$$

and the value a for which the number of variations in sign is to be determined.

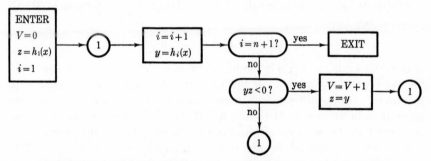

Figure 11–12: Determination of sign variations in a sturm sequence

The FORTRAN subroutine given below will find the number of variations in sign L, for the point X and the Sturm sequence generated by subroutine STURM given in Section 11.54.   If X happens to be a root, the subroutine indicates this fact by assigning to L a value one greater than the highest degree in the Sturm sequence,

```
        SUBROUTINE STURMVA(S,M,X,L)
        DIMENSION S(20,20),M(20)
        L=0
        Z=S(1,1)
        LL=M(1)
        DO 1 I=1,LL
   1    Z=Z*X+S(1,I+1)
        J=1
```

```
      IF(Z)2,10,2
   2  J=J+1
      Y=S(J,1)
      LL=M(J)
      DO 3 I=1,LL
   3  Y=Y*X+S(J,I+1)
      IF(Y*Z)4,6,5
   4  L=L+1
   5  Z=Y
   6  IF(M(J))7,7,2
  10  L=M(1)+1
   7  RETURN
      END
```

11.56   Flow Chart and Program for Isolating Roots

With programs available for constructing a STURM sequence and computing the number of variations of sign, the roots can be isolated by using the technique of halving the interval.   Since by Theorem V of Section 11.21, all roots are less than:

$$U = (|a_1| + |a_2| + \cdots + |a_n|)/|a_1|$$

in absolute value, we begin by finding the number of variations in sign, $V(x)$ for $x = U$ and for $x = -U$.   If $V(U)$ and $V(-U)$ are the same, there are no real roots.   If they differ by one, there is exactly one real root, and we may proceed as in Section 11.51 to find it.   If they differ by more than one we compute $V(0)$, the number of variations at the midpoint of the interval, and if necessary continue subdividing until all the real roots are isolated.   This is a slow process compared to many other techniques for finding real roots. As mentioned above, finding the number of variations in sign at one point for a Sturm sequence involves about $[n(n + 1)]/2$ multiplications, whereas finding a value of an nth degree polynomial $f(x)$ at one point requires only about n multiplications.   Hence for a 10th degree equation the use of a Sturm sequence might be expected to take roughly 5 times as long as some iteration type techniques.   In many instances, though, this slowness is more than compensated for by the relatively high assurance that the method will indeed isolate the roots in a reasonable number of steps instead of overlooking some of them or irresponsibly refusing to converge as some of the faster methods may do.

Given subroutines for constructing a Sturm sequence and computing the number of variations in sign, the flow chart, Figure 11–13, shows how the largest root can be isolated, that is, two values x_1 and x_2 determined such that for the root x, $x_1 \leqslant x \leqslant x_2$.   Once this is done, the process could be repeated to isolate the other roots, if desired.

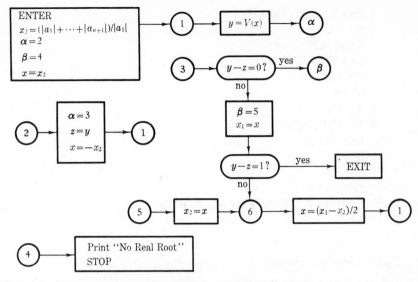

Figure 11–13: Isolation of largest real root

The FORTRAN subroutine given below isolates the maximum root, following the above flow chart and using the subroutines given in the preceding sections:

```
      SUBROUTINE ISOROOT(A,N,X1,X2)
      DIMENSION A(20),S(20,20),M(20)
      CALL STURM(A,N,S,M)
      B=ABSF(A(1))
      X2=B
      DO 1 I=1,N
    1 X2=X2+ABSF(A(I+1))
      X2=X2/B
      J=1
      K=1
      X=X2
    2 CALL STURMVA(S,M,X,LY)
      IF(M(1)−LY)20,21,21
   20 X1=X
      X2=X
      RETURN
   21 GO TO (3,4),J
    3 J=2
      LZ=LY
      X=−X2
      GO TO 2
```

```
 4 IF(LY−LZ−1)6,5,10
 5 X1=X
   RETURN
 6 GO TO(7,8),K
 7 PRINT 101
   STOP
 8 X2=X
 9 X=(X1+X2)/2.
   GO TO 2
10 K=2
   X1=X
   GO TO 9
101 FORMAT(14H NO REAL ROOTS)
   END
```

11.57 Multiple Roots

It was mentioned above that the Sturm sequence can be used only when the equation does not have multiple roots.   This is not a very serious restriction, since there are methods for factoring an equation into factors containing only simple roots.   The most common method is based on the fact that if c is a multiple root of the equation:

$$f(x) = 0$$

it is also a root of the equation:

$$f'(x) = 0$$

and, conversely, if c is a root of both:

$$f(x) = 0 \quad \text{and} \quad f'(x) = 0$$

it is a multiple root of $f(x) = 0$.   From Theorem II of Section 11.2, then, it follows that $x - c$ is a factor of both $f(x)$ and $f'(x)$.

Now suppose $g(x)$ is the highest common factor of $f(x)$ and $f'(x)$; that is to say, $g(x)$ is the polynomial of highest degree which divides into both $f(x)$ and $f'(x)$ without leaving a remainder.   The $f(x)$ can be written:

$$f(x) = g(x)g_1(x)$$

where $g_1(x)$ contains only simple roots.   The factor $g(x)$ will contain all the multiple roots of $f(x)$ with multiplicity reduced by one.   Hence if $f(x)$ contained only double roots, $g(x)$ contains only simple roots.   If $f(x)$ contained roots of higher multiplicity, $g(x)$ will still contain multiple roots. The factor $g_1(x)$ contains only simple roots, and it contains all roots of $f(x)$. Hence if we find the polynomial $g_1(x)$, and solve for all its roots, we will have found all roots of $f(x)$. The process of finding the highest common factor described in Section 11.42, can be used for this purpose.

Given a polynomial:

$$A(1)X^N + A(2)X^{N-1} + \cdots + A(N+1)$$

which may have multiple roots, the FORTRAN subroutine given below will generate another polynomial:

$$B(1)X^M + B(2)X^{M-1} + \cdots + B(M+1)$$

which has all the roots of the original polynomial as simple roots:

```
      SUBROUTINE SIMPRTS(A,N,B,M)
      DIMENSION A(20),B(20),F(20),R(20)
      DO 1 I=1,N
      FN=N+1-I
    1 B(I)=FN*A(I)
      M=N-1
      CALL HIFACT(A,N,B,M,F,K)
      CALL POLYDIV(A,N,F,K,B,M,R,L)
      RETURN
      END
```

11.6 COMPLEX ROOTS

As for real roots, there are a variety of methods for finding complex roots of polynomial equation.   Ordinarily if all roots are required, it is best to find all real roots first, and then solve the reduced equation for the complex roots. If the reduced equation is of second or fourth degree (it will certainly be of even degree) the complex roots can be found by formula.   Only if it is of sixth degree or higher (i.e., there are at least three pairs of complex roots) must a special technique be used.   Only one method of finding complex zeros will be described, that known as Bairstow's method.

The complex roots for a polynomial with real coefficients occur in conjugate pairs, each pair being the solution of a quadratic equation:

$$x^2 + px + q = 0$$

where p and q are real numbers.   Hence the process of finding the complex roots of the polynomial:

$$f(x) = a_1 x^n + a_2 x^{n-1} + \cdots + a_{n+1}$$

can be regarded as equivalent to finding quadratic expressions which are factors of $f(x)$. Bairstow's method consists of taking a trial quadratic expression, i.e., trial values for p and q, dividing the expression into $f(x)$, and obtaining a remainder. The values of p and q are then adjusted to make the remainder smaller, and the process repeated until the remainder is considered small enough. Since it is basically an iteration technique, it is subject to the usual convergence problems.

The method goes as follows: having chosen trial values of p and q, divide $x^2 + px + q$ into $f(x)$. In skeleton form, this division gives:

$$
\begin{array}{ccccccc}
 & & & q_1 & q_2 \cdots\cdots\cdots & q_{n-1} & \\
1 & p & q\,) \overline{a_1} & a_2 & a_3 \cdots\cdots & a_{n+1} & \\
 & & a_1 & a_1 p & a_1 q & & \\
\hline
 & & & & r_1 & r_2 &
\end{array}
$$

The remainder is $r_1 x + r_2$. If the binomial expression were an exact factor, r_1 and r_2 would both be zero. If we were to change the values of p and q, the values of r_1 and r_2 would be changed also, i.e., r_1 and r_2 are functions of p and q:

$$r_1 = r_1(p, q)$$

$$r_2 = r_2(p, q)$$

By Taylor's theorem, the values of r_1 and r_2 if p and q are changed slightly are:

$$r_1(p + \Delta p, q + \Delta q) = r_1(p, q) + \frac{\partial r_1}{\partial p}\Delta p + \frac{\partial r_1}{\partial q}\Delta q + \cdots$$

$$r_2(p + \Delta p, q + \Delta q) = r_2(p, q) + \frac{\partial r_2}{\partial p}\Delta p + \frac{\partial r_2}{\partial q}\Delta q + \cdots$$

We would like to choose Δp and Δq so that r_1 and r_2 become zero. This is approximately the case if:

$$r_1(p, q) + \frac{\partial r_1}{\partial p}\Delta p + \frac{\partial r_1}{\partial q}\Delta q = 0$$

$$r_2(p, q) + \frac{\partial r_2}{\partial p}\Delta p + \frac{\partial r_2}{\partial q}\Delta q = 0$$

If we knew the partial derivatives of r_1 and r_2 with respect to p and q, we could solve these equations for Δp and Δq. The derivation of the formulae for $\partial r_1/\partial p$, etc. is somewhat involved, and will not be reproduced here. The actual expressions for these quantities turn out to be rather simple. They are obtained as follows:

Construct a new polynomial:

$$q(x) = b_1 x^n + b_2 x^{n-1} + \cdots + b_{n+1}$$

where:

$$b_1 = q_1,\, b_2 = q_2,\, \cdots,\, b_{n-1} = q_{n-1},\, b_n = r_1,\, b_{n+1} = r_2.$$

Divide this polynomial by $x^2 + px + q$, obtaining a quotient:

$$c_1 x^{n-2} + c_2 x^{n-3} + \cdots + c_{n-2}x + c_{n-1}$$

and a remainder:

$$t_1 x + t_2$$

The values of the partial derivatives we need are:

$$\frac{\partial r_1}{\partial p} = -c_{n-1}, \qquad \frac{\partial r_2}{\partial p} = -(t_1 - r_1 + pc_{n-1})$$

$$\frac{\partial r_1}{\partial q} = -c_{n-2}, \qquad \frac{\partial r_2}{\partial q} = -(c_{n-1} - pc_{n-2})$$

Hence the expressions for Δp and Δq become:

$$r_1 - c_{n-1}\Delta p - c_{n-2}\Delta q = 0$$
$$r_2 - (t_1 - r_1 + pc_{n-1})\Delta p - (c_{n-1} - pc_{n-2})\Delta q = 0$$

or, solving for Δp and Δq:

$$\Delta p = [r_1(c_{n-1} - pc_{n-2}) - r_2 c_{n-2}]/d$$
$$\Delta q = [r_2 c_{n-1} - r_1(t_1 - r_1 + pc_{n-1})]/d$$

where:

$$d = [c_{n-1}(c_{n-1} - pc_{n-2}) - c_{n-2}(t_1 - r_1 + pc_{n-1})]$$

These values of Δp and Δq can be added to p and q to obtain a new, and hopefully, better quadratic expression $x^2 + px + q$. The flow chart, Figure 11–14, shows how this process might be used to obtain a quadratic factor.

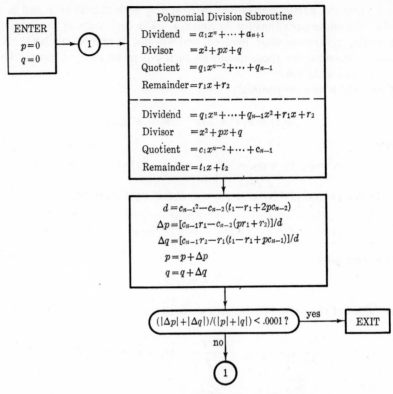

Figure 11–14: **Finding a binomial factor**

The FORTRAN subroutine below finds the real and imaginary parts of a set of complex roots, XRL and XIM, and also the reduced polynomial:

$$Q(1)X^K + Q(2)X^{K-1} + \cdots + Q(K+1)$$

which must be examined for the remaining roots. If the program has not converged in 100 tries, this program prints out that fact and quits trying:

```
      SUBROUTINE PLEXROO (A,N,XRL,XIM,Q,K,ERR)
      DIMENSION  A(20),B(3),Q(20),R(2),C(20),T(2)
      B(1)=1.
      B(2)=0.
      B(3)=0.
      J=1
    1 CALL POLYDIV(A,N,B,2,Q,K,R,L)
      IF(R(1))3,6,3
    3 Q(N)=R(1)
      Q(N+1)=R(2)
```

```
      CALL POLYDIV(Q,N,B,2,C,K,T,M)
      D=C(N−1)*(C(N−1)−B(2)*C(N−2))
      D=D−C(N−2)*(T(1)−R(1)+B(2)*C(N−1))
      IF(D)21,20,21
   20 B(2)=B(2)+.1
      B(3)=B(3)+.1
      GO TO 4
   21 DB2=(R(1)*(C(N−1)−B(2)*C(N−2))−R(2)*C(N−2))/D
      DB3=(C(N−1)*R(2)−R(1)*(T(1)−R(1)+B(2)*C(N−1)))/D
      B(2)=B(2)+DB2
      B(3)=B(3)+DB3
      IF((ABSF(DB2)+ABSF(DB3))/(ABSF(B(2))+ABSF(B(3)))
     −ERR)6,6,4
    4 J=J+1
      IF(100−J)5,1,1
    5 PRINT 1001
      STOP
    6 P=B(2)
      U=B(3)
      CALL QUADROO(1.,P,U,I,XRL,XIM,ERR)
      RETURN
 1001 FORMAT(26H PLEXROO DOES NOT CONVERGE)
      END
```

EXERCISE XXI

1. In each of the following, find the only real root to an accuracy of .01 by the bisection method:

   a. $x^5 + x + 1 = 0$
   b. $x^3 − 3x^2 − 2 = 0$
   c. $x^7 + x^6 + x^2 + 1 = 0$

2. Write a FORTRAN program that will input a polynomial and two limits X_1 and X_2, call subroutine FINDROO given in Section 11.51, and print the value of the root to four places.

3. Write a modified version of subroutine FINDROO that will switch to the Newton-Raphson method when an accuracy of .1 has been reached.

4. Write a Sturm sequence for each of the following:

   a. $x^3 − 7x^2 + 14x − 8$
   b. $x^3 − x^2 − x − 2$
   c. $x^4 − x^3 − 2x^2 − 9x − 9$

5. Estimate the time required for a fast machine to :

   a. Construct a Sturm sequence for a 10th degree polynomial.
   b. Construct a Sturm sequence for a 6th degree polynomial.
      Find the number of variations in a Sturm sequence for one point for:
   c. A 12th degree polynomial
   d. A 6th degree polynomial.

6. a. Write a program MAXROOT which will use subroutine ISOROOT of Section 11.55 to isolate the maximum root and subroutine FINDROO of Section 11.51 to find the root to an accuracy of .0001.
   b. Estimate the time required to find the maximum root of an 8th degree equation on a fast machine with this program, if 6 steps of using STURMVAR are required, followed by 10 iterations of the bisection method in FINDROO.

7. Using three iterations of the procedure described by the flow chart of Section 11.6, find estimates for one pair of complex roots for each of the following:

$$\text{a.} \quad x^4 + x^2 + 1 = 0$$
$$\text{b.} \quad x^8 + 2x^6 + 3x^4 + 1 = 0$$
$$\text{c.} \quad x^4 + x^3 + x^2 + x + 1 = 0$$

8. Write a FORTRAN program ALLROOT that will use the subroutines given in this chapter to completely solve equations of degree up to 19.

CHAPTER XII *Systems of Linear Equations*

12.1 INTRODUCTION

In this chapter, we turn to a problem of finding the values of unknowns, x_1, x_2, etc., which satisfy systems of equations of the type:

$$a_{11}x_1 + a_{12}x_2 + a_{13}x_3 + \cdots + a_{1n}x_n = b_1$$

$$a_{21}x_1 + a_{22}x_2 + a_{23}x_3 + \cdots + a_{2n}x_n = b_2$$

$$a_{31}x_1 + a_{32}x_2 + a_{33}x_3 + \cdots + a_{3n}x_n = b_3 \tag{12-1}$$

$$\cdot$$
$$\cdot$$
$$\cdot$$

$$a_{n1}x_1 + a_{n2}x_2 + a_{n3}x_3 + \cdots + a_{nn}x_n = b_n$$

In college algebra we have learned that for systems of this type, when the number of equations is equal to the number of unknowns, there will ordinarily be a unique solution, i.e., one set of values of x_1, x_2, ... , x_n which satisfy all of the equations. We shall find that the methods of finding this solution which are learned in a college algebra course are not necessarily the best ones for computer use, and we shall also find that problems of this type which are so large as to be out of the question for hand calculations are easily done on the computer.

12.2 CRAMER'S RULE

Probably the most widely known method for the solution of systems of linear equations is that known as Cramer's Rule. For a two-by-two system of equations:

$$a_{11}x_1 + a_{12}x_2 = b_1$$
$$a_{21}x_1 + a_{22}x_2 = b_2$$

the solution is:

$$x_1 = \frac{\begin{vmatrix} b_1 & a_{12} \\ b_2 & a_{22} \end{vmatrix}}{\begin{vmatrix} a_{11} & a_{12} \\ a_{21} & a_{22} \end{vmatrix}} \qquad x_2 = \frac{\begin{vmatrix} a_{11} & b_1 \\ a_{21} & b_2 \end{vmatrix}}{\begin{vmatrix} a_{11} & a_{12} \\ a_{21} & a_{22} \end{vmatrix}}$$

For a three-by-three system:

$$a_{11}x_1 + a_{12}x_2 + a_{13}x_3 = b_1$$
$$a_{21}x_1 + a_{22}x_2 + a_{23}x_3 = b_2$$
$$a_{31}x_1 + a_{32}x_2 + a_{33}x_3 = b_3$$

the solution is:

$$x_1 = \frac{\begin{vmatrix} b_1 & a_{12} & a_{13} \\ b_2 & a_{22} & a_{23} \\ b_3 & a_{32} & a_{33} \end{vmatrix}}{D} \qquad x_2 = \frac{\begin{vmatrix} a_{11} & b_1 & a_{13} \\ a_{21} & b_2 & a_{23} \\ a_{31} & b_3 & a_{33} \end{vmatrix}}{D} \qquad x_3 = \frac{\begin{vmatrix} a_{11} & a_{12} & b_1 \\ a_{21} & a_{22} & b_2 \\ a_{31} & a_{32} & b_3 \end{vmatrix}}{D}$$

where:

$$D = \begin{vmatrix} a_{11} & a_{12} & a_{13} \\ a_{21} & a_{22} & a_{23} \\ a_{31} & a_{32} & a_{33} \end{vmatrix}$$

This form of solution works for systems of equations of any order, and can be stated in words as follows: In the solution of n linear equations in n

unknowns, the value of the *i*th unknown is given by the ratio of two determinants. The denominator is the determinant of coefficients and the numerator is the same determinant except for having the *i*th column replaced by the column of constants.

12.21 Evaluation of a Determinant

The numerical value of a determinant is determined as follows: We form all possible terms containing as factors exactly one element from each row, no two of which come from the same column. To each such term we assign a plus or minus sign in accordance with a rule to be stated shortly. The sum of these terms is the value of the determinant. The sign to be assigned to a term is determined by the following procedure. The factors in the term are arranged in order according to the row from which each factor was chosen:

$$a_{1k_1}a_{2k_2}a_{3k_3} \cdots a_{nk_n}$$

We then rearrange these factors so that they are in order according to the column from which each was chosen, i.e., so that the subscripts $k_1, k_2, \ldots, k_n$ are in their natural order, and count the number of interchanges required to do this. We assign the term a plus sign if the number of interchanges was even and a minus sign if it was odd. For a two-by-two determinant, then:

$$\begin{vmatrix} a_{11} & a_{12} \\ a_{21} & a_{22} \end{vmatrix} = a_{11}a_{22} - a_{21}a_{12}$$

For a three-by-three system:

$$\begin{vmatrix} a_{11} & a_{12} & a_{13} \\ a_{21} & a_{22} & a_{23} \\ a_{31} & a_{32} & a_{33} \end{vmatrix} = \begin{matrix} a_{11}a_{22}a_{33} - a_{11}a_{23}a_{32} - a_{12}a_{21}a_{33} \\ + a_{12}a_{23}a_{31} + a_{13}a_{21}a_{32} - a_{13}a_{22}a_{31} \end{matrix}$$

It is clear that, by utilizing the programming methods of the earlier chapters, we can cause a computer to perform such calculations and provide the solution to a system of equations. It is not so obvious, but it can be shown that such a procedure is quite inefficient in machine time, particularly for systems involving a very large number of unknowns. According to the rule just stated for evaluating a determinant, an *n* by *n* determinant is the sum of $n!$ terms, each of which is the product of *n* numbers. If we were to calculate the value of a determinant by the most direct method, then, about $n \times n!$ multiplications would be required. By a judicious grouping of terms, the number of multiplications can be reduced somewhat, to about $2n!$* Table I shows the number for various sizes of n:

TABLE I

n	Number of Multiplications
2	2
3	9
4	40
5	205
10	6×10^6
20	4×10^{18}

It is seen that, if this procedure is followed, the evaluation of a 20×20 determinant requires a time of about one hundred billion years even on our fast computer.

There is another method of evaluation of a determinant that is very much faster than the brute force approach. We recall that if all elements on one row of a determinant are changed by adding or subtracting a constant multiple of the corresponding elements of another row, the value of the determinant is unchanged. By repeated application of this rule, we can reduce a determinant to a "triangular" form, in which all elements below the main diagonal are zero. For example:

$$
\begin{vmatrix}
b_{11} & b_{12} & b_{13} & \cdots & & b_{1n} \\
0 & b_{22} & b_{23} & \cdots & & b_{2n} \\
0 & 0 & b_{33} & \cdots & & b_{3n} \\
0 & 0 & 0 & b_{44} & \cdots & b_{4n} \\
& & & \cdot & & \\
& & & \cdot & & \\
& & & \cdot & & \\
0 & 0 & 0 & \cdots & & b_{nn}
\end{vmatrix}
$$

The value of a determinant when written in this form turns out to be just the product of the diagonal elements, $b_{11}b_{22}b_{33} \cdots b_{nn}$, since all other terms formed in accordance with the definition of a determinant's value contain at least one factor whose value is zero. Hence, after a determinant is written in triangular form, only $n - 1$ multiplications are required to find its value.

* Actually to $n!\ [1 + 1/2! + 1/3! + \cdots + 1/(n - 1)!]$, which for all n is less than $e \times n!$

The procedure for putting a determinant in diagonal form may be described as follows:

STEP 1: Multiply each of the elements of the first row by the ratio a_{21}/a_{11} and subtract the result from each corresponding element of the second row. This will put a zero in the first position of the second row. Then multiply each of the elements of the first row by the ratio a_{31}/a_{11} and subtract the result from each corresponding element of the third row. This will put a zero in the first position of the third row. Proceed in this fashion until a new determinant is obtained with zeros all the way down the column except for the first row.

STEP 2: Now consider the portion of the determinant excluding first row and first column as a new determinant of order one less than the original one, and use the same procedure to obtain zeros down the first column of this determinant.

STEP 3, etc. Continue this process through the remainder of the determinant.

The total number of multiplications (and divisions) involved is as follows:

To obtain $n - 1$ zeros in first column $n(n - 1)$
To obtain $n - 2$ zeros in second column $(n - 1)(n - 2)$
To obtain $n - 3$ zeros in third column $(n - 2)(n - 3)$

.
.
.

To obtain one zero in next to last column $(2)(1)$

Adding these quantities:

$$(1)(2) + (2)(3) + \cdots + (n - 1)(n) = (1/3)n(n^2 - 1)$$

Adding on the $n - 1$ multiplications required to evaluate the determinant once it is in triangular form, we have a total of $(1/3)(n^3 + 2n - 3)$ multiplications required to evaluate the determinant. Table II shows this number for various values of n. For large n, the value is about $(1/3)n^3$.

TABLE II

n	Number of Multiplications
2	3
3	10
4	23
5	44
10	339
20	2679
100	333,399
1000	333,333,999

It is seen that, if this procedure is followed, a 100×100 determinant will require only 3 seconds on our fast machine, and a 1000×1000 determinant about an hour. The procedure makes evaluation of very large determinants practicable on computers. (Practicable but not trivial. Loss of accuracy can be a serious problem when such large numbers of calculations are involved.)

Example 1. Evaluate the determinant:

$$\begin{vmatrix} 2 & 3 & 5 \\ 3 & 4 & 7 \\ 1 & 3 & 2 \end{vmatrix}$$

by first placing it in triangular form.

We multiply the elements of the first row by 3/2 and subtract from corresponding elements of the second row, giving:

$$\begin{vmatrix} 2 & 3 & 5 \\ 0 & -1/2 & -1/2 \\ 1 & 3 & 2 \end{vmatrix}$$

Then we multiply the elements of the first row by 1/2 and subtract from the third row, giving:

$$\begin{vmatrix} 2 & 3 & 5 \\ 0 & -1/2 & -1/2 \\ 0 & 3/2 & -1/2 \end{vmatrix}$$

Then we multiply the elements of the second row by -3 and subtract from the third row (or multiply by $+3$ and add), giving:

$$\begin{vmatrix} 2 & 3 & 5 \\ 0 & -1/2 & -1/2 \\ 0 & 0 & -2 \end{vmatrix}$$

The value of the determinant is thus $(2)(-1/2)(-2) = 2$.

12.22 *Flow Chart and Subroutine for Evaluation of a Determinant*

In order to demonstrate clearly how a machine program can be organized to evaluate a determinant of any order, we shall first demonstrate the process for a 3 × 3 determinant with the aid of some diagrams. We start with:

$$\begin{vmatrix} a_{11} & a_{12} & a_{13} \\ a_{21} & a_{22} & a_{23} \\ a_{31} & a_{32} & a_{33} \end{vmatrix}$$

We are first to divide the first row by a_{11} and multiply by a_{21} and subtract it from the second row, giving:

$$\begin{vmatrix} a_{11} & a_{12} & a_{13} \\ 0 & a_{22} - \dfrac{a_{21}a_{12}}{a_{11}} & a_{23} - \dfrac{a_{21}a_{13}}{a_{11}} \\ a_{31} & a_{32} & a_{33} \end{vmatrix}$$

Doing the same thing for the third row, we obtain:

$$\begin{vmatrix} a_{11} & a_{12} & a_{13} \\ 0 & a_{22} - \dfrac{a_{21}a_{12}}{a_{11}} & a_{23} - \dfrac{a_{21}a_{13}}{a_{11}} \\ 0 & a_{32} - \dfrac{a_{31}a_{12}}{a_{11}} & a_{33} - \dfrac{a_{31}a_{13}}{a_{11}} \end{vmatrix}$$

We must then do the same thing for the 2 × 2 determinant made up of the second and third rows of the second and third columns. For a larger determinant the situation is analogous. We can build a flow chart based on this situation. We first note that the elements a_{12} and a_{13} in the above determinant do not make any further contribution after we have the zeros in the first column, for any product involving one of these elements must also involve one of the zeros. Hence it does not matter if we change these elements to some other values. With this freedom available to us, we see that the operations leading to the last determinant above can be represented by the following statements:

$$\frac{a_{1i}}{a_{11}} \rightarrow a_{1i} \qquad \text{for } i = 2 \text{ and } 3$$

$$a_{ij} - a_{i1}a_{1j} \rightarrow a_{ij} \qquad \text{for } i \text{ and } j = 2 \text{ and } 3$$

Following these steps would lead to the determinant:

$$\begin{vmatrix} a_{11} & \dfrac{a_{12}}{a_{11}} & \dfrac{a_{13}}{a_{11}} \\[2ex] (a_{21}) & a_{22} - \dfrac{a_{21}a_{12}}{a_{11}} & a_{23} - \dfrac{a_{21}a_{13}}{a_{11}} \\[2ex] (a_{31}) & a_{32} - \dfrac{a_{31}a_{12}}{a_{11}} & a_{33} - \dfrac{a_{31}a_{13}}{a_{11}} \end{vmatrix}$$

The elements in the first column have been unaffected, but we know they should be zero, so we can arrange to neglect them later without going to the extra effort of having the machine store zeros in these locations.   A flow chart for the evaluation of an $n \times n$ determinant can be developed by extending the above.   Figure 12–1 shows such a flow chart.

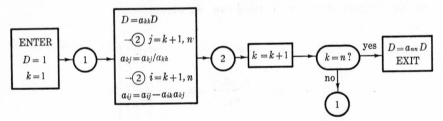

Figure 12–1: Evaluation of a determinant

A calculation based on the flow chart, Figure 12–1, could run into trouble if a_{kk} ever becomes zero, since there is a division by this quantity.   This problem can be avoided by taking the additional precaution of checking to see if a_{kk} is zero and if so interchanging two rows to obtain a nonzero value for a_{kk}.   Since interchanging two rows in a determinant changes the sign of the determinant's value, we must also change the signs of the elements in one of the rows to correct this.

There can also be accuracy problems associated with evaluating a determinant using the above flow chart, particularly for determinants of large order.   These problems tend to be alleviated if the rows and columns are rearranged at each step so that a_{kk} is not only nonzero, but is actually the largest element in absolute value.   On a computer this choice of the largest, or so-called "pivotal" element and rearrangement of the determinant does not require an appreciable amount of time.

Another step which should be taken to avoid accuracy loss is in connection with the computation:

$$a_{ij} = a_{ij} - a_{ik}a_{kj}$$

If the result of this subtraction is supposed to be zero, then this subtraction will be subject to the trouble mentioned many times earlier in the text, loss of accuracy caused by introduction of leading zeros.   The method of protection against this trouble is the same one used in division of polynomials in Section 11.43.   We check the result of the subtraction, and if the difference is much smaller than the numbers being subtracted, we set the difference equal to zero.   The operation can be described by a section of flow chart (as in Figure 12–2) in which a_{ij} is set equal to zero if more than four significant figures have been lost in the subtraction.

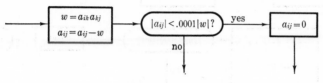

Figure 12–2

A flow chart for finding the value of a determinant incorporating the above safety features can be written as in Figure 12–3.   Here most of the boxes are devoted to the bookkeeping process of interchanging rows and columns. The basic calculation is the same as that in the previous chart.

The FORTRAN subroutine given below evaluates the Nth order determinant:

$$\begin{vmatrix} A(1, 1) & A(1, 2) & \dots & A(1, N) \\ A(2, 1) & A(2, 2) & \dots & A(2, N) \\ & & \cdot & \\ & & \cdot & \\ & & \cdot & \\ A(N, 1) & A(N, 2) & \dots & A(N, N) \end{vmatrix}$$

for values of N up to 20, following the flow chart, Figure 12–3.   In the first

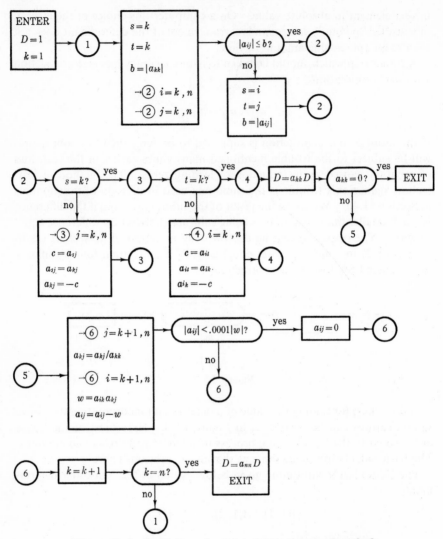

Figure 12–3: Evaluation of a determinant—improved method

statement, the determinant is given the name AA, and the statements up to 200 redefine elements $A(I,J) = AA(I,J)$, so that the original determinant will not be destroyed during the calculation. For ease in relating the FORTRAN program to the flow chart, each remote connector in the flow chart is represented as a CONTINUE statement having the identical number in the FORTRAN program. Statements 1 to 2 search through the elements and find the location of the largest one in absolute value (row IS, column IT). Statements 2 through 3 interchange rows IS and K, multiplying one row by -1 to preserve the sign of the determinant, unless IS happens to be K.

Statements 3 through 4 likewise interchange columns IT and K. Statements 4 through 6 do the actual calculation.

```
      SUBROUTINE DETERM(AA,N,D)
      DIMENSION AA(20,20),A(20,20)
      DO 200 I=1,N
      DO 200 J=1,N
  200 A(I,J)=AA(I,J)
      D=1.
      K=1
    1 CONTINUE
      KK=K+1
      IS=K
      IT=K
      B=ABSF(A(K,K))
      DO 2 I=K,N
      DO 2 J=K,N
      IF(ABSF(A(I,J))-B)2,2,21
   21 IS=I
      IT=J
      B=ABSF(A(I,J))
    2 CONTINUE
      IF(IS-K)3,3,31
   31 DO 32 J=K,N
      C=A(IS,J)
      A(IS,J)=A(K,J)
   32 A(K,J)=-C
    3 CONTINUE
      IF(IT-K)4,4,41
   41 DO 42 I=K,N
      C=A(I,IT)
      A(I,IT)=A(I,K)
   42 A(I,K)=-C
    4 CONTINUE
      D=A(K,K)*D
      IF(A(K,K))5,71,5
    5 CONTINUE
      DO 6 J=KK,N
      A(K,J)=A(K,J)/A(K,K)
      DO 6 I=KK,N
      W=A(I,K)*A(K,J)
      A(I,J)=A(I,J)-W
      IF(ABSF(A(I,J))-.0001*ABSF(W))61,6,6
   61 A(I,J)=0.
```

```
   6 CONTINUE
     K=KK
     IF(K−N)1,70,1
  70 D=A(N,N)*D
  71 RETURN
     END
```

12.23   Disadvantage of Cramer's Rule

Even with the rather efficient method of evaluating a determinant just described, for large systems Cramer's Rule still involves a somewhat larger number of multiplications than some other methods. A total of $n+1$ different determinants must be evaluated, each one requiring about $(1/3)n^3$ multiplications, so that a total of about $(1/3)n^4$ multiplications are required. We will discuss some more efficient methods of solving such systems.

12.3   THE ELIMINATION METHOD

The elimination method is used in elementary algebra for solving systems of linear equations. In this method, an appropriate multiple of the first equation is added to each of the other equations so that the resulting $n-1$ equations have zero coefficients for the x_1 term. (If the first equation does not have a term involving x_1, we must first interchange two equations to obtain one with an x_1 term as the first equation.) Then an appropriate multiple of the next equation is added to each of the remaining equations so that the x_2 term is eliminated from these. (Again, if the second equation contains no x_2 term, we would first have to interchange two equations.) The process is continued until a system of the following form is obtained:

$$b_{11}x_1 + b_{12}x_2 + b_{13}x_3 + \cdots + b_{1n}x_n = d_1$$

$$b_{22}x_2 + b_{23}x_3 + \cdots + b_{2n}x_n = d_2$$

$$b_{33}x_3 + \cdots + b_{3n}x_n = d_3$$

$$\vdots$$

(12-2)

$$b_{nn}x_n = d_n$$

Then from the last equation we have $x_n = d_n/b_{nn}$, and by substituting this result in the next to last equation we find x_{n-1}, and so forth, until x_1 is finally found from the first equation. It is seen that this process bears a definite relation to that of putting a determinant in triangular form described in the preceding section. For large n, the number of multiplications involved is about $(2/3)n^3$.

The equation used to eliminate an unknown at any stage is referred to as a pivotal equation. The final set of equations above is the set of pivotal equations.

Accuracy is frequently improved if at each stage we rearrange the equations and unknowns so as to use the term with largest coefficient (in absolute value) for eliminating the next variable. Even with this improvement, the elimination method frequently suffers from accuracy problems because of the many subtractions involved.

Example 1. Solve the system:

$$2x_1 + 3x_2 + 5x_3 = 5 \qquad \text{(12-3)}$$

$$3x_1 + 4x_2 + 7x_3 = 6 \qquad \text{(12-4)}$$

$$x_1 + 3x_2 + 2x_3 = 5 \qquad \text{(12-5)}$$

We will solve this problem in the way in which we would do it on a computer. Since the term $7x_3$ has the largest coefficient, let us rewrite the system as:

$$7x_3 + 4x_2 + 3x_1 = 6 \qquad \text{(12-6)}$$

$$5x_3 + 3x_2 + 2x_1 = 5 \qquad \text{(12-7)}$$

$$2x_3 + 3x_2 + x_1 = 5 \qquad \text{(12-8)}$$

Multiplying equation (12-6) by 5/7 and subtracting from equation (12-7), we obtain:

$$(1/7)x_2 - (1/7)x_1 = 5/7 \qquad \text{(12-9)}$$

Multiplying equation (12-6) by 2/7 and subtracting from equation (12-8), we obtain:

$$(13/7)x_2 + (1/7)x_1 = 23/7 \qquad \text{(12-10)}$$

Rearranging equations (12-9) and (12-10) so that the largest coefficient occurs first, we have:

$$(13/7)x_2 + (1/7)x_1 = 23/7 \qquad \text{(12-11)}$$

$$(1/7)x_2 - (1/7)x_1 = 5/7 \qquad \text{(12-12)}$$

Multiplying equation (12-11) by 1/13 and subtracting from (12-12), we have:

$$-(14/13)x_1 = 42/13$$

Our system of equations is now:

$$7x_3 + 4x_2 + 3x_1 = 6$$

$$(13/7)x_2 + (1/7)x_1 = 23/7$$

$$-(14/13)x_1 = 42/13$$

Solving them in reverse order, we obtain:

$$x_1 = -3, \qquad x_2 = 2, \qquad x_3 = 1$$

If we were doing this calculation in typical hand calculation fashion, we would have arranged things a little differently and cleared of fractions to simplify the arithmetic. The above calculation is more as it would be done on a computer, where the particular values of the coefficients are not of great importance but an orderly procedure is quite essential.

12.31   *Flow Chart and Program for the Elimination Method*

For the purposes of making it easier to write the flow chart, we will denote the constants $b_1, b_2, \ldots, b_n$ in the original set of equations, (12-1), as a_{1n+1}, $a_{2n+1}, \ldots, a_{nn+1}$. The flow chart, following the description of the process as given in the preceding section, can be written as in Figure 12–4. This involved flow chart is mostly concerned with rearranging the equations and unknowns at each step so that the largest coefficient becomes the first co-efficient in the first equation, and then unscrambling the unknowns at the end to identify them correctly. This procedure, though not essential, is advisable for accuracy purposes for equations of degree larger than four. The boxes entered by connector 2 determine the largest $|a_{ij}|$ at each stage. The boxes entered by connectors 3 and 4 rearrange the equations, and also set an identifier number d_k to keep track of which unknown has been eliminated. The boxes entered by connector 6 find the new coefficients for the system obtained by eliminating the first remaining unknown. The section entered by connector 8 solves the set of pivotal equations, identifying the answers as $y_1, y_2, \ldots, y_n$. These values are the answers, scrambled in some fashion because of the rearrangments in equations and unknowns mentioned earlier. The remainder of the flow chart, entered by connector 9, matches up the y_j's with the original unknowns, the x_i's. If the determinant of the coefficients

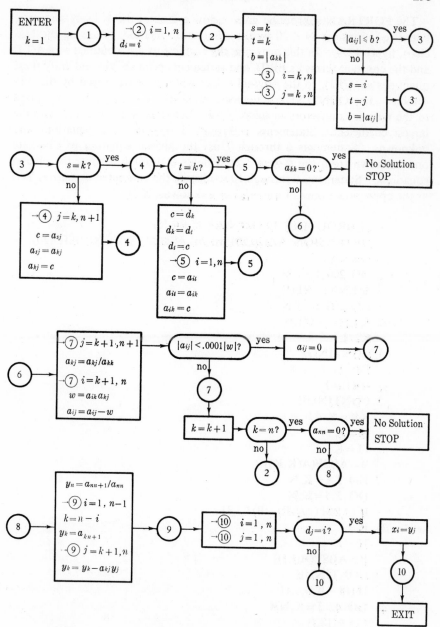

Figure 12–4: Solution of linear equations—elimination method

is zero, a system of equations of this sort ordinarily has no solution. This will be the case if a_{kk}, after rearrangement, is ever zero. The flow chart indicates the places where this condition would be discovered.

The FORTRAN subroutine given below evaluates the N-by-N system of linear equations for $N \leqslant 20$ by the elimination method, following the flow chart, figure 12–4. In this program, the coefficients are identified as AA(I,J) and the constant terms as BB(I), and statements prior to 200 reidentify these quantities as A(I,J), so the original values will not be destroyed by the subroutine. The CONTINUE statements numbered 1 through 10 correspond to the remote connectors in figure 12–4. Statements 2 through 3 find the largest coefficient. Statements 3 through 5 rearrange the equations and unknowns. Statements 6 through 7 use the pivotal equation to eliminate one unknown from the system. Statements 8 through 9 solve the pivotal equations. Statements 9 through 10 re-identify the computed quantities Y(J) as the appropriate ones of the original unknowns, X(I).

```
     SUBROUTINE ELIMIN(AA,N,BB,X)
     DIMENSION AA(20,20),BB(20),A(20,21),Y(20),X(20),ID(20)
     NN=N+1
     DO 200 I=1,N
     A(I,NN)=BB(I)
     DO 200 J=1,N
 200 A(I,J)=AA(I,J)
     K=1
   1 CONTINUE
     DO 21 I=1,N
  21 ID(I)=I
   2 CONTINUE
     KK=K+1
     IS=Kᵉ
     IT=K
     B=ABSF(A(K,K))
     DO 3 I=K,N
     DO 3 J=K,N
     IF(ABSF(A(I,J))−B)3,3,31          Goto  3
  31 IS=I
     IT=J
     B=ABSF(A(I,J))
   3 CONTINUE
     IF(IS−K)4,4,41                    Goto  4
  41 DO 42 J=K,NN
     C=A(IS,J)
     A(IS,J)=A(K,J)
  42 A(K,J)=C
   4 CONTINUE
     IF(IT−K)5,5,51
  51 IC=ID(K)
```

```
      ID(K)=ID(IT)
      ID(IT)=IC
      DO 52 I=1,N
      C=A(I,IT)
      A(I,IT)=A(I,K)
   52 A(I,K)=C
    5 CONTINUE
      IF(A(K,K))6,102,6
    6 CONTINUE
      DO 7 J=KK,NN
      A(K,J)=A(K,J)/A(K,K)
      DO 7 I=KK,N
      W=A(I,K)*A(K,J)
      A(I,J)=A(I,J)-W
      IF(ABSF(A(I,J))≥.0001*ABSF(W))71,7,7
   71 A(I,J)=0.
    7 CONTINUE
      K=KK
      IF(K-N)2,81,102
   81 IF(A(N,N))8,102,8
    8 CONTINUE
      Y(N)=A(N,NN)/A(N,N)
      NM=N-1
      DO 9 I=1,NM
      K=N-I
      KK=K+1
      Y(K)=A(K,NN)
      DO 9 J=KK,N
      Y(K)=Y(K)-A(K,J)*Y(J)
    9 CONTINUE
      DO 10 I=1,N
      DO 10 J=1,N
      IF(ID(J)-I)10,101,10
  101 X(I)=Y(J)
   10 CONTINUE
      RETURN
  102 PRINT 1000
      RETURN
 1000 FORMAT(19H NO UNIQUE SOLUTION)
      END
```

12.4 GAUSS-SEIDEL METHOD

Another and quite different method of solving a system of linear equations is the so-called Gauss-Seidel method, in which the equations (12-1) are rewritten in the following form:

$$a_{11}x_1 = b_1 - a_{12}x_2 - a_{13}x_3 \qquad - \cdots - a_{1n}x_n$$

$$a_{22}x_2 = b_2 - a_{21}x_1 - a_{23}x_3 \qquad - \cdots - a_{2n}x_n$$

$$a_{33}x_3 = b_3 - a_{31}x_1 - a_{32}x_2 - a_{34}x_4 - \cdots - a_{3n}x_n \qquad \textbf{(12-13)}$$

.

.

.

$$a_{nn}x_n = b_n - a_{n1}x_1 - a_{n2}x_2 \qquad - \cdots - a_{nn-1}x_{n-1}$$

In words, in each of the equations all but one unknown is taken to the right hand side of the equation. We then guess a set of values for $x_2, x_3, \ldots, x_n$ and substitute these in the right hand side of the first equation and solve for x_1. Then we substitute this value and the original values of $x_3, \ldots, x_n$ in the right hand side of the second equation and solve for x_2. We discard the old value of x_2 and keep this as a better one. We then substitute in the right hand side of the third equation and obtain a new value for x_3. After we have proceeded through all the equations in this fashion, we have a new set of values $x_1, x_2, \ldots, x_n$. (We must first arrange the equations so that none of the $a_{ii} = 0$.) We then start again with the first equation and find a new x_1, then a new x_2, etc. Each time through this process gives us a new, and, we hope, better set of values for $x_1, x_2, \ldots, x_n$. When the new values obtained agree with the previous set to within the accuracy we desire, we have the solution. This is an iteration process similar in nature to those discussed in Chapter X. It is not absolutely certain that this process will converge, that is, that the differences between succeeding sets of values will get smaller and smaller. We shall discuss the convergence problem more fully a little later. It is not certain, either, how many multiplications will be required to obtain the solution to a desired accuracy. Each trip through the set of equations, or iteration, requires n^2 multiplications. If $(1/3)n$ iterations happen to be required, then, the method will take about as long as the elimination method. It may take more or less time depending entirely on the speed of convergence and the accuracy required.

Example 1. Solve the system:

$$x_1 - 2x_2 = 1$$
$$x_1 + 4x_2 = 4$$

by the Gauss-Seidel method.

We write the equations as:

$$x_1 = 1 + 2x_2 \qquad \text{(12-14)}$$

$$x_2 = 1 - x_1/4 \qquad \text{(12-15)}$$

Let us take as starting values $x_1 = x_2 = 0$:

Putting $x_2 = 0$ in equation (12-14), we obtain:

$$x_1 = 1$$

Putting $x_1 = 1$ in equation (12-15), we obtain:

$$x_2 = 3/4$$

At the end of the first iteration, then, we have:

$$x_1 = 1, \qquad x_2 = 3/4$$

Putting $x_2 = 3/4$ in equation (12-14), we have:

$$x_1 = 5/2$$

Putting $x_1 = 5/2$ in equation (12-15), we have:

$$x_2 = 3/8$$

At the end of the second iteration, then, we have:

$$x_1 = 5/2, \qquad x_2 = 3/8$$

We can continue this process. The results for the first several steps, starting from the beginning, are:

x_1	x_2
0	0
1	.75
2.5	.375
1.75	.5625
2.125	.46875
1.9375	.515625
2.03125	.4921875
1.984375	.51390625

It is easily verified from the equation that the correct solution is $x_1 = 2$, $x_2 = 1/2$. This solution is slowly converging toward those values.

Example 2. Solve the system:

$$x_1 + 4x_2 = 4$$

$$x_1 - 2x_2 = 1$$

by the Gauss-Seidel method.

This is the same problem as Example 1, with the equations reversed. We write the equations as:

$$x_1 = 4 - 4x_2$$

$$x_2 = -1/2 + x_1/2$$

Then the successive iterations give the following values:

x_1	x_2
0	0
4	1.5
-2	-1
8	3.5
-10	-5.5
26	12.5
-46	-23.5

It is clear that the process is diverging, and the solution will not be obtained.

Example 3. Apply the Gauss-Seidel to Example 1, Section 12.3.

The equations are:

$$2x_1 + 3x_2 + 5x_3 = 3$$

$$3x_1 + 4x_2 + 7x_3 = 6$$

$$x_1 + 3x_4 + 2x_3 = 5$$

We write them as:

$$2x_1 = 5 - 3x_2 - 5x_3$$

$$4x_2 = 6 - 3x_1 - 7x_3$$

$$2x_3 = 5 - x_1 - 3x_2$$

Successive iterations give (to four decimal places):

x_1	x_2	x_3
0	0	0
2.5	−.375	1.8125
−1.4688	.5703	2.3789
−4.3027	.5640	3.8054
−7.8595	.7352	5.3270
−11.9203	1.1180	6.7831

In Section 12.3, we found that the solution to this system was:

$$x_1 = -3, \qquad x_2 = 2, \qquad x_3 = 1$$

Our iteration scheme is not converging toward those values.

12.41   Convergence of the Gauss-Seidel Method

Some insight into the convergence problem can be obtained by following Examples 1 and 2 of Section 12.4 in graphical form. Figure 12–5 illustrates the scheme followed in Example 1. Starting at the point P_0, we change x_1

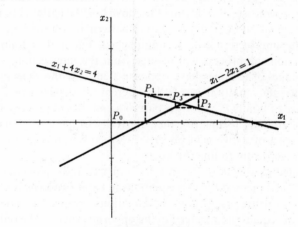

Figure 12–5

(that is, move horizontally) to arrive on the line $x_1 - 2x_2 = 1$, and then change x_2 (that is, move vertically) to arrive on the line $x_1 + 4x_2 = 4$, bringing us to the point P_1. This is the point given by the first iteration. On the second iteration we move horizontally, then vertically to arrive at P_2. On the third we move horizontally, then vertically to arrive at P_3, etc. It is clear from the figure that this process is bringing us closer and closer to the true point of intersection.

Figure 12–6 illustrates the scheme followed in Example 2. The same straight lines are involved, but this time we always move horizontally to reach the line $x_1 + 4x_2 = 4$ and vertically to reach the line $x_1 - 2x_2 = 1$. The points P_0, P_1, P_2, ... , are the results of the successive iterations in this case.

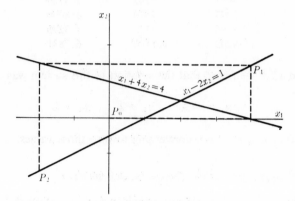

Figure 12–6

It appears that graphically the Gauss-Seidel method for two equations in two unknowns consists of following the above boxlike pattern about the point of intersection of the two lines: if this pattern is followed in the correct direction the intersection will be approached, but if it is followed in the wrong direction the process will diverge from the intersection. This is the case if the slopes of the lines have opposite signs. If the signs of the slopes are the same, the situation is a little different, as depicted in Figure 12–7. The sequence of points P_0, P_1, P_2 is part of a convergent process, in which we proceed horizontally to line (*b*), then vertically to line (*a*). The points P_0, P_1', P_2' are part of a divergent process, in which we proceed horizontally to line (*a*) then vertically to line (*b*).

As indicated by the above figures, the situation regarding convergence for the Gauss-Seidel method for two equations in two unknowns is as follows:

The process will converge for the equations arranged in one order and diverge for the equations arranged in the opposite order. The only exception occurs when the equations represent perpendicular lines, in which case the process will not converge for either arrangement. It is interesting to note that, contrary to our experience with iteration methods in the preceding chapters, the convergence or nonconvergence for these linear equations does *not* depend on choice of initial estimate.

For larger systems of equations the situation becomes much more complex. The necessary and sufficient conditions for convergence are known, but are not easily expressed in a very usable form. Sometimes a rearrangement of the equations will produce convergence, but this is not at all guaranteed.

The likelihood of convergence is usually increased if the equations are re-arranged so that the coefficients $a_{11}, a_{22}, a_{33}, \ldots, a_{nn}$ which appear on the left hand side in the system as written in Section 12.4 are the largest coefficients in absolute value. In fact convergence is assured in this case if in each equation the absolute value of the coefficient a_{ii} is larger than the sum of the

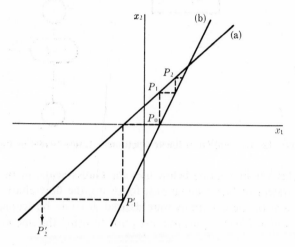

Figure 12-7

absolute values of the remaining coefficients. This condition is not often met. In fact, as in Example 3 of Section 12.4, it is often impossible even to write all the equations with largest terms on the left hand side.

12.42 Flow Chart and Program for the Gauss-Seidel Method

The flow chart in Figure 12-8 describes the Gauss-Seidel method. This flow chart uses the equations arranged just as they are, with no attempt to rearrange the equations to increase the likelihood of convergence. If desired, it could be preceded by another section of flow chart which would rearrange the equations in attempt to enhance the likelihood of convergence. In order to cut down on the number of divisions required, each of the equations is first divided through by the coefficient a_{ii}, so that in the set of new coefficients, c_{ij}, the c_{ii}'s are all one. This flow chart computes at each iteration a quantity:

$$E = \sum_{i=1}^{n} |x_i^{new} - x_i^{old}|,$$

and when this quantity becomes smaller than the given number d, the iteration stops. Note that, in the way the expression for P is written, P is precisely $x_i^{new} - x_i^{old}$.

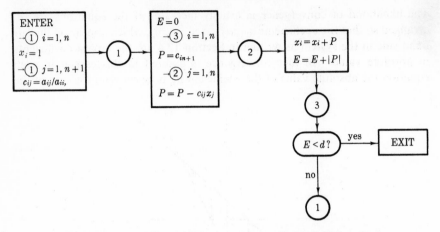

Figure 12–8: Solution of linear equations—Gauss-Seidel method

The FORTRAN subroutine below uses the Gauss-Seidel method to solve an N-by-N system of linear equations, following the flow chart. Again, if a rearrangement of the equations were desired, it could be accomplished by using a subroutine for that purpose just prior to using the one given below:

```
      SUBROUTINE GAUSID(A,N,B,X,ERR)
      DIMENSION A(20,20), B(20),C(20,21),X(20)
      K=0
      NN=N+1
      DO 11 I=1,N
      IF(A(I,I))12,6,12
   12 X(I)=1.
      C(I,NN)=B(I)/A(I,I)
      DO 11 J=1,N
   11 C(I,J)=A(I,J)/A(I,I)
    1 CONTINUE
      E=0.
      DO 3 I=1,N
      P=C(I,NN)
      DO 2 J=1,N
      P=P-C(I,J)*X(J)
    2 CONTINUE
      X(I)=X(I)+P
      E=E+ABSF(P)
    3 CONTINUE
      IF(E-ERR)4,4,5
    4 RETURN
    5 K=K+1
```

```
    IF(100 − K)6,1,1
  6 PRINT 1000
    RETURN
1000 FORMAT(25H GAUSID DOES NOT CONVERGE)
    END
```

EXERCISE XXII

1. Following the flow chart of Section 12.22, evaluate the following determinants:

a.
$$\begin{vmatrix} 1 & 3 & 2 \\ 2 & -1 & 4 \\ 4 & 1 & -3 \end{vmatrix}$$

b.
$$\begin{vmatrix} 2 & 0 & 1 \\ 0 & 2 & 0 \\ 1 & 0 & 3 \end{vmatrix}$$

c.
$$\begin{vmatrix} 1 & 2 & -1 & 3 \\ 2 & 0 & -1 & 2 \\ 1 & 4 & -2 & -1 \\ 3 & 0 & 0 & 2 \end{vmatrix}$$

d.
$$\begin{vmatrix} 1 & 0 & 0 & 1 \\ 0 & 2 & 0 & 3 \\ 1 & 0 & 4 & 2 \\ 3 & 0 & 0 & 1 \end{vmatrix}$$

2. Following the flow chart, Figure 12–4, solve the following systems of equations.

a. $x + y = 2$
    $x - y = 4$

b. $x + 2y = 7$
    $4x + y = 5$

c. $2x + 3y + z = 2$
    $x + 2y - 4z = 3$
    $4x - 2y + z = -2$

d. $x + y + z = 4$
    $3x - y - z = 1$
    $x + 2y - z = 5$

3. Following the flow chart, Figure 12–8, perform the first four iterations for the following systems of equations:

a. $2x + y = 3$
    $x + 2y = 3$

b. $4x - y = 6$
    $x + 3y = -5$

c. $3x + 2y + z = 5$
    $2x + 5y + 4z = 8$
    $x + 4y + 6z = 4$

d. $x + 2y + 4z = 6$
    $3x + y + 2z = 5$
    $2x + 4y + z = 4$

4. Write a FORTRAN program that will input a determinant up to order 20, call subroutine DETERM of Section 12.22, and print the result.

5. Write a FORTRAN program that will input a system of linear equations up to size 20 × 20, call subroutine ELIMIN of Section 12.31 to solve them, and print the result.

6. a. Write a FORTRAN subroutine which will rearrange a set of linear equations, for use of subroutine GAUSID of Section 12.42, so that after rearrangement:

$$a_{ii} \geqslant a_{ki} \qquad \text{for } k > i$$

b. Show that your subroutine will correctly arrange the equations:

$$x_1 + 8x_2 + x_3 = 10$$
$$x_1 + x_2 + 7x_3 = 9$$
$$9x_1 + x_2 + x_3 = 11$$

so that the Gauss-Seidel method will converge.

c. Explain what may go wrong with this method of arrangement if some of the coefficients are zero.

CHAPTER XIII *Matrices*

13.1 INTRODUCTION

In all the methods of solving linear equations by computer, we have seen that only the coefficients and the constants appear within the machine. The formalism of writing down the unknowns x_1, x_2, etc., when we write the equations longhand, merely serves to identify the proper locations of the coefficients and constants. In other words, the solution of the system of equations:

$$a_{11}x_1 + a_{12}x_1 + \cdots + a_{1n}x_n = b_1$$

$$a_{21}x_1 + a_{22}x_2 + \cdots + a_{2n}x_n = b_2$$

.

.

.

$$a_{n1}x_1 + a_{n2}x_2 + \cdots + a_{nn}x_n = b_n$$

is determined completely by the array of coefficients:

$$\begin{pmatrix} a_{11} & a_{12} & \cdot & \cdot & \cdot & a_{1n} \\ a_{21} & a_{22} & \cdot & \cdot & \cdot & a_{2n} \\ \cdot & & & & & \\ \cdot & & & & & \\ \cdot & & & & & \\ a_{n1} & a_{n2} & \cdot & \cdot & \cdot & a_{nn} \end{pmatrix}$$

and the array of constants:

$$\begin{pmatrix} b_1 \\ b_2 \\ \cdot \\ \cdot \\ \cdot \\ b_n \end{pmatrix}$$

If we are given any two such arrays, we can write the set of equations they represent. If we were to change the numerical value of any number in one of these arrays, a different set of equations would be represented. Further, if we were to interchange the position of any two of the numbers, a still different set of equations would be represented. All this suggests that it may be useful to consider these arrays of numbers as separate entities, establish rules for manipulating them, and perhaps free ourselves somewhat from the repetitious writing of the basically nonessential symbols $x_1 +, x_2 +,$ ... $x_3 +$, etc. Considerations such as these have led to the definition of a matrix as an array of numbers, and to the development of an "algebra" of matrices, a set of rules for combining matrices to form other matrices. Once developed, matrix algebra has come to have far-reaching applications, completely apart from systems of linear equations.

13.2 DEFINITIONS AND ELEMENTARY OPERATIONS

A matrix is a rectangular array of quantities or numbers, such as:

$$a_{11} \quad a_{12} \quad a_{13}$$

$$a_{21} \quad a_{22} \quad a_{23}$$

$$a_{31} \quad a_{32} \quad a_{33}$$

In order to distinguish a matrix from a determinant, which also frequently *looks like* an array of numbers, it is customary to enclose a matrix in square brackets, or large parentheses, or double bars, as:

$$\begin{bmatrix} a_{11} & a_{12} & a_{13} \\ a_{21} & a_{22} & a_{23} \\ a_{31} & a_{32} & a_{33} \end{bmatrix}, \quad \begin{pmatrix} a_{11} & a_{12} & a_{13} \\ a_{21} & a_{22} & a_{23} \\ a_{31} & a_{32} & a_{33} \end{pmatrix}, \quad \text{or} \quad \begin{Vmatrix} a_{11} & a_{12} & a_{13} \\ a_{21} & a_{22} & a_{23} \\ a_{31} & a_{32} & a_{33} \end{Vmatrix}$$

A determinant is usually written between single bars, as:

$$\begin{vmatrix} a_{11} & a_{12} & a_{13} \\ a_{21} & a_{22} & a_{23} \\ a_{31} & a_{32} & a_{33} \end{vmatrix}$$

This determinant only looks like an array. Really the symbol only stands for a single quantity, which is obtained by multiplying and adding the individual a_{ij}'s in the manner described in Section 12.21. The matrix, on the other hand, has no single numerical value, but is instead the entire array. We shall be using a single letter or symbol to stand for a matrix, such as:

$$A = \begin{pmatrix} a_{11} & a_{12} & \cdot & \cdot & \cdot & a_{1n} \\ a_{21} & a_{22} & \cdot & \cdot & \cdot & a_{2n} \\ \cdot & & & & & \\ \cdot & & & & & \\ \cdot & & & & & \\ a_{m1} & a_{m2} & \cdot & \cdot & \cdot & a_{mn} \end{pmatrix}$$

When we do this, it is important to remember that A is not a number, and so does not act like a number, i.e., it does not obey the ordinary laws of algebra.

Occasionally, we will be interested in the value of a determinant made up of exactly the same elements as some square matrix A. When we do we shall refer to it as the determinant of the matrix A.

A matrix of m rows and n columns is an m-by-n matrix. If $m = n$, the matrix is a square matrix of order m.

The sum of the diagonal elements of a square matrix is called the "trace" of the matrix, $\mathrm{tr}A = a_{11} + a_{22} + \cdots + a_{nn}$.

If a matrix consists of a single column it is called a column matrix, or sometimes a column vector.

If all the elements in the main diagonal of a square matrix are ones, and all the other elements are zeros, the matrix is called a unit matrix, or identity matrix. Thus:

$$\begin{pmatrix} 1 & 0 & 0 \\ 0 & 1 & 0 \\ 0 & 0 & 1 \end{pmatrix}$$

is a unit matrix of order 3. Unit matrices of any order are usually denoted by the symbol *I*.

If all the elements are zero, the matrix is called a zero matrix.

Two matrices *A* and *B* are said to be equal if:

(*1*)   They have the same number of rows.

(*2*)   They have the same number of columns.

(*3*)   Each pair of corresponding elements are equal.

13.21   Addition and Subtraction of Matrices

The operations of addition and subtraction are defined for two matrices *A* and *B* if:

(*1*)   They have the same number of rows.

(*2*)   They have the same number of columns.

The sum of two matrices is the matrix obtained by adding corresponding pairs of elements. Thus if:

$$A = \begin{pmatrix} a_{11} & a_{12} & a_{13} \\ a_{21} & a_{22} & a_{23} \\ a_{31} & a_{32} & a_{33} \end{pmatrix} \quad \text{and} \quad B = \begin{pmatrix} b_{11} & b_{12} & b_{13} \\ b_{21} & b_{22} & b_{23} \\ b_{31} & b_{32} & b_{33} \end{pmatrix}$$

then:

$$A + B = \begin{pmatrix} a_{11} + b_{11} & a_{12} + b_{12} & a_{13} + b_{13} \\ a_{21} + b_{21} & a_{22} + b_{22} & a_{23} + b_{23} \\ a_{31} + b_{31} & a_{32} + b_{32} & a_{33} + b_{33} \end{pmatrix}$$

The difference $A - B$ is the matrix obtained by subtracting the elements of *B* from the corresponding elements of *A*.

$$A - B = \begin{pmatrix} a_{11} - b_{11} & a_{12} - b_{12} & a_{13} - b_{13} \\ a_{21} - b_{21} & a_{22} - b_{22} & a_{23} - b_{23} \\ a_{31} - b_{31} & a_{32} - b_{32} & a_{33} - b_{33} \end{pmatrix}$$

Example 1.   Find $A + B$ and $A - B$, where:

$$A = \begin{pmatrix} 3 & 0 & -2 \\ 1 & 3 & 1 \end{pmatrix}, \quad B = \begin{pmatrix} 2 & 1 & 2 \\ -1 & 3 & -2 \end{pmatrix}$$

SOLUTION:

$$A + B = \begin{pmatrix} 5 & 1 & 0 \\ 0 & 6 & -1 \end{pmatrix}, \qquad A - B = \begin{pmatrix} 1 & -1 & -4 \\ 2 & 0 & 3 \end{pmatrix}$$

Example 2. Find $A + B$ and $A - B$, where:

$$A = \begin{pmatrix} 3 & 0 & -2 \\ 1 & 3 & 2 \end{pmatrix}, \qquad B = \begin{pmatrix} 2 & -1 \\ 1 & 3 \\ 2 & -2 \end{pmatrix}$$

SOLUTION: Since there are not the same number of rows or columns in A and B, they cannot be added or subtracted. The symbols $A + B$ and $A - B$ are meaningless in this case.

Example 3. Given two matrices A and B, each with N columns and M rows, write FORTRAN statements which would form the sum, $C = A + B$.

SOLUTION: The matrix A can be represented by a doubly subscripted variable $A(I,J)$, where I runs from 1 to M and J runs from 1 to N. The same is true for B and C. Then the required FORTRAN statements are:

```
    DO 20 I=1,M
    DO 20 J=1,N
20  C(I,J)=A(I,J)+B(I,J)
```

A total of N × M additions are required to obtain C.

As a direct extension of addition, it would be natural to be able to say:

$$A + A = 2A$$

This leads to the definition of multiplication of a matrix by a constant as follows:

A constant times a matrix is the matrix obtained by multiplying *all* elements of the original matrix by the constant.

13.22 Multiplication of the Matrices

At first acquaintance, the operation of multiplication of two matrices seems to be defined in a most peculiar way. There are very good reasons for choosing to call this seemingly awkward process "multiplication," and these will appear shortly.

The product *AB* of two matrices, *A* and *B*, is defined only if the number of *columns* in *A* is equal to the number of *rows* in *B*. In all other cases the product is undefined. If the number of columns in *A* is equal to the number of rows in *B*, then *A* and *B* are said to be "conformable" in the order *AB*.

The product *AB* of two conformable matrices is itself a matrix, whose elements are found according to the following rule:

The element in the *i*th row and the *j*th column of the product is the sum of the products by pairs of the elements of the *i*th row of *A* and *j*th column of *B*.

Example 1. If:

$$A = \begin{pmatrix} 1 & 2 \\ 3 & -1 \end{pmatrix}, \quad B = \begin{pmatrix} 3 & -2 \\ 2 & 1 \end{pmatrix}$$

find **AB**.

SOLUTION: Since *A* has 2 columns and *B* has 2 rows, *A* and *B* are conformable in the order *AB*, so the product is indeed defined. To find the element in the first row, first column of the product matrix, we take the first row of *A*, which is:

$$1 \quad 2$$

and the first column of *B*, which is:

$$3$$

$$2$$

and form the sum of the products by pairs:

$$1 \times 3 + 2 \times 2 = 7$$

Hence 7 is the element in the first row, first column of the product.

In like manner, the element in the first row and second column of the product is obtained from combining the first row of *A* with the second column of *B*, thus:

$$1 \times (-2) + 2 \times 1 = 0$$

and for the second row, first column:

$$3 \times 3 + (-1) \times 2 = 7$$

and the second row, second column:

$$3 \times (-2) + (-1) \times 1 = -7$$

Hence the product is:

$$\begin{pmatrix} 1 & 2 \\ 3 & -1 \end{pmatrix} \begin{pmatrix} 3 & -2 \\ 2 & 1 \end{pmatrix} = \begin{pmatrix} 7 & 0 \\ 7 & -7 \end{pmatrix}$$

Example 2. If:

$$A = \begin{pmatrix} 1 & 3 & 1 \\ -2 & 1 & -1 \end{pmatrix}, \qquad B = \begin{pmatrix} 1 \\ 2 \\ 3 \end{pmatrix}$$

find **AB**.

SOLUTION: Since *A* has 3 columns and *B* has 3 rows, they are conformable in the order *AB*. We can expedite the process of finding the product by writing the two matrices side by side, and then going across a row of *A* and down a column of *B* forming products by pairs, thus:

$$\begin{pmatrix} 1 & 3 & 1 \\ -2 & 1 & -1 \end{pmatrix} \begin{pmatrix} 1 \\ 2 \\ 3 \end{pmatrix} = \begin{pmatrix} 1 \times 1 + 3 \times 2 + 1 \times 3 \\ -2 \times 1 + 1 \times 2 - 1 \times 3 \end{pmatrix} = \begin{pmatrix} 10 \\ -3 \end{pmatrix}$$

Example 3. For the matrices **A** and **B** of Example 2, find **BA**.

SOLUTION: Since *B* has 1 column and *A* has 2 rows, they are not conformable in the order *BA*. The product *BA* is not defined!

Example 4. If:

$$A = \begin{pmatrix} a_{11} & a_{12} & \cdot & \cdot & \cdot & a_{1n} \\ a_{21} & a_{22} & \cdot & \cdot & \cdot & a_{2n} \\ \cdot & & & & & \\ \cdot & & & & & \\ \cdot & & & & & \\ a_{m1} & a_{m2} & \cdot & \cdot & \cdot & a_{mn} \end{pmatrix}, \qquad B = \begin{pmatrix} b_{11} & b_{12} & \cdot & \cdot & \cdot & b_{1l} \\ b_{21} & b_{22} & \cdot & \cdot & \cdot & b_{2l} \\ \cdot & & & & & \\ \cdot & & & & & \\ \cdot & & & & & \\ b_{n1} & b_{n2} & \cdot & \cdot & \cdot & b_{nl} \end{pmatrix}$$

and:

$$AB = C$$

write a formula for finding c_{ij}, the element in the ith row and jth column of C.

SOLUTION: The ith row of A is:

$$a_{i1} \qquad a_{i2} \qquad \cdots \qquad a_{in}$$

and the jth column of B is:

$$b_{1j}$$

$$b_{2j}$$

$$\cdot$$

$$\cdot$$

$$\cdot$$

$$b_{nj}$$

and the sum of the products by pairs gives:

$$c_{ij} = a_{i1}b_{1j} + a_{i2}b_{2j} + \cdots + a_{in}b_{nj}$$

or in more abbreviated form:

$$c_{ij} = \sum_{k=1}^{n} a_{ik}b_{kj}$$

Example 5.   Given matrix A with M rows and N columns and matrix B with N rows and L columns, write a set of FORTRAN statements which will form the product $C = AB$.

SOLUTION: A suitable set of statements is:

```
        DO 10 I=1,M
        DO 10 J=1,L
        C(I,J)=0.
        DO 10 K=1,N
     10 C(I,J)=C(I,J)+A(I,K)*B(K,J)
```

We note that statement 10 is in three DO loops, and will be performed

$N \times M \times L$ times, or $N \times M \times L$ multiplications are required to find the product matrix C.

Example 6. If:

$$A = \begin{pmatrix} a_{11} & a_{12} & a_{13} \\ a_{21} & a_{22} & a_{23} \\ a_{31} & a_{32} & a_{33} \end{pmatrix}, \qquad x = \begin{pmatrix} x_1 \\ x_2 \\ x_3 \end{pmatrix}$$

write the product Ax.

SOLUTION:

$$Ax = \begin{pmatrix} a_{11}x_1 + a_{12}x_2 + a_{13}x_3 \\ a_{21}x_1 + a_{22}x_2 + a_{23}x_3 \\ a_{31}x_1 + a_{32}x_2 + a_{33}x_3 \end{pmatrix}$$

Note that this product Ax is actually a column vector, having three elements.

Example 7. Write the system of linear equations:

$$a_{11}x_1 + a_{12}x_2 + a_{13}x_3 = b_1$$
$$a_{21}x_1 + a_{22}x_2 + a_{23}x_3 = b_2$$
$$a_{31}x_1 + a_{32}x_2 + a_{33}x_3 = b_3$$

in matrix form.

SOLUTION: From Example 6, if we define:

$$A = \begin{pmatrix} a_{11} & a_{12} & a_{13} \\ a_{21} & a_{22} & a_{23} \\ a_{31} & a_{32} & a_{33} \end{pmatrix}, \qquad x = \begin{pmatrix} x_1 \\ x_2 \\ x_3 \end{pmatrix}$$

then the left hand sides of the equations above are just the three elements of the column vector Ax. Now let us define the column vector:

$$b = \begin{pmatrix} b_1 \\ b_2 \\ b_3 \end{pmatrix}$$

We recall that two matrices are equal if and only if every pair of corresponding elements are equal. Thus, the statement:

$$Ax = b$$

is a matrix equation. The expressions on each side of the equals sign are matrices. The equation means that:

(*1*) The first element of Ax, that is, $a_{11}x_1 + a_{12}x_2 + a_{13}x_3$, is equal to b_1.

(*2*) The second element of Ax, that is, $a_{21}x_1 + a_{22}x_2 + a_{23}x_3$, is equal to b_2.

(*3*) The third element of Ax, that is, $a_{31}x_1 + a_{32}x_2 + a_{33}x_3$, is equal to b_3.

Hence the matrix equation:

$$Ax = b$$

says exactly the same thing as the system of linear equations above.

We see from Examples 6 and 7 that any system of linear equations, with any number of unknowns, can be represented by a matrix equation:

$$Ax = b$$

where A is a matrix and x and b are column vectors of the correct order. This simple expression is one of the several happy results of the seemingly odd definition of multiplication.

13.23   Laws of Matrix Algebra

We have defined three operations with matrices and have given them the names "addition," "subtraction," and "multiplication," names we use in the ordinary algebra of numbers. Actually this is a little dangerous, since it suggests that these new matrix operations will obey the same rules as the ordinary arithmetic operations, and we really have no right to expect that they will do so.

The fundamental laws of ordinary algebra are the following:

I.   Addition is *commutative*. $a + b = b + a$, i.e., if we add b to a, or a to b, we will get the same result.

II.   Addition is *associative*. $(a + b) + c = a + (b + c)$, i.e., if we add $a + b$, and then add c to this sum, we get the same result as if we add b and c first, and then add a to the sum.

III.   Multiplication is *distributive* with respect to addition. $a(b + c) = ab + ac$, i.e., if we add b to c and then multiply by a, we get the same result as if we multiply a by b, multiply a by c, and then add the result.

IV.   Multiplication is *commutative*. $ab = ba$, i.e., if we multiply a by b or b by a, we get the same result.

V. Multiplication is *associative*. $(ab)c = a(bc)$. If we take the product ab and multiply by c we get the same answer as if we take the product bc and multiply by a.

When these laws for the algebra of numbers are investigated for matrices, it is found that they all hold *except* law IV above, the commutative law for multiplication. As was seen in Examples 2 and 3 of Section 13.22, it is possible to have two matrices whose product AB could be found but whose product BA was not even defined.

In summary, then, we can say that, in expressions involving sums, differences, and products of matrices, we can use the same laws for combining these operations as for ordinary numbers except that the order of any two matrices in a product cannot be reversed. In a matrix equation, we may add the same matrix to both sides or subtract the same matrix from both sides without changing the equality. We also may *multiply* both sides by the same matrix, provided that:

(*1*) The matrix is conformable with those by which it is to be multiplied.

(*2*) The order of multiplication is made the same on both sides of the equation.

Example 1. If A, B, and C are square matrices of order n, and if:

$$A + B = C$$

solve for A.

Subtracting B from both sides, we have:

$$A = C - B$$

Example 2. If A; B, C, and D are square matrices of order n, and if $A = B + C$, find AD and DA.

Multiplying the equation:

$$A = B + C$$

on the right by D, we have:

$$AD = (B + C)D = BD + CD$$

Multiplying the above equation on the left by D, we have:

$$DA = D(B + C) = DB + DC$$

13.24   Matrix Inversion

We have given definitions and rules for the addition, subtraction, and multiplication of matrices which parallel to some extent the rules of ordinary algebra.   As yet we have not mentioned division, for the very good reason that division as such is not defined for matrices.   There is another operation which serves a somewhat analogous purpose, however.   That operation is the "inversion" of a matrix.

In ordinary algebra, b/a stands for the number which, when multiplied by a, gives b.   Thus if $ax = b$, we can say that $x = b/a$.   Instead of treating division in this manner, we could define an "inverse" of a number as follows: For any number "a," the inverse, a^{-1}, is that number which, when multiplied by "a" gives 1.   Every nonzero number has a unique inverse, for example, the inverse of 2 is .5, and .5 is the *only* inverse of 2.   Then if we have $ax = b$, we do not even have to have a process of division in order to find x, for we can multiply both sides of the equation by a^{-1}, giving:

$$a^{-1}ax = a^{-1}b, \qquad \text{or } x = a^{-1}b$$

For square matrices, we define the inverse in a manner analogous to that above.   For a square matrix A of order n, the inverse matrix, A^{-1} is that matrix which when multiplied by A gives the identity matrix of order n; that is:

$$AA^{-1} = I$$

Example 1.   Show that the inverse of:

$$\begin{pmatrix} 2 & -1 \\ -1 & 1 \end{pmatrix}$$

is:

$$\begin{pmatrix} 1 & 1 \\ 1 & 2 \end{pmatrix}$$

SOLUTION: We form the product:

$$\begin{pmatrix} 2 & -1 \\ -1 & 1 \end{pmatrix}\begin{pmatrix} 1 & 1 \\ 1 & 2 \end{pmatrix} = \begin{pmatrix} 1 & 0 \\ 0 & 1 \end{pmatrix}$$

Since the product is the identity matrix, the second matrix is indeed the inverse of the first.

It can be shown that any square matrix A has a unique inverse if and only if its determinant is different from zero.   It can also be shown that A

commutes with its inverse; that is:

$$AA^{-1} = A^{-1}A = I$$

The inverse is not defined for nonsquare matrices.

A formula for the inverse of a matrix A can be found as follows. Consider the set of linear equations:

$$y_1 = a_{11}x_1 + a_{12}x_2 + \cdots + a_{1n}x_n$$

$$y_2 = a_{21}x_1 + a_{22}x_2 + \cdots + a_{2n}x_n$$

.

.   (13-2)

.

$$y_n = a_{n1}x_1 + a_{n2}x_2 + \cdots + a_{nn}x_n$$

connecting one set of variables $x_1, x_2, \ldots, x_n$ with another set $y_1, y_2, \ldots, y_n$. In matrix form we can write this set of equations as:

$$y = Ax$$

where:

$$y = \begin{pmatrix} y_1 \\ y_2 \\ \cdot \\ \cdot \\ \cdot \\ y_n \end{pmatrix} \qquad x = \begin{pmatrix} x_1 \\ x_2 \\ \cdot \\ \cdot \\ \cdot \\ x_n \end{pmatrix}$$

If we multiply this set of equations by A^{-1}, we obtain:

$$A^{-1}y = A^{-1}Ax$$

or

$$A^{-1}y = Ix = x$$

Hence the elements of A^{-1} are just the coefficients of the y's if we solve the set of equations (13-2) for the x's in terms of the y's.

One way of solving for the x's in terms of the y's is to apply Cramer's Rule. We have, for example:

$$x_1 = \frac{\begin{vmatrix} y_1 & a_{12} & \cdot & \cdot & \cdot & a_{1n} \\ y_2 & a_{22} & \cdot & \cdot & \cdot & a_{2n} \\ \cdot & \cdot & & & & \cdot \\ \cdot & \cdot & & & & \cdot \\ y_n & a_{n2} & \cdot & \cdot & \cdot & a_{nn} \end{vmatrix}}{\begin{vmatrix} a_{11} & a_{12} & \cdot & \cdot & \cdot & a_{1n} \\ a_{21} & a_{22} & & & & a_{2n} \\ \cdot & \cdot & & & & \cdot \\ \cdot & \cdot & & & & \cdot \\ a_{n1} & a_{n2} & \cdot & \cdot & \cdot & a_{nn} \end{vmatrix}}$$

If we evaluate the determinant in the numerator by expanding by minors down the first column, we have:

$$x_1 = \frac{A_{11}y_1 + A_{21}y_2 + \cdots + A_{n1}y_n}{\det A}$$

where by A_{ij} we mean the cofactor of a_{ij} in the determinant $\det A$, i.e., the determinant obtained by crossing out the row and columns containing a_{ij} in $\det A$, and multiplying by $(-1)^{i+j}$. In like manner by Cramer's Rule:

$$x_2 = \frac{A_{12}y_1 + A_{22}y_2 + \cdots + A_{n2}y_n}{\det A}$$

If we solve for all the x_i's by Cramer's Rule in similar fashion, we may write the result in matrix form as:

$$
\begin{pmatrix} x_1 \\ x_2 \\ \cdot \\ \cdot \\ \cdot \\ x_n \end{pmatrix} = \begin{pmatrix} \dfrac{A_{11}}{\det A} & \dfrac{A_{21}}{\det A} & \cdots & \dfrac{A_{n1}}{\det A} \\[2mm] \dfrac{A_{12}}{\det A} & \dfrac{A_{22}}{\det A} & \cdots & \dfrac{A_{n2}}{\det A} \\[2mm] \cdot & & & \\ \cdot & & & \\ \cdot & & & \\ \dfrac{A_{1n}}{\det A} & \dfrac{A_{2n}}{\det A} & & \dfrac{A_{nn}}{\det A} \end{pmatrix} \begin{pmatrix} y_1 \\ y_2 \\ y_3 \\ \cdot \\ \cdot \\ y_n \end{pmatrix}
$$

and the large square matrix is the inverse of A. By studying it, we can see that the rules for finding the inverse of a matrix A can be summarized as follows:

1.   Interchange rows and columns.
2.   Replace each element by its cofactor.
3.   Divide by the determinant.

Example 2. Find the inverse of the matrix:

$$
\begin{pmatrix} 1 & 2 & 1 \\ -1 & 0 & 2 \\ 0 & 1 & 1 \end{pmatrix}
$$

SOLUTION:

STEP 1:   We interchange rows and columns, obtaining:

$$
\begin{pmatrix} 1 & -1 & 0 \\ 2 & 0 & 1 \\ 1 & 2 & 1 \end{pmatrix}
$$

STEP 2:   We replace each element by its cofactor, obtaining:

$$
\begin{pmatrix}
\begin{vmatrix} 0 & 1 \\ 2 & 1 \end{vmatrix} & -\begin{vmatrix} 2 & 1 \\ 1 & 1 \end{vmatrix} & \begin{vmatrix} 2 & 0 \\ 1 & 2 \end{vmatrix} \\[12pt]
-\begin{vmatrix} -1 & 0 \\ 2 & 1 \end{vmatrix} & \begin{vmatrix} 1 & 0 \\ 1 & 1 \end{vmatrix} & -\begin{vmatrix} 1 & -1 \\ 1 & 2 \end{vmatrix} \\[12pt]
\begin{vmatrix} -1 & 0 \\ 0 & 1 \end{vmatrix} & -\begin{vmatrix} 1 & 0 \\ 2 & 1 \end{vmatrix} & \begin{vmatrix} 1 & -1 \\ 2 & 0 \end{vmatrix}
\end{pmatrix}
=
\begin{pmatrix}
-2 & -1 & 4 \\
1 & 1 & -3 \\
-1 & -1 & 2
\end{pmatrix}
$$

STEP 3:   We divide each element by the value of the determinant, which is -1, obtaining as the inverse:

$$
\begin{pmatrix}
2 & 1 & -4 \\
-1 & -1 & 3 \\
1 & 1 & -2
\end{pmatrix}
$$

The procedure just given could be programmed for a computer to obtain inverses of matrices.   However, as is apparent from the derivation, this method is analogous to solving a set of linear equations by Cramer's Rule, which is a rather slow process.   It requires the evaluation of one nth order determinant and n $n-$ 1st order determinants.   From Section 12.21, this involves about n^4 multiplications.   A considerably more rapid way of obtaining the inverse of a matrix A is to solve the set of equations (13-2) by the elimination method.   As in Section 12.3, accuracy is frequently improved if at each stage the equations are rearranged to place the largest coefficient in the lead position, a step usually worth while for large systems despite the increased bookkeeping introduced.

Example 3.   Invert the matrix:

$$
\begin{pmatrix}
1 & 2 & 1 \\
-1 & 0 & 2 \\
0 & 1 & 1
\end{pmatrix}
$$

by the elimination method.

SOLUTION: We will write the steps in matrix notation, but it may help the reader if he rewrites each in terms of ordinary algebraic equations.   Consider the matrix equation:

$$
\begin{pmatrix} 1 & 2 & 1 \\ -1 & 0 & 2 \\ 0 & 1 & 1 \end{pmatrix}
\begin{pmatrix} x_1 \\ x_2 \\ x_3 \end{pmatrix} =
\begin{pmatrix} 1 & 0 & 0 \\ 0 & 1 & 0 \\ 0 & 0 & 1 \end{pmatrix}
\begin{pmatrix} y_1 \\ y_2 \\ y_3 \end{pmatrix}
$$

It can also be written:

$$
\begin{pmatrix} 2 & 1 & 1 \\ 0 & -1 & 2 \\ 1 & 0 & 1 \end{pmatrix}
\begin{pmatrix} x_2 \\ x_1 \\ x_3 \end{pmatrix} =
\begin{pmatrix} 1 & 0 & 0 \\ 0 & 1 & 0 \\ 0 & 0 & 1 \end{pmatrix}
\begin{pmatrix} y_1 \\ y_2 \\ y_3 \end{pmatrix}
$$

This interchange of x_1 and x_2 places the largest coefficient, 2, in the lead position. If we multiply the first equation by 1/2, we obtain:

$$
\begin{pmatrix} 1 & 1/2 & 1/2 \\ 0 & -1 & 2 \\ 1 & 0 & 1 \end{pmatrix}
\begin{pmatrix} x_2 \\ x_1 \\ x_3 \end{pmatrix} =
\begin{pmatrix} 1/2 & 0 & 0 \\ 0 & 1 & 0 \\ 0 & 0 & 1 \end{pmatrix}
\begin{pmatrix} y_1 \\ y_2 \\ y_3 \end{pmatrix}
$$

Subtracting the first equation from the third,

$$
\begin{pmatrix} 1 & 1/2 & 1/2 \\ 0 & -1 & 2 \\ 0 & -1/2 & 1/2 \end{pmatrix}
\begin{pmatrix} x_2 \\ x_1 \\ x_3 \end{pmatrix} =
\begin{pmatrix} 1/2 & 0 & 0 \\ 0 & 1 & 0 \\ -1/2 & 0 & 1 \end{pmatrix}
\begin{pmatrix} y_1 \\ y_2 \\ y_3 \end{pmatrix}
$$

Interchanging x_1 and x_3 to make the largest coefficient, 2, be the leading coefficient in the last two equations:

$$
\begin{pmatrix} 1 & 1/2 & 1/2 \\ 0 & 2 & -1 \\ 0 & 1/2 & -1/2 \end{pmatrix}
\begin{pmatrix} x_2 \\ x_3 \\ x_1 \end{pmatrix} =
\begin{pmatrix} 1/2 & 0 & 0 \\ 0 & 1 & 0 \\ -1/2 & 0 & 1 \end{pmatrix}
\begin{pmatrix} y_1 \\ y_2 \\ y_3 \end{pmatrix}
$$

Multiplying the second equation by 1/2:

$$
\begin{pmatrix} 1 & 1/2 & 1/2 \\ 0 & 1 & -1/2 \\ 0 & 1/2 & -1/2 \end{pmatrix}
\begin{pmatrix} x_2 \\ x_3 \\ x_1 \end{pmatrix}
=
\begin{pmatrix} 1/2 & 0 & 0 \\ 0 & 1/2 & 0 \\ -1/2 & 0 & 1 \end{pmatrix}
\begin{pmatrix} y_1 \\ y_2 \\ y_3 \end{pmatrix}
$$

Multiplying the second equation by 1/2 and subtracting from the third:

$$
\begin{pmatrix} 1 & 1/2 & 1/2 \\ 0 & 1 & -1/2 \\ 0 & 0 & -1/4 \end{pmatrix}
\begin{pmatrix} x_2 \\ x_3 \\ x_1 \end{pmatrix}
=
\begin{pmatrix} 1/2 & 0 & 0 \\ 0 & 1/2 & 0 \\ -1/2 & -1/4 & 1 \end{pmatrix}
\begin{pmatrix} y_1 \\ y_2 \\ y_3 \end{pmatrix}
$$

Multiplying the third equation by -4:

$$
\begin{pmatrix} 1 & 1/2 & 1/2 \\ 0 & 1 & -1/2 \\ 0 & 0 & 1 \end{pmatrix}
\begin{pmatrix} x_2 \\ x_3 \\ x_1 \end{pmatrix}
=
\begin{pmatrix} 1/2 & 0 & 0 \\ 0 & 1/2 & 0 \\ 2 & 1 & -4 \end{pmatrix}
\begin{pmatrix} y_1 \\ y_2 \\ y_3 \end{pmatrix}
$$

The third equation now gives x_1 in terms of y_1 y_2, and y_3. We can use it to eliminate x_1 from the second equation by adding one-half the third equation to the second, obtaining:

$$
\begin{pmatrix} 1 & 1/2 & 1/2 \\ 0 & 1 & 0 \\ 0 & 0 & 1 \end{pmatrix}
\begin{pmatrix} x_2 \\ x_3 \\ x_1 \end{pmatrix}
=
\begin{pmatrix} 1/2 & 0 & 0 \\ 1 & 1 & -2 \\ 2 & 1 & -4 \end{pmatrix}
\begin{pmatrix} y_1 \\ y_2 \\ y_3 \end{pmatrix}
$$

Now the second and third equations can be used to eliminate x_3 and x_1 from the first. Subtract one-half the second equation from the first, giving:

$$
\begin{pmatrix} 1 & 0 & 1/2 \\ 0 & 1 & 0 \\ 0 & 0 & 1 \end{pmatrix}
\begin{pmatrix} x_2 \\ x_3 \\ x_1 \end{pmatrix}
=
\begin{pmatrix} 0 & -1/2 & 1 \\ 1 & 1 & -2 \\ 2 & 1 & -4 \end{pmatrix}
\begin{pmatrix} y_1 \\ y_2 \\ y_3 \end{pmatrix}
$$

Subtract one-half the third equation from the first, giving:

$$\begin{pmatrix} 1 & 0 & 0 \\ 0 & 1 & 0 \\ 0 & 0 & 1 \end{pmatrix} \begin{pmatrix} x_2 \\ x_3 \\ x_1 \end{pmatrix} = \begin{pmatrix} x_2 \\ x_3 \\ x_1 \end{pmatrix} = \begin{pmatrix} -1 & -1 & 3 \\ 1 & 1 & -2 \\ 2 & 1 & -4 \end{pmatrix} \begin{pmatrix} y_1 \\ y_2 \\ y_3 \end{pmatrix}$$

Rearranging these equations:

$$\begin{pmatrix} x_1 \\ x_2 \\ x_3 \end{pmatrix} = \begin{pmatrix} 2 & 1 & -4 \\ -1 & -1 & 3 \\ 1 & 1 & -2 \end{pmatrix} \begin{pmatrix} y_1 \\ y_2 \\ y_3 \end{pmatrix}$$

and the inverse matrix is:

$$\begin{pmatrix} 2 & 1 & -4 \\ -1 & -1 & 3 \\ 1 & 1 & -2 \end{pmatrix}$$

The flow chart, Figure 13–1, describes the inversion of a matrix by the elimination process as demonstrated above. It parallels closely the flow chart of Section 12.31, except that the y_i's are not constants and their coefficients must be kept separate, increasing the bookkeeping process. In the chart, the coefficients of the y_i's, which eventually become the elements a'_{ij} of the inverse matrix, are denoted by a_{ij} with j running from $n + 1$ to $2n$.

The FORTRAN subroutine below inverts the matrix A following the flow chart, Figure 13–1 (another matrix inversion subroutine is given in Section 13.42):

```
SUBROUTINE MATINV(AA,N,AINV)
DIMENSION AA(20,20),AINV(20,20),A(20,40),ID(20)
NN=N+1
N2=2*N
DO 200 I=1,N
DO 200 J=1,N
200 A(I,J)=AA(I,J)
K=1
DO 1 I=1,N
```

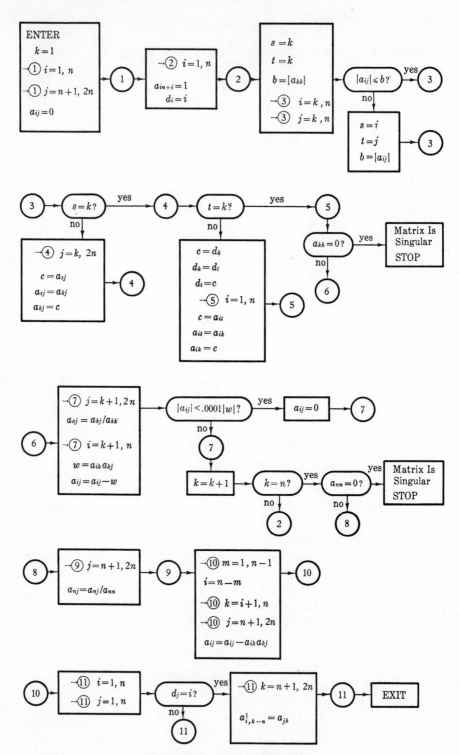

Figure 13–1: Inverse of a matrix

```
      DO 1 J=NN,N2
      A(I,J)=0.
  1 CONTINUE
      DO 21 I=1,N
      A(I,N+I)=1.
 21 ID(I)=I
  2 CONTINUE
      KK=K+1
      IS=K
      IT=K
      B=ABSF(A(K,K))
      DO 3 I=K,N
      DO 3 J=K,N
      IF(ABSF(A(I,J))−B)3,3,31
 31 IS=I
      IT=J
      B=ABSF(A(I,J))
  3 CONTINUE
      IF(IS−K)4,4,41
 41 DO 42 J=K,N2
      C=A(IS,J)
      A(IS,J)=A(K,J)
 42 A(K,J)=C
  4 CONTINUE
      IF(IT−K)5,5,51
 51 IC=ID(K)
      ID(K)=ID(IT)
      ID(IT)=IC
      DO 52 I=1,N
      C=A(I,IT)
      A(I,IT)=A(I,K)
 52 A(I,K)=C
  5 CONTINUE
      IF(A(K,K))6,120,6
  6 CONTINUE
      DO 7 J=KK,N2
      A(K,J)=A(K,J)/A(K,K)
      DO 7 I=KK,N
      W=A(I,K)*A(K,J)
      A(I,J)=A(I,J)−W
      IF(ABSF(A(I,J))−.0001*ABSF(W))71,7,7
 71 A(I,J)=0.
  7 CONTINUE
      K=KK
```

```
      IF(K−N)2,81,120
   81 IF(A(N,N))8,120,8
    8 CONTINUE
      DO 9 J=NN,N2
      A(N,J)=A(N,J)/A(N,N)
    9 CONTINUE
      N1=N−1
      DO 10 M=1,N1
      I=N−M
      II=I+1
      DO 10 K=II,N
      DO 10 J=NN,N2
      A(I,J)=A(I,J)−A(I,K)*A(K,J)
   10 CONTINUE
      DO 11 I=1,N
      DO 11 J=1,N
      IF(ID(J)−I)11,111,11
  111 DO 112 K=NN,N2
  112 AINV(I,K−N)=A(J,K)
   11 CONTINUE
      RETURN
  120 PRINT 1000
      RETURN
 1000 FORMAT(19H MATRIX IS SINGULAR)
      END
```

Comparison of the flow chart, Figure 13–1, and the above program with those of Section 12.31 for solving a system of linear equations shows that the matrix inversion requires essentially all the steps of the elimination method, plus many more. Hence while it makes for a mathematically elegant presentation to write a system of linear equations as:

$$Ax = b$$

and its solution as:

$$x = A^{-1}b$$

the use of matrix subroutines to perform the solution in this manner on a computer tends to be somewhat inefficient.

One advantage of using a matrix inversion routine rather than the elimination method for a system of equations is that in some cases enhanced accuracy can be attained. As was mentioned in Section 12.31, the large number of subtractions involved in the elimination method can sometimes lead to accuracy problems despite the precautions taken. When this occurs, the inverse matrix as obtained by the above method will be subject to the same accuracy problems. However, once an approximate inverse matrix has been obtained, more accurate approximations of the inverse matrix can be obtained as follows:

Let A be the matrix to be inverted, and $\mathbf{D}_1$ be the matrix obtained by following the above flow chart. Then, because of inaccuracies:

$$AD_1 \neq I$$

but instead:

$$I - AD_1 = F_1$$

where F_1 is a matrix which, if D_1 was a reasonably good estimate, has small elements. If for each row (or each column) of F_1 the sum of the absolute values of the elements is less than one, then the matrix D_2 defined by:

$$D_2 = D_1(I + F_1)$$

is an improved estimate of A^{-1}. If the error matrix $F_2 = I - AD_2$ still has elements which are too large, then the matrix D_3 defined by $D_3 = D_2(I + F_2)$ is a still better estimate, etc. Thus, repetition of a process involving some matrix multiplications can be used to improve the accuracy of the inverse to the extent desired.

EXERCISE XXIII

1. Given the following matrices:

$$A = \begin{pmatrix} 2 & 2 \\ 1 & -1 \\ -2 & 1 \end{pmatrix} \qquad B = \begin{pmatrix} 1 & -1 \\ 2 & 3 \end{pmatrix} \qquad C = \begin{pmatrix} 2 \\ 1 \\ -2 \end{pmatrix}$$

$$D = \begin{pmatrix} 4 & 1 & 3 \\ 2 & -1 & 1 \\ -3 & 2 & 1 \end{pmatrix} \qquad E = \begin{pmatrix} 1 \\ 2 \end{pmatrix} \qquad F = \begin{pmatrix} 1 & -1 & 2 \\ 2 & -3 & 1 \end{pmatrix}$$

Evaluate the following expressions, or, if the expression is meaningless, so state:

a.	AB	f.	$DA + A$
b.	DC	g.	$FA + B$
c.	BE	h.	$FC + BE$
d.	BA	i.	$FDABE$
e.	ABE	j.	$AF + D$

2. Using the method of Example 2, Section 13.24, invert the following matrices:

a. $\begin{pmatrix} 3 & 2 \\ 4 & 3 \end{pmatrix}$

c. $\begin{pmatrix} 2 & 3 & 1 \\ 1 & -1 & 2 \\ -3 & 1 & -1 \end{pmatrix}$

b. $\begin{pmatrix} 1 & -3 \\ 2 & 4 \end{pmatrix}$

d. $\begin{pmatrix} 1 & 0 & 0 \\ 0 & 3 & 2 \\ 0 & 4 & 3 \end{pmatrix}$

3. Following the flow chart, Figure 13–1, invert the matrices of Problem 2.

4. Find A^{-1}, then solve $Ax = b$ by multiplying both sides by A^{-1}, if:

a. $A = \begin{pmatrix} 2 & 3 \\ 3 & 4 \end{pmatrix}$, $b = \begin{pmatrix} 2 \\ 1 \end{pmatrix}$

b. $A = \begin{pmatrix} 2 & 4 & -1 \\ -1 & -3 & 1 \\ 3 & -1 & 2 \end{pmatrix}$, $b = \begin{pmatrix} 4 \\ -2 \\ 6 \end{pmatrix}$

5. Determine the number of multiplications necessary to find the product of two 20×20 matrices, and estimate the time required on a fast machine.

6. Determine the number of multiplications necessary to invert a 20×20 matrix following the flow chart, Figure 13–1, and estimate the time required on a fast machine.

7. Write a simplified version of the subroutine MATINV of Section 13.24 that does not bother to interchange rows and columns.

8. Write a FORTRAN subroutine INVIMPR that will take the trial inverse obtained from MATINV and use the method described at the end of Section 13.24 to improve the inverse until all the elements of the error matrix F_n are less than .001 in absolute value.

13.3 OVERDETERMINED AND UNDERDETERMINED SYSTEMS OF LINEAR EQUATIONS

In Chapter XII, and again in Section 13.24, methods were discussed for solving systems of linear equations. In all these discussions it was assumed that there was a unique solution and that there were just as many equations as unknowns. Further, it was tacitly assumed that the equations were non-homogeneous, i.e., not all the constant terms were zero, and also that the determinant of the coefficients was not zero. With these conditions satisfied there *is* a unique solution. In many important cases, however, these conditions are not all satisfied—yet there may still be a unique solution, or there may be no solution or an infinite number of solutions. In this section we will discuss a method for finding which situation prevails and for completely describing the solutions when there is an infinite number of them.

13.31 *Rank of a Matrix*

As a tool for further study of systems of equations we will need the concept of rank of a matrix.

DEFINITION: The rank of a matrix is the order of the highest order non-vanishing determinant within the matrix.

By a "determinant within the matrix" we mean any determinant that can be made by crossing out rows or columns in the matrix.

Example 1. Find the rank of the matrix:

$$\begin{pmatrix} -1 & 1 & 2 \\ -3 & 3 & 1 \end{pmatrix}$$

The largest order determinant we can construct is second order, so the rank is 2 or less. To see if it is 2, we must check all second order determinants. If we cross out the third column, we can construct the determinant:

$$\begin{vmatrix} -1 & 1 \\ -3 & 3 \end{vmatrix}$$

which has the value zero. Since this one vanishes, we must check other second order determinants. Crossing out the second column in the matrix, we obtain the determinant:

$$\begin{vmatrix} -1 & 2 \\ -3 & 1 \end{vmatrix}$$

which has the value 5. Since there is a nonvanishing second order determinant, the rank is 2.

Example 2. Find the rank of the matrix:

$$\begin{pmatrix} 1 & 2 & 3 \\ -1 & -2 & -3 \\ 2 & 4 & 6 \end{pmatrix}$$

The largest order determinant we can construct is third order, so the rank is 3 or less. The only third order determinant is:

$$\begin{vmatrix} 1 & 2 & 3 \\ -1 & -2 & -3 \\ 2 & 4 & 6 \end{vmatrix} = 0$$

so the rank is not 3. If we cross out the third row and third column, we have the determinant:

$$\begin{vmatrix} 1 & 2 \\ -1 & -2 \end{vmatrix} = 0$$

Similarly, if we check all other second order determinants, we find that they all vanish.

Hence the rank is less than 2. If we cross out the second and third rows, and the second and third columns, we can form the determinant $|1| = 1$. Since the highest order nonvanishing determinant is first order, the rank of the matrix is 1.

It is seen from the above examples that finding the rank of a matrix is a straightforward process. For matrices of higher order, however, the process as just demonstrated is extremely laborious, sometimes involving the evaluation of many determinants. Fortunately, however, a less laborious method is available, based on the following theorem:

Theorem I.   *The rank of a matrix is unchanged if any multiple of the elements of one row (or column) is added to the corresponding elements of another row (or column).*

This theorem means that we can proceed, just as in evaluating a determinant, to combine rows or columns to obtain zeros where we choose.

Example 3. Find the rank of:

$$\begin{pmatrix} 1 & -1 & -1 & -2 \\ 2 & 1 & -2 & 2 \\ 4 & 3 & -4 & 6 \end{pmatrix}$$

Using Theorem I, we may proceed as follows:

$$\text{rank} \begin{pmatrix} 1 & -1 & -1 & -2 \\ 2 & 1 & -2 & 2 \\ 4 & 3 & -4 & 6 \end{pmatrix} = \text{rank} \begin{pmatrix} 1 & -1 & -1 & -2 \\ 0 & 3 & 0 & 6 \\ 4 & 3 & -4 & 6 \end{pmatrix}$$

(twice first row subtracted from second)

$$= \text{rank} \begin{pmatrix} 1 & -1 & -1 & -2 \\ 0 & 3 & 0 & 6 \\ 0 & 7 & 0 & 14 \end{pmatrix}$$

(four times first row subtracted from third

$$= \text{rank} \begin{pmatrix} 1 & -1 & -1 & -2 \\ 0 & 3 & 0 & 6 \\ 0 & 0 & 0 & 0 \end{pmatrix}$$

(7/3 times second row subtracted from third)

It is obvious in this last matrix all third order determinants are zero, but at least one second order determinant:

$$\begin{vmatrix} 1 & -1 \\ 0 & 3 \end{vmatrix}$$

is not zero. Hence the rank of the original matrix is 2.

Note that in the above example, we have *not* said the *matrices* obtained at each step are equal, but only that the *ranks* are equal. Each step has created a new matrix, one differing from the preceding in many respects, but having the rank in common.

It is seen that the method of determining rank as demonstrated in Example 3 above is closely akin to the method of evaluation of a determinant given in Section 12.22. Minor modifications to the flow chart and program given there will give a flow chart and program for finding rank. The flow chart, Figure 13–2, contains these modifications, and will find the rank of matrix having n rows and m columns with no more effort than that involved in evaluating the largest determinant in the matrix.

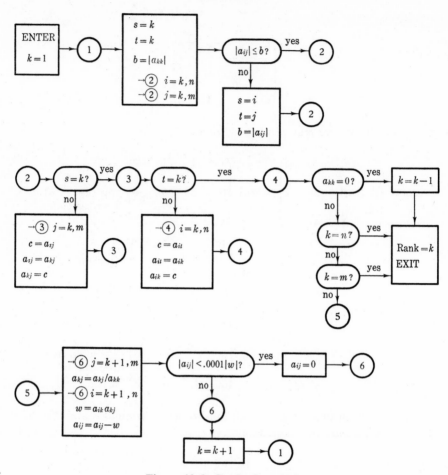

Figure 13–2: Rank of a matrix

In the flow chart, Figure 13–2, it is quite essential that the check for loss of significant figures before connector 6 be used, and a_{ij} be set equal to zero if too many figures have been lost. As in Example 3 above, the determination of rank is based on the fact that some elements become zero during the process. If due to roundoff or other error these elements are recorded as small, nonzero numbers, the rank would not be correctly determined.

The FORTRAN subroutine below finds the rank, K, of a matrix having N rows and M columns, where neither N nor M exceed 20.

```
SUBROUTINE MARANK(AA,N,M,K)
DIMENSION AA(20,20),A(20,20)
DO 200 I=1,N
DO 200 J=1,M
```

```
200 A(I,J)=AA(I,J)
    K=1
  1 CONTINUE
    KK=K+1
    IS=K
    IT=K
    B=ABSF(A(K,K))
    DO 2 I=K,N
    DO 2 J=K,M
    IF(ABSF(A(I,J))-B)2,2,21
 21 IS=I
    IT=J
    B=ABSF(A(I,J))
  2 CONTINUE
    IF(IS-K)3,3,31
 31 DO 32 J=K,M
    C=A(IS,J)
    A(IS,J)=A(K,J)
 32 A(K,J)=C
  3 CONTINUE
    IF(IT-K)4,4,41
 41 DO 42 I=K,N
    C=A(I,IT)
    A(I,IT)=A(I,K)
 42 A(I,K)=C
  4 CONTINUE
    IF(A(K,K))51,7,51
 51 IF(K-N)52,8,52
 52 IF(K-M)5,8,5
  5 CONTINUE
    DO 6 J=KK,M
    A(K,J)=A(K,J)/A(K,K)
    DO 6 I=KK,N
    W=A(I,K)*A(K,J)
    A(I,J)=A(I,J)-W
    IF(ABSF(A(I,J))-.0001*ABSF(W))61,6,6
 61 A(I,J)=0.
  6 CONTINUE
    K=KK
    GO TO 1
  7 K=K-1
  8 RETURN
    END
```

13.32   Consistent and Inconsistent Equations

A set of linear equations:

$$a_{11}x_1 + \quad \cdots \quad + a_{1m}x_m = b_1$$

$$a_{21}x_1 + \quad \cdots \quad + a_{2m}x_m = b_2$$

$$\cdot$$

$$\cdot$$

$$\cdot$$

$$a_{n1}x_1 + \quad \cdots \quad + a_{nm}x_m = b_n$$

is said to be consistent if there exists at least one solution and inconsistent if there is no solution. We are now in a position to give a criterion for determining whether a set of equations is consistent or inconsistent. We will refer to the matrix:

$$\begin{pmatrix} a_{11} & a_{12} & \cdots & a_{1m} \\ a_{21} & a_{22} & \cdots & a_{2m} \\ & \cdot & & \\ & \cdot & & \\ & \cdot & & \\ a_{n1} & a_{n2} & \cdots & a_{nm} \end{pmatrix}$$

as the *coefficient* matrix, and to the matrix:

$$\begin{pmatrix} a_{11} & a_{12} & \cdots & a_{1m} & b_1 \\ a_{21} & a_{22} & \cdots & a_{2m} & b_2 \\ & \cdot & & \\ & \cdot & & \\ & \cdot & & \\ a_{n1} & a_{n2} & \cdots & a_{nm} & b_n \end{pmatrix}$$

as the *augmented* matrix.   Then the following theorem applies:

Theorem II: *A set of linear equations is consistent if and only if the coefficient matrix and augmented matrix have the same rank.*

Example 1.   Determine if the following equations are consistent:

$$x + 3y = 4$$
$$2x + 6y = 2$$

The coefficient matrix is:

$$\begin{pmatrix} 1 & 3 \\ 2 & 6 \end{pmatrix}$$

which has rank 1.
The augmented matrix is:

$$\begin{pmatrix} 1 & 3 & 4 \\ 2 & 6 & 2 \end{pmatrix}$$

which has rank 2.
Hence the system is inconsistent.

Example 2.   Determine if the following equations are consistent:

$$x + 2y = 3$$
$$2x - y = 2$$
$$3x + y = 5$$

The coefficient matrix is:

$$\begin{pmatrix} 1 & 2 \\ 2 & -1 \\ 3 & 1 \end{pmatrix}$$

which has rank 2.
The augmented matrix is:

$$\begin{pmatrix} 1 & 2 & 3 \\ 2 & -1 & 2 \\ 3 & 1 & 5 \end{pmatrix}$$

which has rank 2.

Hence the equations are consistent, and there is a solution, despite the fact that there are more equations than unknowns! Upon closer scrutiny, it will be observed that the third equation is merely the sum of the first two.

The last example illustrates an important principle, that consistency or inconsistency cannot be ascertained merely from the numbers of equations and unknowns. A system with more equations than unknowns can be consistent, and a system with more unknowns than equations can be inconsistent. The subroutine for finding rank given in the preceding section is the tool needed to investigate consistency in the larger systems.

13.33   Linear Independence of Vectors

Consistent systems of linear equations may have infinitely many solutions. It is possible, however, to investigate these solutions systematically and to characterize them completely. To do so. we need first the concept of linear dependence and independence. Consider the set of column vectors

$$u_1 = \begin{pmatrix} u_{11} \\ u_{21} \\ \cdot \\ \cdot \\ \cdot \\ u_{n1} \end{pmatrix}, \quad u_2 = \begin{pmatrix} u_{12} \\ u_{22} \\ \cdot \\ \cdot \\ \cdot \\ u_{n2} \end{pmatrix}, \text{ etc.}, \quad u_r = \begin{pmatrix} u_{1r} \\ u_{2r} \\ \cdot \\ \cdot \\ \cdot \\ u_{nr} \end{pmatrix}$$

If $c_1, c_2, \ldots, c_r$ are any constants, the expression:

$$c_1 u_1 + c_2 u_2 + \cdots + c_r u_r$$

is called a "linear combination" of the vectors $u_1, \ldots, u_r$. If there is some set of constants $c_1, \ldots, c_r$, not all zero, such that:

$$c_1 u_1 + c_2 u_2 + \cdots + c_r u_r = 0$$

then the vectors are said to be "linearly dependent." If, on the other hand, every linear combination of the vectors $u_1, \ldots, u_r$ is nonzero except for the case $c_1 = c_2 = \cdots = c_r = 0$, then the vectors are said to be "linearly independent."

Example 1. Are the vectors:

$$\begin{pmatrix} 0 \\ 1 \end{pmatrix} \quad \text{and} \quad \begin{pmatrix} 1 \\ 0 \end{pmatrix}$$

linearly independent?

The sum

$$c_1 \begin{pmatrix} 0 \\ 1 \end{pmatrix} + c_2 \begin{pmatrix} 1 \\ 0 \end{pmatrix} = \begin{pmatrix} c_2 \\ c_1 \end{pmatrix}$$

is zero only if both c_1 and c_2 are zero. Hence they are linearly independent.

Example 2. Are the vectors:

$$\begin{pmatrix} 1 \\ -1 \\ 2 \end{pmatrix}, \quad \begin{pmatrix} 2 \\ 1 \\ 1 \end{pmatrix}, \quad \text{and} \quad \begin{pmatrix} 3 \\ 0 \\ 3 \end{pmatrix}$$

linearly independent?

The sum:

$$c_1 \begin{pmatrix} 1 \\ -1 \\ 2 \end{pmatrix} + c_2 \begin{pmatrix} 2 \\ 1 \\ 1 \end{pmatrix} + c_3 \begin{pmatrix} 3 \\ 0 \\ 3 \end{pmatrix} = \begin{pmatrix} c_1 + 2c_2 + 3c_3 \\ -c_1 + c_2 \\ 2c_1 + c_2 + 3c_3 \end{pmatrix}$$

is zero if $c_1 = 1$, $c_2 = 1$, $c_3 = -1$. Hence the vectors are not linearly independent.

13.34 *Complete Solution of Systems of Linear Equations*

The following theorem gives a complete picture of the situation regarding solutions for systems of linear equations.

Theorem III. *Let $Ax = b$ be a consistent system having m unknowns, and let the rank of A be r. Then:*

(1) If $r = m$, there is a unique solution vector x.

(2) If $r < m$, then there is at least one solution vector x. In addition $m - r$ linearly independent vectors $u_1, u_2, \ldots, u_{m-r}$ can be found which are solutions to the set of homogeneous equations $Ax = 0$. The vector x plus any linear combination of these is also a solution of the given equation, and there are no other solutions. If $b = 0$, the vector x can be taken as $x = 0$.

Hereafter we will refer to the vector **x** described in this theorem as the *particular* solution.

A method of obtaining all these solutions in a systematic fashion is illustrated by the example below:

Example 1.   Solve the system:

$$\begin{pmatrix} 4 & 2 & -1 & 1 \\ 1 & -1 & 2 & -1 \\ 3 & 3 & -3 & 2 \\ 2 & -2 & 4 & -2 \end{pmatrix} \begin{pmatrix} x_1 \\ x_2 \\ x_3 \\ x_4 \end{pmatrix} = \begin{pmatrix} 6 \\ 1 \\ 5 \\ 2 \end{pmatrix}$$

We will proceed as in the elimination method as illustrated in Section 12.31. Dividing the first equation by 4 and using it to eliminate x_1 from the remaining equations:

$$\begin{pmatrix} 1 & .5 & -.25 & .25 \\ 0 & -1.5 & 2.25 & -1.25 \\ 0 & 1.5 & -2.25 & 1.25 \\ 0 & -3 & 4.5 & -2.5 \end{pmatrix} \begin{pmatrix} x_1 \\ x_2 \\ x_3 \\ x_4 \end{pmatrix} = \begin{pmatrix} 1.5 \\ -.5 \\ .5 \\ -1 \end{pmatrix}$$

Rearranging to make the largest element to be in the proper position:

$$\begin{pmatrix} 1 & -.25 & .5 & .25 \\ 0 & 4.5 & -3 & -2.5 \\ 0 & -2.25 & 1.5 & 1.25 \\ 0 & 2.25 & -1.5 & -1.25 \end{pmatrix} \begin{pmatrix} x_1 \\ x_3 \\ x_2 \\ x_4 \end{pmatrix} = \begin{pmatrix} 1.5 \\ -1 \\ .5 \\ -.5 \end{pmatrix}$$

Dividing the second equation by 4.5 and using it to eliminate x_3 from the other two equations:

$$\begin{pmatrix} 1 & -.25 & .5 & .25 \\ 0 & 1 & -2/3 & -5/9 \\ 0 & 0 & 0 & 0 \\ 0 & 0 & 0 & 0 \end{pmatrix} \begin{pmatrix} x_1 \\ x_3 \\ x_2 \\ x_4 \end{pmatrix} = \begin{pmatrix} 1.5 \\ -2/9 \\ 0 \\ 0 \end{pmatrix}$$

At this point we see that the rank of A is 2, and that the system now has two equations. If the system had been inconsistent, there would be more than two nonzero elements remaining on the right hand side of the equation at this point.

Since there are four unknowns and the rank of A is 2, Theorem II tells us that the complete solution is made up of a particular solution and any linear combination of two linearly independent solution vectors. We can find the complete solution as follows: Add .25 times row 2 to row 1, obtaining:

$$\begin{pmatrix} 1 & 0 & 1/3 & 1/9 \\ 0 & 1 & -2/3 & -5/9 \\ 0 & 0 & 0 & 0 \\ 0 & 0 & 0 & 0 \end{pmatrix} \begin{pmatrix} x_1 \\ x_3 \\ x_2 \\ x_4 \end{pmatrix} = \begin{pmatrix} 13/9 \\ -2/9 \\ 0 \\ 0 \end{pmatrix}$$

We can find the particular solution by setting $x_2 = x_4 = 0$. Then the system becomes:

$$x_1 = 13/9$$

$$x_3 = -2/9$$

Hence the particular solution is:

$$\begin{pmatrix} x_1 \\ x_2 \\ x_3 \\ x_4 \end{pmatrix} = \begin{pmatrix} 13/9 \\ 0 \\ -2/9 \\ 0 \end{pmatrix}$$

To find two linearly independent solution vectors, we take the homogeneous equation:

$$\begin{pmatrix} 1 & 0 & 1/3 & 1/9 \\ 0 & 1 & -2/3 & -5/9 \\ 0 & 0 & 0 & 0 \\ 0 & 0 & 0 & 0 \end{pmatrix} \begin{pmatrix} x_1 \\ x_3 \\ x_2 \\ x_4 \end{pmatrix} = \begin{pmatrix} 0 \\ 0 \\ 0 \\ 0 \end{pmatrix}$$

and choose arbitrary values for x_2 and x_4.

Taking $x_2 = 1$, $x_4 = 0$, we have:

$$x_1 + 1/3 = 0$$

$$x_3 - 2/3 = 0$$

which has the solution:

$$x_1 = -1/3, \qquad x_3 = 2/3$$

so one of the linearly independent vectors is:

$$\boldsymbol{u}_1 = \begin{pmatrix} -1/3 \\ 1 \\ 2/3 \\ 0 \end{pmatrix}$$

Taking $x_2 = 0$, $x_4 = 1$, we have:

$$x_1 + 1/9 = 0$$

$$x_3 - 5/9 = 0$$

which has the solution:

$$x_1 = -1/9, \qquad x_3 = 5/9$$

and so the other solution is:

$$\boldsymbol{u}_2 = \begin{pmatrix} -1/9 \\ 0 \\ 5/9 \\ 1 \end{pmatrix}$$

and the general solution is:

$$x = \begin{pmatrix} 13/9 \\ 0 \\ -2/9 \\ 0 \end{pmatrix} + c_1 \begin{pmatrix} -1/3 \\ 1 \\ 2/3 \\ 0 \end{pmatrix} + c_2 \begin{pmatrix} -1/9 \\ 0 \\ 5/9 \\ 1 \end{pmatrix}$$

where c_1 and c_2 are arbitrary constants.

For convenience in organizing a computer solution, we note that these vectors (apart from a constant multiple of -1 in some cases), can be obtained from the last set of equations by the following somewhat artificial steps:

1. Add -1's down the last two columns of the diagonal of the coefficient matrix so that it becomes:

$$\begin{pmatrix} 1 & 0 & 1/3 & 1/9 \\ 0 & 1 & -2/3 & -5/9 \\ 0 & 0 & -1 & 0 \\ 0 & 0 & 0 & -1 \end{pmatrix}$$

2. Rearrange these last two columns and the column of constants as if they were ordered just as the x's are:

$$\begin{pmatrix} x_1 \\ x_3 \\ x_2 \\ x_4 \end{pmatrix}$$

and needed to be correctly ordered. They become:

$$\begin{pmatrix} 1/3 & 1/9 & 13/9 \\ -1 & 0 & 0 \\ -2/3 & -5/9 & -2/9 \\ 0 & -1 & 0 \end{pmatrix}$$

The column of constants has become the particular solution and the other two columns two linearly independent vectors that can be used to form the complete solution.

The method just demonstrated is a general one, and can be used for computer solution of larger systems. It requires only a few modifications and extensions of the elimination method given in Section 12.31.

The flow chart, Figure 13–3, extends the one given in Section 12.31 along the lines illustrated in the example of the preceding section. If the equations are inconsistent, it so indicates. If the system has a unique solution, it gives the solution $x_1, x_2, \dots, x_m$. If the system has more than one solution, it gives a particular solution, $x_1, x_2, \dots, x_m$, indicates the number of linearly independent vectors, K, and gives a set of them, $u_{1i}, u_{2i}, \dots, u_{mi}, i = 1, \dots, K$.

The FORTRAN subroutine given below solves a system of N equations in M unknowns, where N and M are both 20 or less. Inputs are: **AA**, the coefficient matrix; **BB**, the constant vector; and NI and M, the dimensions of the system. Outputs are: **X**, a particular solution vector, K, the number of linearly independent solution vectors for the homogeneous system, and **U**, a set of linearly independent solution vectors.

```
      SUBROUTINE SOLINEQ(AA,NI,M,BB,X,K,U)
      DIMENSION  AA(20,20),BB(20),A(20,21),X(20),ID(20),U(20,20)
      N=NI
      MM=M+1
      DO  200  I=1,N
      A(I,MM)=BB(I)
      DO  200  J=1,M
  200 A(I,J)=AA(I,J)
      K=1
      IF(N−M)15,1,1
   15 IT=N+1
      N=M
      DO  16  I=IT,M
      DO  16  J=1,MM
   16 A(I,J)=0.
    1 CONTINUE
      DO  21  I=1,M
   21 ID(I)=I
    2 CONTINUE
      KK=K+1
      IS=K
      IT=K
      B=ABSF(A(K,K))
      DO  3  I=K,N
      DO  3  J=K,M
```

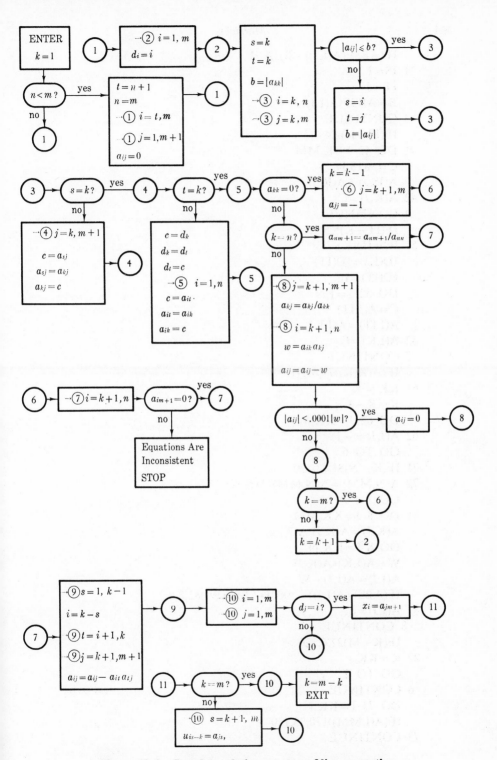

Figure 13–3: Complete solution—system of linear equations

```
         IF(ABSF(A(I,J)) − B)3,3,31
31  IS = I
    IT = J
    B = ABSF(A(I,J))
 3  CONTINUE
    IF(IS − K)4,4,41
41  DO 42 J = K,MM
    C = A(IS,J)
    A(IS,J) = A(K,J)
42  A(K,J) = C
 4  CONTINUE
    IF(IT − K)5,5,51
51  IC = ID(K)
    ID(K) = ID(IT)
    ID(IT) = IC
    DO 52 I = 1,N
    C = A(I,IT)
    A(I,IT) = A(I,K)
52  A(I,K) = C
 5  CONTINUE
    IF(A(K,K))71,61,71
61  KK = K
    K = K − 1
    DO 62 J = KK,M
62  A(J,J) = −1.
    GO TO 6
71  IF(K − N)81,72,120
72  A(N,MM) = A(N,MM)/A(N,N)
    GO TO 7
81  DO 8 J = KK,MM
    A(K,J) = A(K,J)/A(K,K)
    DO 8 I = KK,N
    W = A(I,K)*A(K,J)
    A(I,J) = A(I,J) − W
    IF(ABSF(A(I,J)) − .0001*ABSF(W))82,8,8
82  A(I,J) = 0.
 8  CONTINUE
    IF(K − M)22,6,120
22  K = KK
    GO TO 2
 6  CONTINUE
    DO 73 I = KK,N
    IF(A(I,MM))120,73,120
73  CONTINUE
```

```
      7 CONTINUE
        K1 = K - 1
        DO 9 IS = 1,K1
        I = K - IS
        II = I + 1
        DO 9 IT = II,K
        DO 9 J = KK,MM
        A(I,J) = A(I,J) - A(I,IT)*A(IT,J)
      9 CONTINUE
        DO 10 I = 1,M
        DO 10 J = 1,M
        IF(ID(J) - I)10,111,10
    111 X(I) = A(J,MM)
     11 CONTINUE
        IF(K - M)101,10,101
    101 DO 102 IS = KK,M
    102 U(I,IS - K) = A(J,IS)
     10 CONTINUE
        K = M - K
        RETURN
    120 PRINT 1000
        RETURN
   1000 FORMAT(27H EQUATIONS ARE INCONSISTENT)
        END
```

13.4   EIGENVALUES AND EIGENVECTORS

A surprisingly large number of problems in physics and engineering can be reduced to the following mathematical problem:

Given a square nth order matrix A, find a nonzero vector x and a constant λ such that:

$$Ax = \lambda x$$

that is to say, find a vector x such that Ax is simply a multiple of the vector x itself. We can rewrite this equation as:

$$Ax - \lambda x = 0$$

or

$$(A - \lambda I)x = 0 \tag{13-3}$$

In this form, the equation appears as a set of homogeneous, linear equations for $x_1, x_2, \ldots, x_n$. The matrix of coefficients is $(A - \lambda I)$, and the augmented matrix is the same with a column of zeros added, so by Theorem II of Section

13.33 the equations are consistent. By Theorem III of Section 13.34 there is a unique solution if the rank of the coefficient matrix is n. We already know that solution, it is $x_1 = x_2 = \cdots = x_n = 0$. Hence there is a nonzero vector x only if the rank of $(A - \lambda I)$ is less than n. This will be true if:

$$\det (A - \lambda I) = 0 \qquad (13\text{-}4)$$

If this determinant is zero, then by Theorem III of Section 13.34 there are one or more linearly independent solution vectors that can be used to describe the complete solution. Thus we are interested in the values of λ for which:

$$\begin{vmatrix} a_{11} - \lambda & a_{12} & \cdots & a_{1n} \\ a_{21} & a_{22} - \lambda & & a_{2n} \\ \cdot & & \cdot & \\ \cdot & & & \cdot \\ \cdot & & & \cdot \\ a_{n1} & a_{n2} & \cdots & a_{nn} - \lambda \end{vmatrix} = 0$$

In Chapter XII it was stated that the value of a determinant could be obtained by forming all possible terms containing as factors exactly one element from each row and each column. If we were to attempt to do this with the determinant above, we would find that the various terms would contain different powers of λ. If we were to collect the terms having like powers, we would obtain an expression of the form:

$$(-1)^n[\lambda^n - p_1\lambda^{n-1} - p_2\lambda^{n-2} - \cdots - p_n] \qquad (13\text{-}5)$$

where the constants $p_1, p_2, \ldots, p_n$ are numbers resulting from some very complicated manipulations of the numbers a_{ij} in the determinant.

From Chapter XI, there are exactly n values of λ (not necessarily distinct) which will make (13-5) be equal to zero. These values are called the "eigenvalues" (or "characteristic roots," or "latent roots," or "proper values") of the matrix A. For any eigenvalue λ_i, the vector x which satisfies equation (13-3) is called the "eigenvector" (or "characteristic vector," or "latent vector," or "proper vector") corresponding to λ_i. The polynomial (13-5) is called the "characteristic polynomial" of the matrix A, and the equation:

$$\lambda^n - p_1\lambda^{n-1} - p_2\lambda^{n-2} - \cdots - p_n = 0 \qquad (13\text{-}6)$$

is called the "characteristic equation."

Example 1. Find the eigenvalues and eigenvectors for the matrix:

$$\begin{pmatrix} 1 & 3 \\ 2 & 2 \end{pmatrix}$$

To find the eigenvalues, we set:

$$\begin{vmatrix} 1 - \lambda & 3 \\ 2 & 2 - \lambda \end{vmatrix} = 0$$

Expanding, we obtain the characteristic equation:

$$(1 - \lambda)(2 - \lambda) - 6 = \lambda^2 - 3\lambda - 4 = 0$$

This factors into:

$$(\lambda - 4)(\lambda + 1) = 0$$

so the eigenvalues are:

$$\lambda_1 = 4, \qquad \lambda_2 = -1$$

To find the eigenvector corresponding to λ_1, we set:

$$\begin{pmatrix} 1 - \lambda_1 & 3 \\ 2 & 2 - \lambda_1 \end{pmatrix} \begin{pmatrix} x_1 \\ x_2 \end{pmatrix} = \mathbf{0}$$

or

$$\begin{pmatrix} -3 & 3 \\ 2 & -2 \end{pmatrix} \begin{pmatrix} x_1 \\ x_2 \end{pmatrix} = \mathbf{0}$$

Since there are two unknowns and the coefficient matrix has rank 1, Theorem III of Section 13.34 tells us that these equations have one linearly independent vector solution U_1, and that all other solutions are multiples of this one. We see by inspection that the vector:

$$\begin{pmatrix} 1 \\ 1 \end{pmatrix}$$

is a solution, and hence is an eigenvector corresponding to λ_1. All other solutions are of the form:

$$c_1 \begin{pmatrix} 1 \\ 1 \end{pmatrix}$$

where c_1 is an arbitrary constant.   Hence the eigenvector is really determined only up to an arbitrary constant multiple.

To find the eigenvector corresponding to λ_2, we set:

$$\begin{pmatrix} 1 - \lambda_2 & 3 \\ 2 & 2 - \lambda_2 \end{pmatrix} \begin{pmatrix} x_1 \\ x_2 \end{pmatrix} = 0$$

or

$$\begin{pmatrix} 2 & 3 \\ 2 & 3 \end{pmatrix} \begin{pmatrix} x_1 \\ x_2 \end{pmatrix} = 0$$

Again there is one linearly independent solution vector.   We see by inspection that:

$$\begin{pmatrix} 3 \\ -2 \end{pmatrix}$$

is a solution.   All solutions are of the form:

$$c_2 \begin{pmatrix} 3 \\ -2 \end{pmatrix}$$

where c_2 is an arbitrary constant.

Hence the eigenvalues are:

$$4, \quad -1$$

and the corresponding eigenvectors are:

$$\begin{pmatrix} 1 \\ 1 \end{pmatrix} \quad \text{and} \quad \begin{pmatrix} 3 \\ -2 \end{pmatrix}$$

(We ordinarily ignore the arbitrary constant multiple when writing an eigenvector.)

Example 2. Find the eigenvalues and eigenvectors for the matrix:

$$\begin{pmatrix} 3 & 2 & 4 \\ 1 & 4 & 4 \\ -1 & -2 & -2 \end{pmatrix}$$

To determine the eigenvalues, we set:

$$\begin{vmatrix} 3-\lambda & 2 & 4 \\ 1 & 4-\lambda & 4 \\ -1 & -2 & -2-\lambda \end{vmatrix} = 0$$

Expanding, we obtain the characteristic equation:

$$-\lambda^3 + 5\lambda^2 - 8\lambda + 4 = 0$$

which has the roots:

$$\lambda_1 = 1, \qquad \lambda_2 = \lambda_3 = 2$$

To find the eigenvector corresponding to λ_1, we set:

$$\begin{pmatrix} 3-\lambda_1 & 2 & 4 \\ 1 & 4-\lambda_1 & 4 \\ -1 & -2 & -2-\lambda_1 \end{pmatrix} \begin{pmatrix} x_1 \\ x_2 \\ x_3 \end{pmatrix} = 0$$

or

$$\begin{pmatrix} 2 & 2 & 4 \\ 1 & 3 & 4 \\ -1 & -2 & -3 \end{pmatrix} \begin{pmatrix} x_1 \\ x_2 \\ x_3 \end{pmatrix} = 0$$

The coefficient matrix has rank 2, so this system has one linearly independent vector solution. If we solve by the method of Section 13.34, we find that the eigenvector is:

$$\begin{pmatrix} 1 \\ 1 \\ -1 \end{pmatrix}$$

To find the eigenvector corresponding to λ_2, we set:

$$\begin{pmatrix} 3 - \lambda_2 & 2 & 4 \\ 1 & 4 - \lambda_2 & 4 \\ -1 & -2 & -2 - \lambda_2 \end{pmatrix} \begin{pmatrix} x_1 \\ x_2 \\ x_3 \end{pmatrix} = 0$$

or

$$\begin{pmatrix} 1 & 2 & 4 \\ 1 & 2 & 4 \\ -1 & -2 & -4 \end{pmatrix} \begin{pmatrix} x_1 \\ x_2 \\ x_3 \end{pmatrix} = 0$$

The coefficient matrix has rank 1, so this system has two linearly independent vector solutions. Solving by the method of Section 13.34, we find two linearly independent eigenvectors:

$$\begin{pmatrix} -4 \\ 0 \\ 1 \end{pmatrix} \quad \text{and} \quad \begin{pmatrix} -2 \\ 1 \\ 0 \end{pmatrix}$$

The root λ_3, being the same as λ_2, has the same eigenvectors. Hence we have a single root, 1, with its eigenvector:

$$\begin{pmatrix} 1 \\ 1 \\ -1 \end{pmatrix}$$

and a double root, 2, with two eigenvectors:

$$\begin{pmatrix} -4 \\ 0 \\ 1 \end{pmatrix} \quad \text{and} \quad \begin{pmatrix} -2 \\ 1 \\ 0 \end{pmatrix}$$

Example 3. Find the eigenvalues and eigenvectors for the matrix:

$$\begin{pmatrix} 0 & 1 & 0 \\ 0 & 0 & 1 \\ -8 & -12 & -6 \end{pmatrix}$$

We set:

$$\begin{vmatrix} -\lambda & 1 & 0 \\ 0 & -\lambda & 1 \\ -8 & -12 & -6-\lambda \end{vmatrix} = 0$$

and obtain the characteristic equation:

$$-\lambda^3 - 6\lambda^2 - 12\lambda - 8 = 0$$

which has the roots:

$$\lambda_1 = -2, \qquad \lambda_2 = -2, \qquad \lambda_3 = -2$$

To find the eigenvectors, we set:

$$\begin{pmatrix} 2 & 1 & 0 \\ 0 & 2 & 1 \\ -8 & -12 & -4 \end{pmatrix} \begin{pmatrix} x_1 \\ x_2 \\ x_3 \end{pmatrix} = 0$$

Since the coefficient matrix has rank 2, there is only one linearly independent eigenvector. It turns out to be:

$$\begin{pmatrix} 1 \\ -2 \\ 4 \end{pmatrix}$$

Since all roots are the same, we can obtain no more eigenvectors. Hence in this case we have a triple eigenvalue, -2, and only one eigenvector (which might be considered as a triple eigenvector):

$$\begin{pmatrix} 1 \\ -2 \\ 4 \end{pmatrix}$$

The above examples have illustrated all the possibilities concerning real eigenvalues and their corresponding eigenvectors. These possibilities can be summarized in the following.

Theorem IV. *An nth order square matrix has n eigenvalues. If these are discrete, there is one eigenvector corresponding to each eigenvalue. If an eigenvalue is of multiplicity r, it may have from one to r linearly independent eigenvectors associated with it.*

13.41   Complex Eigenvalues

From Chapter XI it is known that the characteristic equation may have complex roots, occurring in conjugate pairs. In this case, the eigenvectors are also complex, and the equation:

$$(A - \lambda I)x = 0$$

instead of being n equations in n unknowns, is really $2n$ equations in $2n$ unknowns, for both the real and imaginary part of x must satisfy the equation. Let:

$$\lambda = \alpha + \beta i$$

be a complex eigenvalue, and let the eigenvector be:

$$x = \begin{pmatrix} x_1 + y_1 i \\ x_2 + y_2 i \\ \cdot \\ \cdot \\ \cdot \\ x_n + y_n i \end{pmatrix}$$

If we substitute these in the above equation and separate real and imaginary parts, the result can be written in the form:

$$
\begin{pmatrix}
a_{11} - \alpha & a_{12} & \cdots & a_{1n} & \beta & 0 & \cdots & 0 \\
a_{21} & a_{22} - \alpha & \cdots & a_{2n} & 0 & \beta & \cdots & 0 \\
\cdot & & & & & & & \\
\cdot & & & & & & & \\
\cdot & & & & & & & \\
a_{n1} & a_{n2} & \cdots & a_{nn} - \alpha & 0 & 0 & \cdots & \beta \\
-\beta & 0 & \cdots & 0 & a_{11} - \alpha & a_{12} & \cdots & a_{1n} \\
0 & -\beta & \cdots & 0 & a_{21} & a_{22} - \alpha & \cdots & a_{2n} \\
\cdot & & & & & & & \\
\cdot & & & & & & & \\
\cdot & & & & & & & \\
0 & 0 & \cdots & -\beta & a_{n1} & a_{n2} & \cdots & a_{nn} - \alpha
\end{pmatrix}
\begin{pmatrix}
x_1 \\ x_2 \\ \cdot \\ \cdot \\ \cdot \\ x_n \\ y_1 \\ y_2 \\ \cdot \\ \cdot \\ \cdot \\ y_n
\end{pmatrix} = 0
$$

These are $2n$ real equations in $2n$ real unknowns which can be solved for the x_i's and y_i's. The eigenvector corresponding to the complex conjugate of λ is the complex conjugate of the eigenvector for λ, so the process needs to be done only once for each pair of complex roots.

Example 1. Find the eigenvalues and eigenvectors of:

$$
\begin{pmatrix} -1 & -5 \\ 1 & 3 \end{pmatrix}
$$

We set:

$$
\begin{vmatrix} -1 - \lambda & -5 \\ 1 & 3 - \lambda \end{vmatrix} = 0
$$

and obtain the characteristic equation:

$$\lambda^2 - 2\lambda + 2 = 0$$

which has roots:

$$\lambda_1 = 1 + i, \qquad \lambda_2 = 1 - i$$

To find the eigenvector corresponding to λ_1, using the method described above, we write:

$$\begin{pmatrix} -2 & -5 & 1 & 0 \\ 1 & 2 & 0 & 1 \\ -1 & 0 & -2 & -5 \\ 0 & -1 & 1 & 2 \end{pmatrix} \begin{pmatrix} x_1 \\ x_2 \\ y_1 \\ y_2 \end{pmatrix} = 0$$

Applying the method of Section 13.34, this reduces to:

$$\begin{pmatrix} 1 & 0 & -.2 & .4 \\ 0 & 1 & .4 & .2 \\ 0 & 0 & 0 & 0 \\ 0 & 0 & 0 & 0 \end{pmatrix} \begin{pmatrix} x_2 \\ y_2 \\ y_1 \\ x_1 \end{pmatrix} = 0$$

This has two linearly independent solution vectors:

$$\begin{pmatrix} x_1 \\ x_2 \\ y_1 \\ y_2 \end{pmatrix} = \begin{pmatrix} 0 \\ .2 \\ 1 \\ -.4 \end{pmatrix} \quad \text{and} \quad \begin{pmatrix} 1 \\ -.4 \\ 0 \\ -.2 \end{pmatrix}$$

These vectors of themselves are not of interest to us, except to use the numbers in them to construct the complex vectors:

$$\begin{pmatrix} x_1 + y_1 i \\ x_2 + y_2 i \end{pmatrix} = \begin{pmatrix} i \\ .2 - .4i \end{pmatrix} \quad \text{and} \quad \begin{pmatrix} x_1 + y_1 i \\ x_2 + y_2 i \end{pmatrix} = \begin{pmatrix} 1 \\ -.4 - .2i \end{pmatrix}$$

These two vectors are not linearly independent at all, for if we multiply the second by i, we obtain the first. Hence we have really obtained only one eigenvector corresponding to the eigenvalue $1 + i$, and that is:

$$\begin{pmatrix} i \\ .2 - .4i \end{pmatrix}$$

The eigenvector corresponding to $1 - i$ is the conjugate of this:

$$\begin{pmatrix} -i \\ .2 + .4i \end{pmatrix}$$

13.42   Computer Methods

It is seen that the process of finding eigenvalues and eigenvectors consists of:
(*1*)   Finding the characteristic polynomial.
(*2*)   Solving the characteristic equation for its roots.
(*3*)   Solving sets of linear equations for the eigenvectors.

Chapter XI gave methods for solving polynomial equations, so we already have computer methods for step (*2*).   Section 13.35 gave a computer method for solving systems of linear equations which is satisfactory for step (*3*). Hence the only thing really required is a computer method for generating the characteristic polynomial.   In the examples above, we have used very small matrices and found the characteristic polynomial by brute force expansion of the determinant, but this process is inefficient for large order matrices. A more efficient method is the Leverrier-Faddeev method, which proceeds as follows:

$$\text{Let } A_1 = A \qquad\qquad \text{and } p_1 = \text{tr}A$$

$$\text{Let } A_2 = A(A_1 - p_1 I), \qquad \text{and } p_2 = (1/2)\,\text{tr}A_2$$

$$\text{Let } A_3 = A(A_2 - p_2 I), \qquad \text{and } p_3 = (1/3)\,\text{tr}A_3$$

$$\cdot$$
$$\cdot$$
$$\cdot$$

$$A_n = A(A_{n-1} - p_{n-1} I) \qquad \text{and } p_n = (1/n)\,\text{tr}A_n$$

The numbers $p_1, p_2, \ldots, p_n$ are the required coefficients in the characteristic equation:

$$\lambda^n - p_1\lambda^{n-1} - p_2\lambda^{n-2} - \cdots - p_n = 0$$

In addition, as a bonus side product of this process, it can be shown that the inverse of A is given by:

$$A^{-1} = (1/p_n)(A_{n-1} - p_{n-1}I) \tag{13-7}$$

and also, as a sometimes helpful check:

$$A_n - p_nI = 0 \tag{13-8}$$

Example 1. Find the characteristic equation of:

$$\begin{pmatrix} 1 & 3 & 2 \\ -2 & 1 & 1 \\ 1 & -2 & -1 \end{pmatrix}$$

Following the above procedure, we have:

$$A_1 = \begin{pmatrix} 1 & 3 & 2 \\ -2 & 1 & 1 \\ 1 & -2 & -1 \end{pmatrix}, \qquad p_1 = 1 + 1 - 1 = 1$$

$$A_2 = \begin{pmatrix} 1 & 3 & 2 \\ -2 & 1 & 1 \\ 1 & -2 & -1 \end{pmatrix} \begin{pmatrix} 0 & 3 & 2 \\ -2 & 0 & 1 \\ 1 & -2 & -2 \end{pmatrix} = \begin{pmatrix} -4 & -1 & 1 \\ -1 & -8 & -5 \\ 3 & 5 & 2 \end{pmatrix}$$

$$p_2 = (1/2)(-4 - 8 + 2) = -5$$

$$A_3 = \begin{pmatrix} 1 & 3 & 2 \\ -2 & 1 & 1 \\ 1 & -2 & -1 \end{pmatrix} \begin{pmatrix} 1 & -1 & 1 \\ -1 & -3 & -5 \\ 3 & 5 & 7 \end{pmatrix} = \begin{pmatrix} 4 & 0 & 0 \\ 0 & 4 & 0 \\ 0 & 0 & 4 \end{pmatrix}$$

$$p_3 = (1/3)(4 + 4 + 4) = 4$$

As a check, we see that:

$$A_3 - p_3 I = \begin{pmatrix} 4 & 0 & 0 \\ 0 & 4 & 0 \\ 0 & 0 & 4 \end{pmatrix} - \begin{pmatrix} 4 & 0 & 0 \\ 0 & 4 & 0 \\ 0 & 0 & 4 \end{pmatrix} = 0$$

Hence the characteristic equation is:

$$\lambda^3 - \lambda^2 + 5\lambda - 4 = 0$$

The flow chart, Figure 13–4, describes this process for an nth order matrix. According to equation (13-8), the matrix A_n is simply the identity matrix multiplied by p_n, so only the first element of A_n need be calculated to give p_n.

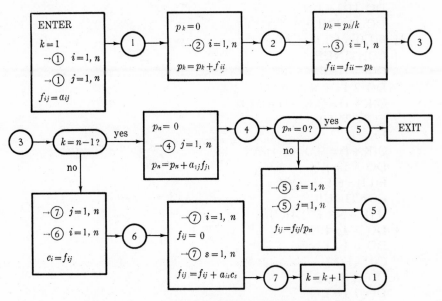

Figure 13–4: Generation of characteristic polynomial

The value of p_n is in fact the determinant of A, so that if p_n is zero, the matrix is singular. If p_n is not zero, the inverse of A is easily calculated from equation (13-7), and the flow chart includes this calculation. The elements of A^{-1} are the last values obtained for f_{ij}.

The FORTRAN subroutine given below will generate coefficients in accordance with the flow chart, for matrices up to order 20. However, in order that the subscripts will match the notation in the subroutines of Chapter XI, the characteristic equation is written as:

$$Q(1)\lambda^N + Q(2)\lambda^{N-1} + \cdots + Q(N+1) = 0$$

The relationship between the p_k of the flow chart and the $Q(K)$ of the subroutine is given by:

$$Q(1) = 1, \quad Q(K+1) = -p_k \text{ for } k = 1, \ldots, n$$

As in the flow chart, the subscripted variable $F(I,J)$ is the inverse matrix unless $Q(N+1)$ happens to be zero.

```
      SUBROUTINE CHAREQ(A,N,Q,F)
      DIMENSION  A(20,20),F(20,20),Q(21),C(20)
      Q(1)=1.
      K=1
      DO 11 I=1,N
      DO 11 J=1,N
   11 F(I,J)=A(I,J)
    1 CONTINUE
      Q(K+1)=0.
      DO 2 I=1,N
      Q(K+1)=Q(K+1)+F(I,I)
    2 CONTINUE
      FK=K
      Q(K+1)=-Q(K+1)/FK
      DO 3 I=1,N
      F(I,I)=F(I,I)+Q(K+1)
    3 CONTINUE
      IF(K-N+1)71,41,71
   71 DO 7 J=1,N
      DO 6 I=1,N
      C(I)=F(I,J)
    6 CONTINUE
      DO 7 I=1,N
      F(I,J)=0.
      DO 7 IS=1,N
      F(I,J)=F(I,J)+A(I,IS)*C(IS)
    7 CONTINUE
      K=K+1
      GO TO 1
   41 Q(N+1)=0.
      DO 4 J=1,N
      Q(N+1)=Q(N+1)-A(1,J)*F(J,1)
```

```
 4 CONTINUE
   IF(Q(N+1))51,5,51
51 DO 52 I=1,N
   DO 52 J=1,N
52 F(I,J)=−F(I,J)/Q(N+1)
 5 RETURN
   END
```

With the above subroutine and subroutines of Chapter XI and Section 13.34 above, eigenvalues and eigenvectors can be found in a systematic way. Sometimes, however, it is not necessary to find all eigenvalues and eigenvectors, but to find only the largest eigenvalue, or some other specific information. Special purpose programs exist for such uses. There are also methods which, under some conditions, can be used to find eigenvalues directly from the matrix itself, without generating the characteristic equation first. These methods are available in the literature and will not be reported here.

EXERCISE XXIV

1. Determine the rank of the following matrices:

a. $\begin{pmatrix} 1 & 1 \\ 1 & 1 \end{pmatrix}$

b. $\begin{pmatrix} 1 & 2 & 3 & 4 & 5 \\ 1 & 2 & 3 & 4 & 6 \end{pmatrix}$

c. $\begin{pmatrix} 1 & 2 & 3 \\ -2 & 1 & -2 \\ -1 & 3 & 1 \end{pmatrix}$

d. $\begin{pmatrix} 2 & -1 & 3 & 4 \\ 1 & -2 & -2 & -1 \\ 0 & 3 & 7 & 6 \end{pmatrix}$

2. Determine whether the following systems are consistent or inconsistent:

a. $\begin{aligned} x+2y+z &= 4 \\ -2x-4y-2z &= 3 \end{aligned}$

b. $\begin{aligned} x+2y &= 6 \\ x+3y &= 8 \end{aligned}$

c. $\begin{aligned} x+3y &= 7 \\ 2x-y &= 4 \\ 4x+5y &= 18 \end{aligned}$

d. $\begin{aligned} x+2y &= 8 \\ 3x-y &= 2 \\ 2x+y &= 6 \end{aligned}$

3. Solve completely the following systems of equations:

a. $\begin{aligned} x+2y &= 0 \\ -2x-4y &= 0 \end{aligned}$

b. $\begin{aligned} x+y-z &= 2 \\ x-y+z &= 3 \end{aligned}$

c. $\begin{aligned} x+3y-z &= 4 \\ 2x-y+2z &= 3 \\ 3x+2y+z &= 7 \end{aligned}$

d. $\begin{aligned} x+2y+z &= 1 \\ 2x-y+z &= 2 \\ 3x-y+4z &= 3 \end{aligned}$

4. Find all eigenvalues and eigenvectors for the following matrices:

a. $\begin{pmatrix} 0 & 1 \\ 1 & 0 \end{pmatrix}$ b. $\begin{pmatrix} 1 & 3 \\ -2 & -4 \end{pmatrix}$

c. $\begin{pmatrix} 1 & 2 \\ -2 & -3 \end{pmatrix}$ d. $\begin{pmatrix} 1 & 0 & 1 \\ 0 & 1 & 1 \\ 0 & 0 & 2 \end{pmatrix}$

e. $\begin{pmatrix} 2 & 1 & 2 \\ -1 & 0 & 0 \\ -1 & -1 & -1 \end{pmatrix}$

5. Find the number of multiplications required to find the rank of 10 by 15 matrix using SUBROUTINE MARANK of Section 13.32, if the rank turns out to be 8.

6. Write a program that will input a system of linear equations up to 20 by 20, call subroutine SOLINEQ of Section 13.34 to obtain all solutions, and print the result.

7. Write a program that will input a square matrix up to 19 by 19, call subroutine CHAREQ of Section 13.42 to obtain the characteristic equation, call the appropriate subroutine from Chapter XI to find the largest real root, call subroutine SOLINEQ of Section 13.34 to find the corresponding eigenvector, and print the result.

CHAPTER XIV *Curve-Fitting*

14.1 INTRODUCTION

One of the fields of elementary mathematics where the digital computer has most to contribute is that of curve-fitting. This process is one which is extremely laborious for hand computation, so much so that only quite simple curve-fitting operations were ordinarily done before the day of the digital computer. With the digital computer, however, standard types of programs are available that allow very rapid determination of the best-fitting curve from a wide family of possible choices. No attempt will be made here to catalog the ever-growing variety of standard subroutines available. Instead, we shall concern ourselves with the fundamentals of curve-fitting and with some of the basic techniques employed in machine programs for curve-fitting, in order to lay a proper foundation upon which the reader can build in areas of his own particular interest.

The basic problem in curve-fitting can be described as follows. We have a set of measured values of a quantity x, and an associated set of measured values of another quantity y. We wish to find some functional relation:

$$y = f(x)$$

between x and y which is satisfied by our sets of measured values (x_1, y_1), (x_2, y_2), etc., and which will allow us to infer reasonable values of y for other values of x, where we have no measurement. If we were to stop here, our description of the problem would be quite incomplete. What do we mean by "reasonable" values of y? In Figure 14–1 are shown five points (x_1, y_1), ... , (x_5, y_5), and three different curves passing through all five points. The dashed curve is made up of straight line segments. The dotted curve is a smooth arc. The solid curve is a wildly oscillating function with a singularity. All pass through all of the given points. How are we to decide which of these is the best fit? If we have no further information upon which

361

to act, we are intuitively drawn to the smooth, dotted curve as the most reasonable fit. This is the type of curve-fitting generally used for interpolation, a process discussed in the next chapter. Quite freqently, however, we know

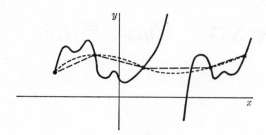

Figure 14–1

that for physical reasons the functional relation $y = f(x)$ must have some particular function form, e.g.:

$$y = c_1 e^{c_2 x}$$

or perhaps:

$$y = c_1 \tan x + c_2 \cos c_3 x$$

where the constants c_1, c_2, c_3 are not known. In such cases, in attempting to find the best fit we are restricted choosing the constants to give the most reasonable fit. We cannot even be sure in this case that our "best" function will pass through all the given points. Ordinarily it will be impossible to choose the constants so that this will happen. The usual practical problem in curve-fitting, then, is of the following type. We have some set of values $(x_1, y_1), (x_2, y_2), \ldots, (x_n, y_n)$, which we wish to fit with a curve of the form:

$$y = f(x, c_1, c_2, c_3, \ldots, c_m) \tag{14-1}$$

where the function f is completely specified except for the particular values of the constants $c_1, c_2, \ldots, c_m$. We wish to choose these constants so that our measured values will most nearly satisfy the above expression.

Again, we have trouble being sufficiently specific. What do we mean by "most nearly satisfy?" Once we have selected the constants $c_1, \ldots, c_m$, if we substitute in our measured values we will find that the equation:

$$f(x_i, c_1, c_2, \ldots, c_m) - y_i = 0$$

is not satisfied exactly, but instead, there is some error in each case:

$$f(x_1, c_1, c_2, \ldots, c_m) - y_1 = \delta_1$$
$$f(x_2, c_1, c_2, \ldots, c_m) - y_2 = \delta_2$$

$$\cdot \qquad \qquad (14\text{-}2)$$

$$\cdot$$

$$\cdot$$

$$f(x_n, c_1, c_2, \ldots, c_m) - y_n = \delta_n$$

the quantities $\delta_1, \delta_2, \ldots, \delta_n$ representing the amount of error in the fit. Depending upon the type of fit desired, we might define that fit to be "best" that causes the quantity $|\delta_1| + |\delta_2| + |\delta_3| + \cdots + |\delta_n|$ to be a minimum, and accept as our solution the values of $c_1, c_2, \ldots, c_m$ which cause this to happen. As another example, we might define that fit to be "best" that causes the quantity $\delta_1{}^2 + \delta_2{}^2 + \cdots + \delta_n{}^2$ to be a minimum, and accept as our solution the values of $c_1, c_2, \ldots, c_m$ which cause this to happen. Ordinarily, the latter set of c's will turn out to be different from the preceding set. This latter criterion of goodness of fit, the so-called "least squares" criterion, is by far the most widely used, and is the one we will discuss in the present chapter.

14.2 LINEAR FORMULAE

An extremely wide variety of curve-fitting problems can be grouped into one category, and can be solved with what is basically one machine program. These consist of all curve-fitting problems where the undetermined constants appear only in linear form, that is to say, the functional relation between x and y is of the form:

$$y = c_1 f_1(x) + c_2 f_2(x) + \cdots + c_m f_m(x) \qquad (14\text{-}3)$$

where the functions $f_1(x)$, $f_2(x)$, $f_3(x)$, etc. are completely known functions of x. Specific examples of this type will be mentioned shortly. In this case if we have n sets of measured values, (x_1, y_1), (x_2, y_2), $\ldots$, (x_n, y_n), and we substitute these into the given equation, we *would like* to satisfy the equations:

$$c_1 f_1(x_1) + c_2 f_2(x_1) + \cdots + c_m f_m(x_1) = y_1$$
$$c_1 f_1(x_2) + c_2 f_2(x_2) + \cdots + c_m f_m(x_2) = y_2$$

$$\cdot$$

$$\cdot$$

$$\cdot$$

$$c_1 f_1(x_n) + c_2 f_2(x_n) + \cdots + c_m f_m(x_n) = y_n$$

Since the quantities x_1, x_2, etc. are known numbers, the quantities $f_1(x_1)$, $f_2(x_1)$, etc. are known numbers, so the above equations are just a set of n linear equations for the m unknowns, $c_1, c_2, \ldots, c_m$. If n is equal to m, there is exactly one solution (provided that the determinant of coefficients is not zero), i.e., there is one set of values for $c_1, c_2, \ldots, c_m$ that will cause the above equations to be satisfied. If n is less than m, there are less equations than unknowns and there are an infinite number of solutions, each of which represents a curve passing through the given points. The problem in this case is not completely determined, and we cannot find a single "best" fit without further information of some sort. If n is greater than m, there are more equations than unknowns, and there is no solution. In this case we look for a solution in the "least squares" sense. We write the equations in the form:

$$c_1 f_1(x_1) + c_2 f_2(x_1) + \cdots + c_m f_m(x_1) - y_1 = \delta_1$$
$$c_1 f_1(x_2) + c_2 f_2(x_2) + \cdots + c_m f_m(x_2) - y_2 = \delta_2$$

$$\cdot$$

$$\cdot \qquad\qquad\qquad\qquad\qquad\qquad\qquad\text{(14-4)}$$

$$\cdot$$

$$c_1 f_1(x_n) + c_2 f_2(x_n) + \cdots + c_m f_m(x_n) - y_n = \delta_n$$

The quantities δ_1, δ_2, etc. are the "residuals." For a perfect fit these residuals would all be zero. Since we cannot make them be zero, we try instead to make them all small by looking for the values of $c_1, c_2, \ldots, c_m$ which will minimize the expression $\delta_1^2 + \delta_2^2 + \cdots + \delta_n^2$. In curve-fitting, this last situation, in which there are more equations than unknowns, is the common one. We will discuss its solution shortly, but first will describe some particular cases of linear formulae.

14.21 Polynomial Fits

If in the general expression (14-3) of the preceding section we take

$$f_1(x) = 1$$
$$f_2(x) = x$$
$$f_3(x) = x^2$$

$$\cdot$$

$$\cdot$$

$$\cdot$$

$$f_m(x) = x^{m-1}$$

we obtain:

$$y = c_1 + c_2 x + c_3 x^2 + \cdots + c_m x^{m-1}$$

that is to say, we are attempting to fit the data with a polynomial of degree $m - 1$. Thus, the general method of fitting with a linear formula contains polynomials as a special case. If we have n points we wish to fit with a polynomial, and if we have a choice of the degree of the polynomial, the following considerations are of interest.

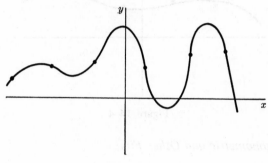

Figure 14–2

From the preceding section it is clear that we can pass one and only one polynomial of degree $n-1$ through all n points. As is indicated in Figure 14–2, this may not be a very satisfying fit, since the polynomial may oscillate violently between the points being fitted. A smoother curve is obtained, at the expense of some error in fit at the points themselves, by using a polynomial

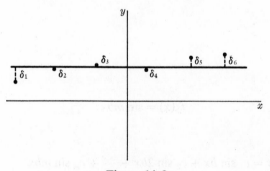

Figure 14–3

of lower degree. As an extreme case, Figure 14–3 shows a fit with a polynomial of degree zero, a horizontal straight line. In most cases, the most satisfying fit is obtained by a polynomial of some intermediate degree, compromising between goodness of fit at the measured values and smoothness of the curve.   Figure 14–4 shows the type of fit that might be attainable in the present example with a polynomial of degree four.   Although no completely general rule can be given, it is frequently desirable to conduct polynomial fits using a polynomial whose degree is from 1/2 to 3/4 of the number of points to be fitted.

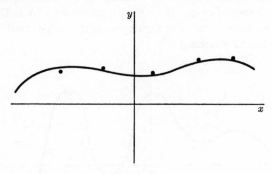

Figure 14–4

14.22   Trigonometric and Other Fits

If in the general expression (14-3) of Section 14.2 we take:

$$f_1(x) = \sin bx$$

$$f_2(x) = \sin 2bx$$

$$f_3(x) = \sin 3bx$$

.

.

.

$$f_m(x) = \sin mbx$$

we obtain:

$$y = c_1 \sin bx + c_2 \sin 2bx + \cdots + c_m \sin mbx$$

that is to say, the fitting function is the first m terms of the so-called Fourier sine series.   An expansion of this type is frequently the natural one to use for problems in physics or engineering.   In applications of this type of fit the constant b would be chosen ahead of time to give the sine functions the desired periodicity.

Instead of sine terms, a series in cosine terms could be used, or a series of mixed sine and cosine terms. These types of series are most useful in problems in which x is constrained to some restricted range of values, and the values outside that region are not of interest.

In passing, it might be mentioned that in some problems it is of interest to express y in terms of some of the more advanced functions of mathematics. In cases in which axial symmetry is present, Bessel functions are frequently the most useful:

$$y = c_1 J_0(\alpha_1 x) + c_2 J_0(\alpha_2 x) + \cdots + c_m J_0(\alpha_m x)$$

In other problems, Legendre polynomials are the natural functions to use:

$$y = c_1 P_0(x) + c_2 P_1(x) + \cdots + c_m P_{m-1}(x)$$

These are mentioned at this point in an elementary treatment only to indicate the wide range of applicability of the formulation given above for fitting by a linear formula. Indeed, it can be applied almost unchanged to problems in more than one dimension, for example, those involving expansions in spherical harmonics.

14.23   Method of Performing the Least Squares Fit

The method of finding the least squares solution to equations (14-4) of Section 14.2 will first be derived symbolically and then described by a flow chart. Those equations can be abbreviated:

$$\sum_{i=1}^{m} c_i f_i(x_j) - y_j = \delta_j, \qquad j = 1, 2, \ldots, n \tag{14-5}$$

and we desire to choose the c_i's so that:

$$\sum_{j=1}^{n} \delta_j^2 = \text{minimum} \tag{14-6}$$

This last quantity is to be regarded as a function of the c_i's. A necessary condition for it to be a minimum is that its partial derivatives by each of the c_i's must vanish, i.e.:

$$\frac{\partial}{\partial c_k} \sum_{j=1}^{n} \delta_j^2 = 0 \qquad \text{for } k = 1, 2, \ldots, m$$

or

$$\sum_{j=1}^{n} \delta_j \frac{\partial \delta_j}{\partial c_k} = 0 \qquad \text{for } k = 1, 2, \ldots, m \tag{14-7}$$

From (14-5):

$$\frac{\partial \delta_j}{\partial c_k} = f_k(x_j)$$

Substituting this, and the value for δ_j from (14-5) into (14-7), we have:

$$\sum_{j=1}^{n} \left[\sum_{i=1}^{m} c_i f_i(x_j) - y_j \right] f_k(x_j) = 0 \qquad \text{for } k = 1, 2, \ldots, m$$

or

$$\sum_{i=1}^{m} c_i \sum_{j=1}^{n} f_i(x_j) f_k(x_j) = \sum_{j=1}^{n} y_j f_k(x_j) \qquad \text{for } k = 1, 2, \ldots, m \qquad \textbf{(14-8)}$$

This is a system of m linear equations for the m unknowns $c_1, c_2, \ldots, c_m$, and can be solved by any of the methods of Chapter XII. In order to clarify the structure of the formula, which is perhaps a little confusing because of the double summation notation, an example will be worked through following the same procedure.

Example 1. Find the formula of the type $y = c_1 e^x + c_2 e^{2x}$ that will give the best least squares fit to the points $(0, 1)$, $(1, -2)$, $(2, -40)$.

We have:

$$c_1 e^0 + c_2 e^0 - 1 = \delta_1$$
$$c_1 e^1 + c_2 e^2 + 2 = \delta_2$$
$$c_1 e^2 + c_2 e^4 + 40 = \delta_3$$

We desire that:

$$\delta_1{}^2 + \delta_2{}^2 + \delta_3{}^2 = \text{minimum}$$

so we set:

$$\delta_1 \frac{\partial \delta_1}{\partial c_1} + \delta_2 \frac{\partial \delta_2}{\partial c_1} + \delta_3 \frac{\partial \delta_3}{\partial c_1} = 0$$

and:

$$\delta_1 \frac{\partial \delta_1}{\partial c_2} + \delta_2 \frac{\partial \delta_2}{\partial c_2} + \delta_3 \frac{\partial \delta_3}{\partial c_2} = 0$$

Now:

$$\frac{\partial \delta_1}{\partial c_1} = e^0, \qquad \frac{\partial \delta_2}{\partial c_1} = e^1, \text{ etc.}$$

so we have:

$$(c_1e^0 + c_2e^0 - 1)e^0 + (c_1e^1 + c_2e^2 + 2)e^1 + (c_1e + c_2e^4 + 40)e^2 = 0$$
$$(c_1e^0 + c_2e^0 - 1)e^0 + (c_1e^1 + c_2e^2 + 2)e^2 + (c_1e^2 + c_2e^4 + 40)e^4 = 0$$

or, regrouping terms:

$$c_1(e^0e^0 + e^1e^1 + e^2e^2) + c_2(e^0e^0 + e^2e^1 + e^4e^2) = e^0 - 2e^1 - 40e^2$$
$$c_1(e^0e^0 + e^1e^2 + e^2e^4) + c_2(e^0e^0 + e^2e^2 + e^4e^4) = e^0 - 2e^2 - 40e^4$$

or, substituting rough numerical values:

$$63c_1 + 424c_2 = -296$$
$$424c_1 + 3036c_2 = -2198$$

So that:

$$c_1 \approx 2, \qquad c_2 \approx -1$$

In order to proceed with the construction of a flow chart, we note that the problem is to solve the set of linear equations:

$$\sum_{i=1}^{m} a_{ki}c_i = b_k \qquad \text{for } k = 1, 2, \ldots, m \tag{14-9}$$

where:

$$a_{ki} = \sum_{j=1}^{n} f_i(x_j)f_k(x_j) \tag{14-10}$$

$$b_k = \sum_{j=1}^{n} y_j f_k(x_j) \tag{14-11}$$

The process can be written in a particularly nice form in matrix notation. Let:

$$F = \begin{pmatrix} f_1(x_1) & f_2(x_1) & \cdots & f_m(x_1) \\ f_1(x_2) & f_2(x_2) & \cdots & f_m(x_2) \\ \cdot & & & \\ \cdot & & & \\ \cdot & & & \\ f_1(x_n) & f_2(x_n) & \cdots & f_m(x_n) \end{pmatrix} \tag{14-12}$$

and:

$$
b = \begin{pmatrix} b_1 \\ b_2 \\ b_3 \\ \cdot \\ \cdot \\ \cdot \\ b_m \end{pmatrix}, \quad
y = \begin{pmatrix} y_1 \\ y_2 \\ \cdot \\ \cdot \\ \cdot \\ \cdot \\ y_m \end{pmatrix}, \quad
c = \begin{pmatrix} c_1 \\ c_2 \\ \cdot \\ \cdot \\ \cdot \\ \cdot \\ c_m \end{pmatrix}
$$

Further let $\tilde{F}$ stand for the matrix obtained by interchanging rows and columns in F. (The symbol $\tilde{F}$ is read "F-transpose.") Then:

$$
\tilde{F} = \begin{pmatrix}
f_1(x_1) & f_1(x_2) & \cdots & f_1(x_n) \\
f_2(x_1) & f_2(x_2) & \cdots & f_2(x_n) \\
\cdot \\
\cdot \\
\cdot \\
f_m(x_1) & f_m(x_2) & \cdots & f_m(x_n)
\end{pmatrix}
$$

Let:

$$
A = \begin{pmatrix}
a_{11} & a_{12} & \cdot & \cdot & \cdot & a_{1m} \\
a_{21} & a_{22} & \cdot & \cdot & \cdot & a_{2m} \\
\cdot \\
\cdot \\
\cdot \\
a_{m1} & a_{m2} & \cdot & \cdot & \cdot & a_{mm}
\end{pmatrix}
$$

With this notation, equations (14-9), (14-10), and (14-11) become:

$$Ac = b$$

$$A = \tilde{F}F$$

$$b = \tilde{F}y$$

These equations really say the following:

If we wish the least squares solution to the system of equations:

$$Fc = y \tag{14-13}$$

where there are more equations than unknowns, we multiply both sides by $\tilde{F}$, and then solve the resulting system, which now has the same number of equations and unknowns:

$$(\tilde{F}F)c = \tilde{F}y$$

In order to illustrate these points further, Example 1 will be redone, in matrix notation.

We have:

$$f_1(x) = e^x, \qquad f_2(x) = e^{2x}, \qquad x_1 = 0$$

$$y_1 = 1, \qquad x_2 = 1, \qquad y_2 = -2, \qquad x_3 = 2, \qquad y_3 = -40$$

Hence the set of equations we wish to solve is:

$$\begin{pmatrix} e^0 & e^0 \\ e^1 & e^2 \\ e^2 & e^4 \end{pmatrix} \begin{pmatrix} c_1 \\ c_2 \end{pmatrix} = \begin{pmatrix} 1 \\ -2 \\ -40 \end{pmatrix}$$

Multiplying both sides by the transpose of the matrix on the left:

$$\begin{pmatrix} e^0 & e^1 & e^2 \\ e^0 & e^2 & e^4 \end{pmatrix} \begin{pmatrix} e^0 & e^0 \\ e^1 & e^2 \\ e^2 & e^4 \end{pmatrix} \begin{pmatrix} c_1 \\ c_2 \end{pmatrix} = \begin{pmatrix} e^0 & e^1 & e^2 \\ e^0 & e^2 & e^4 \end{pmatrix} \begin{pmatrix} 1 \\ -2 \\ -40 \end{pmatrix}$$

Multiplying out the matrices, we have approximately:

$$\begin{pmatrix} 63 & 424 \\ 424 & 3036 \end{pmatrix} \begin{pmatrix} c_1 \\ c_2 \end{pmatrix} = \begin{pmatrix} -296 \\ -2198 \end{pmatrix}$$

These are the same equations for c_1 and c_2 that were obtained in Example 1 earlier.

14.24   Flow Chart and Program for Least Squares Fit

The flow chart, Figure 14–5, describes, in a rather terse form, the performance of a least squares fit as discussed in the preceding section. The process described by the flow chart consists of application of a very limited set of routines, as follows:

(1) m different routines for evaluating the functions $f_1(x), f_2(x), \ldots, f_m(x)$.
(2)   A routine for multiplying a matrix by its transpose.
(3)   A routine for solving an m-by-m system of linear equations.

ENTER

$$z_{ij} = f_i(x_j) \qquad \begin{cases} i=1,\ldots,m \\ j=1,\ldots,n \end{cases}$$

$$a_{ki} = \sum_{j=1}^{n} z_{ij} z_{kj}, \qquad \begin{cases} i=1,\ldots,m \\ k=1,\ldots,i \end{cases}$$

$$a_{ik} = a_{ki}, \qquad \begin{cases} i=1,\ldots,m \\ k=i+1,\ldots,m \end{cases}$$

$$b_k = \sum_{j=1}^{n} y_j z_{kj}, \qquad k=1,\ldots,m$$

EXIT to routine for solving system of linear equations

$$\sum_{i=1}^{m} a_{ki} c_i = b_k, \qquad k=1,\ldots,m$$

Figure 14–5: Least squares fit—expression linear in coefficients

The FORTRAN subroutine given below will perform the least squares fit of a function having M unknown coefficients to N points, where M can be as large as 20 and N as large as 50.   The correct functions FU1F(X), FU2F(X), etc., must be inserted, depending on the type of fit wanted.   It calls the subroutine GAUSID of the preceding chapter to solve the system of linear equations.   Because the symmetry of the coefficients, the Gauss-Seidel method usually converges for this particular type of problem.   (Theoretically it always does, but the use of approximate numbers in the computer sometimes destroys convergence.)

```
SUBROUTINE LSTSQ(X,Y,N,C,M)
DIMENSION X(50),Y(50),C(20),F(20,50),A(20,20),B(20)
FU1F(X)=
FU2F(X)=           insert correct expressions for
   .                 f₁(x), ... , fₘ(x)
   .
FUMF(X)=
```

```
    DO 1 J=1,N
    F(1,J)=FU1F(X(J))
    F(2,J)=FU2F(X(J))
        .
        .
        .
  1 F(M,J)=FUMF(X(J))
    DO 3 I=1,M
    DO 3 K=1,I
    A(K,I)=0.
    DO 2 J=1,N
  2 A(K,I)=A(K,I)+F(I,J)*F(K,J)
  3 A(I,K)=A(K,I)
    DO 4 K=1,M
    B(K)=0
    DO 4 J=1,N
  4 B(K)=B(K)+Y(J)*F(K,J)
    CALL  GAUSID(A,M,B,C)
    RETURN
    END
```

14.25 Machine Time Requirements for the Least Squares Fit

It is interesting to make a rough estimate of the machine time that will be required to make a fit of an expression having m undetermined coefficients to a set of n points. First m different functions must be evaluated, each a total of n times. The time to evaluate these functions may vary considerably. For a polynomial, only one multiplication is required for each function, since each power of x is obtained by multiplying the preceding power by x. For sines, cosines, exponentials, etc., from five to ten multiplication times might be required for each function. Let us first consider only polynomial fits. For these, a total of nm multiplications will be required to form all the functions $f_i(x_j)$. The next step is to perform the multiplications necessary to obtain the elements a_{ij} and b_j. Each element requires n multiplications, and there are:

$$(m + 1) + m + (m - 1) + \cdots + 1 = (m + 1)(m + 2)/2$$

elements, or about $m^2/2$ elements, for a total of about $m^2n/2$ multiplications. From Chapter XII, the solution of an m-by-m set of linear equations will require about $m^3/2$ multiplication times. Thus, for a polynomial fit, we require about:

$$nm + m^2n/2 + m^3/2 \text{ multiplication times}$$

For example, for a 5th degree polynomial (6 coefficients) and 8 points, the time is about:

$$48 + 144 + 108 = 300 \text{ multiplication times}$$

If $t_m = 10$ milliseconds, this is 3 seconds. If $t_m = 10$ microseconds, it is about 3 milliseconds. For a 19th degree polynomial (20 undetermined coefficients) and 30 points, the time is about:

$$600 + 6000 + 4000 = 10{,}000 \text{ multiplication times}$$

If $t_m = 10$ milliseconds, this is about 2 minutes. If $t_m = 10$ microseconds, it is about .1 second. If instead of polynomials, we are making a fit using functions requiring 10 multiplication times to compute, our rough estimate for total time becomes:

$$10nm + m^2n/2 + m^3/2$$

For large values of m and n, this will give times essentially the same as the previous expressions. As has been indicated by the above examples the computer can quite handily accomplish least squares fits on systems involving many data points and many undetermined coefficients.

14.3 WEIGHTED LEAST SQUARES

We have said that the most widely used criterion for goodness of fit is that the sum of squares of the residuals:

$$\delta_1{}^2 + \delta_2{}^2 + \delta_3{}^2 + \cdots + \delta_n{}^2$$

be a minimum. A rather common variation of this criterion is to require instead that the expression:

$$w_1\delta_1{}^2 + w_2\delta_2{}^2 + \cdots + w_n\delta_n{}^2$$

be a minimum, where $w_1, w_2, \ldots, w_n$ are selected positive numbers. In the upper expression above, we are essentially saying that we are willing to accept as big an error for any one of the points (x_i, y_i) as for any other. If we use the lower expression, we are saying, in effect, that we consider a good fit at one point to have more weight than that at another point. The following two examples will illustrate the effect of weighting.

Example 1. Find the best least squares fit of the form $y = c_1 + c_2x$ for the three points (0, 0), (1, 1), and (2, 1).

Following the procedure of Section 14.23, we write:

$$\begin{pmatrix} 1 & 0 \\ 1 & 1 \\ 1 & 2 \end{pmatrix} \begin{pmatrix} c_1 \\ c_2 \end{pmatrix} = \begin{pmatrix} 0 \\ 1 \\ 1 \end{pmatrix}$$

Multiplying by the transpose:

$$\begin{pmatrix} 1 & 1 & 1 \\ 0 & 1 & 2 \end{pmatrix} \begin{pmatrix} 1 & 0 \\ 1 & 1 \\ 1 & 2 \end{pmatrix} \begin{pmatrix} c_1 \\ c_2 \end{pmatrix} = \begin{pmatrix} 1 & 1 & 1 \\ 0 & 1 & 2 \end{pmatrix} \begin{pmatrix} 0 \\ 1 \\ 1 \end{pmatrix}$$

So the equations are:

$$3c_1 + 3c_2 = 2$$
$$3c_1 + 5c_2 = 3$$

and the solution is $c_1 = 1/6$, $c_2 = 1/2$.

Example 2. Find the best least squares fit of the form $y = c_1 + c_2 x$ for the four points $(0, 0)$, $(1, 1)$, $(2,1)$, and $(2, 1)$.

Here we are weighting the point $(2, 1)$ double by using it twice. A little reflection will show that this is the same as minimizing the expression:

$$\delta_1^2 + \delta_2^2 + 2\delta_3^2$$

i.e., assigning double weight to the point. For the moment, let us treat the problem as if we had four points, so that we can use the procedures we have already learned. The equations from which we obtain the coefficients are:

$$\begin{pmatrix} 1 & 0 \\ 1 & 1 \\ 1 & 2 \\ 1 & 2 \end{pmatrix} \begin{pmatrix} c_1 \\ c_2 \end{pmatrix} = \begin{pmatrix} 0 \\ 1 \\ 1 \\ 1 \end{pmatrix}$$

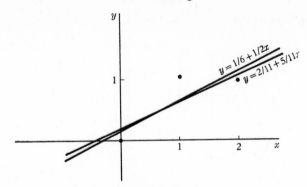

Figure 14–6

Upon multiplying by the transpose, we obtain:

$$4c_1 + 5c_2 = 3$$

$$5c_1 + 9c_2 = 5$$

and the solution is $c_1 = 2/11$, $c_2 = 5/11$.

Figure 14–6 shows the solutions to both Example 1 and Example 2. Clearly the weighting in Example 2 has caused the chosen line to be nearer to the point (2,1). Weighting is usually required when the experimental data is known to be better for some of the points than for others. There are rules from the field of statistics that say what the weighting factor should be. For example, if the measurement error itself is the same at all data points, then the weighting factor w_i for each point should be proportional to the number of independent measurements available at that point. If the measurements have different intrinsic errors at the different points, the weighting factor assigned should be inversely proportional to the square of the intrinsic error (or standard deviation).

The weighting factor can be absorbed directly into the calculation procedure described in Section 13.23 as follows: If the point (x_j, y_j) is to be assigned a weight w_j, we multiply the jth equation by $\sqrt{w_j}$. This will be demonstrated by reworking Example 2, above.

Example 3. Find the best least squares fit of the form $y = c_1 + c_2 x$ for the three points (0, 0), (1, 1), and (2, 1), giving the last point double weight.

We construct the equations:

$$\begin{pmatrix} 1 & 0 \\ 1 & 1 \\ \sqrt{2} & 2\sqrt{2} \end{pmatrix} \begin{pmatrix} c_1 \\ c_2 \end{pmatrix} = \begin{pmatrix} 0 \\ 1 \\ \sqrt{2} \end{pmatrix}$$

Upon multiplying by the transpose, we again obtain the equations:

$$4c_1 + 5c_2 = 3$$
$$5c_1 + 9c_2 = 5$$

and the solution is $c_1 = 2/11$, $c_2 = 5/11$.

14.4 NONLINEAR FORMULAE

Occasions arise when it is desirable or necessary to fit an expression with a nonlinear formula. Here the general principles are the same as with linear formulae, but the equations to be solved for the undetermined coefficients in this case will be nonlinear, and their solution presents a more difficult problem. The particular techniques which are of use in this situation will be discussed.

14.41 *Formulae Reducible to Linear*

If all the undetermined coefficients appear as factors or as exponents in a product, they can be placed in a linear relation by taking logarithms. An example will illustrate this point.

Example 1. Fit a curve of the form $y = c_1 e^{c_2 x}$ to the points $(0, 1)$, $(1, 2)$, $(2, 6)$.

If we take logarithms of both sides, we obtain:

$$\ln y = \ln c_1 + c_2 x$$

Now let:

$$k_1 = \ln c_1 \quad \text{and} \quad z = \ln y$$

and we have:

$$z = \ln y = k_1 + c_2 x$$

so our problem is now to fit three points of the form (x, z) with this linear expression. The points are $(0, 0)$, $(1, \ln 2)$, $(2, \ln 6)$. We can use the method of Section 14.23 to solve this problem. The equations are:

$$\begin{pmatrix} 1 & 0 \\ 1 & 1 \\ 1 & 2 \end{pmatrix} \begin{pmatrix} k_1 \\ c_2 \end{pmatrix} = \begin{pmatrix} 0 \\ \ln 2 \\ \ln 6 \end{pmatrix}$$

Upon multiplying by the transpose, we obtain (roughly):

$$3k_1 + 3c_2 = 2.48$$
$$3k_1 + 5c_2 = 4.28$$

so that:

$$k_1 = -.07, \qquad c_2 = .9$$

and:

$$c_1 = e^{-.07} \approx .9$$

and our fit is:

$$y = .9e^{.9x}$$

The solution we have just obtained bears some closer investigation. It is indeed a least squares fit, but perhaps not the one we really wanted. In taking logarithms of both sides of the initial expression, we have introduced a weighting. We have treated the problem as if it were to minimize:

$$\sum \delta_i^2, \qquad \text{where } \delta_i = k_1 + c_2 x_i - \ln y_i$$

Thus each δ_i is then the error in $\ln y_i$. This is not the same as minimizing:

$$\sum \gamma_i^2, \qquad \text{where } \gamma_i = c_1 e^{c_2 x_i} - y_i$$

In this last expression each γ_i is the error in the corresponding y_i. In the former expression, each δ_i is the error in $\ln y_i$. Now if y is in error by an amount Δy, then $\ln y$ is in error by an amount which is approximately $\Delta y / y$. Hence:

$$\delta_i \approx \gamma_i / y_i$$

and if we minimize:

$$\sum \delta_i^2$$

we are minimizing:

$$\sum (\gamma_i / y_i)^2$$

that is to say, we have weighted each γ_i by the inverse square of y_i. If we wish to weight all the errors in y_i equally, we would have to minimize:

$$\sum y_i^2 \delta_i^2$$

Example 2. Make a least squares fit of the form $y = c_1 e^{c_2 x}$ to the points $(0, 1)$, $(1, 2)$, $(2, 6)$, giving equal weight to errors in y at all three points.

This is the same as Example 1, except that we now insist that weighting factors be used as described above. We do this by again writing:

$$z = \ln y = k_1 + c_2 x$$

and use the method of Section 14.23, multiplying each row by y_i for proper weighting. We obtain:

$$\begin{pmatrix} 1 & 0 \\ 2 & 2 \\ 6 & 12 \end{pmatrix} \begin{pmatrix} k_1 \\ c_2 \end{pmatrix} = \begin{pmatrix} 0 \\ 2\ln 2 \\ 6\ln 6 \end{pmatrix}$$

so the equations are:

$$41k_1 + 76c_2 = 67.2760$$
$$76k_1 + 148c_2 = 131.7793$$

so that:

$$k_1 = -.2000, \qquad c_2 = .9932 \approx 1$$

and:

$$c_i = e^{k_1} = .8187 \approx .8$$

Figure 14–7 shows the curves of Examples 1 and 2.

Table I shows the values of the ordinates of the two curves at the three given points. It will be observed that the curve obtained in Example 2 misses all the points by about the same amount, while the curve obtained in Example 1

TABLE I

x	Given y	$y = .9e^{.9x}$ (Example 1)	$y = .8e^{x}$ (Example 2)
0	1	.9	.8
1	2	2.2	2.2
2	6	5.4	5.9

misses the point having ordinate 1 by .1, that having ordinate 2 by .2, and that having ordinate 6 by .6. That is to say, Example 2 gave us a fit having nearly equal *absolute* errors at the given point, whereas Example 1 gave us a fit having nearly equal *relative* errors.

The situation just demonstrated by the above examples is one that applies in general to curve-fitting problems where the coefficients can be put in a linear relation by taking logarithms of both sides of the fitting equation. If the least squares fit is made directly to the logarithmic expression, the *relative* errors are being given roughly equal weight. If it is desired to give the *absolute* errors equal weight, then weights proportional to the squares of the ordinates at the measured points must be introduced in performing the fit.

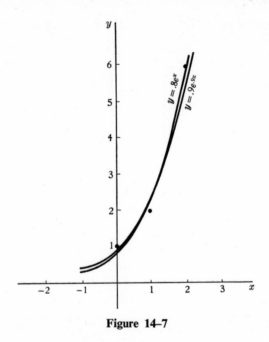

Figure 14–7

14.42 Formulae Not Reducible to Linear

When it is necessary to make a fit with a formula that cannot be written so as to put the undetermined constants in a linear relationship, then the problem of finding the constants becomes much more difficult. This is the general problem posed at the beginning of the chapter, where the fitting function:

$$y = f(x, c_1, c_2, \dots, c_m)$$

has no special properties we can use to simplify the problem. It is fortunately true that a large percentage of the practical problems fall into the easier types already discussed, but on occasion it is necessary to use this less tractable type of fit. In this case, the problem can be described as follows: We have a set of n relations:

$$f(x_1, c_1, c_2, \dots, c_m) - y_i = \delta_i, \qquad i = 1, \dots, n \qquad \textbf{(14-14)}$$

and we wish to choose the c's so as to make:

$$\sum_{i=1}^{n} \delta_i^2 \text{ a minimum}$$

A necessary condition is that:

$$\frac{\partial}{\partial c_j} \sum_{i=1}^{n} \delta_i^2 = 0 \qquad \text{for } j = 1, \dots, m \qquad \text{(14-15)}$$

or

$$\sum_{i=1}^{n} \delta_i \frac{\partial \delta_i}{\partial c_j} = 0 \qquad \text{for } j = 1, \dots, m \qquad \text{(14-16)}$$

Substituting in the value of δ_i, we have:

$$\sum_{=1}^{n} [f(x_i, c_1, c_2, \dots, c_m) - y_i] \frac{\partial f(x_i, c_1, c_2, \dots, c_m)}{\partial c_j}$$

$$= 0 \qquad \text{for } j = 1, \dots, m \qquad \text{(14-17)}$$

This is a system of m nonlinear equations for the c_j's, equations which may be transcendental, depending on the nature of the function f. In Chapter X we discussed methods of solving a transcendental equation in one unknown, and mentioned that these methods could be extended to several equations in several unknowns. The equations may, of course, have more than one root, so the problem of finding a scheme which will converge to the proper root may be a difficult one. Another complication is the fact that the expressions for the partial derivative of f by each of the c_j's is required. If f is a very involved function, the writing of these may in itself be quite a difficult task. Nonetheless the problem is by no means a hopeless one for the digital computer, even if one forces the machine to struggle brute force through the calculation as it has just been outlined. A particular iteration scheme, described in the next section, can sometimes be used to obtain the solution rather easily. Before discussing that scheme, in order to make the various aspects of the problem more clear, we will redo Example 2 of Section 14.41 following the procedure outlined above.

Example 1. Make a least squares fit of the form:

$$y = c_1 e^{c_2 x}$$

to the points $(0, 1)$, $(1, 2)$, and $(2, 6)$, giving equal weights to errors in y at all three points.

Since the formula is reducible to one having a linear relationship among the undetermined constants, the method described in Section 14.41 is the best one for this problem.   However, we will use the method described above in order to clarify the above discussion.   In our case:

$$f(x, c_1, c_2) = c_1 e^{c_2 x}$$

and:

$$\frac{\partial f(x, c_1, c_2)}{\partial c_1} = e^{c_2 x}$$

$$\frac{\partial f(x, c_1, c_2)}{\partial c_2} = x c_1 e^{c_2 x}$$

so that, substituting into (14-17), we obtain:

$$[c_1 e^{c_2 \cdot 0} - 1] e^{c_2 \cdot 0} + [c_1 e^{c_2 \cdot 1} - 2] e^{c_2 \cdot 1} + [c_1 e^{c_2 \cdot 2} - 6] e^{c_2 \cdot 2} = 0$$

and:

$$[c_1 e^{c_2 \cdot 0} - 1] . 0 . c_1 e^{c_2 \cdot 0} + [c_1 e^{c_2 \cdot 1} - 2] 1 . c_1 e^{c_2 \cdot 1} + [c_1 e^{c_2 \cdot 2} - 6] 2 . c_1 e^{c_2 \cdot 2} = 0$$

These simplify to:

$$c_1 e^{4 c_2} + (c_1 - 6) e^{2 c_2} - 2 e^{c_2} + c_1 - 1 = 0$$

and:

$$2 c_1 e^{3 c_2} + (c_1 - 12) e^{c_2} - 2 = 0$$

These are the equations for c_1 and c_2.   In this particular case they are not inordinately difficult to solve, since c_1 appears only to the first power.   We will not complete the solution, since it is not very instructive as to the techniques which might be employed on a digital computer.   We do point out, however, that these equations are indicative of the complexity of the equations one can become involved in even for rather simple functions $f(x, c_1, c_2, \ldots, c_m)$.

14.43   *Iteration Scheme for Formulae Not Reducible to Linear*

Let us suppose that we are attempting to fit a set of n points with the function:

$$y = f(x, c_1, c_2, \ldots, c_m)$$

and that we already have rough estimates for the constants $c_1, c_2, \ldots, c_m$, e.g.:

$$c_1 \approx k_1$$

$$c_2 \approx k_2$$

.

.

.

$$c_m \approx k_m$$

where the k_i are known. More precisely, we can say that:

$$c_1 = k_1 + E_1$$

$$c_2 = k_2 + E_2$$

.

.

.

$$c_m = k_m + E_m$$

where $E_1, E_2, \ldots, E_m$ are unknown but small. Then:

$$y = f(x, k_1 + E_1, k_2 + E_2, \ldots, k_m + E_m)$$

or, by Taylor's Formula:

$$y = f(x, k_1, k_2, \ldots, k_m) + E_1 \frac{\partial f(x, k_1, k_2, \ldots, k_m)}{\partial c_1} +$$

$$\cdots + E_m \frac{\partial f(x, k_1, k_2, \ldots, k_m)}{\partial c_m}$$

This is a different formula for y, one in which everything is known but the coefficients $E_1, E_2, \ldots, E_m$. Since these appear linearly, they can be determined by the method of Section 14.23. Once these are determined, we have a new estimate for the c_j's. If we desire, we can then use these new c values as $k_1, k_2, \ldots, k_m$, and repeat the process. If the initial guess was sufficiently good, the process *may* converge to the desired values $c_1, c_2, \ldots, c_m$.

Example 1. Make a least squares fit of the form:

$$y = c_1 e^{c_2 x}$$

to the points $(0, 1)$, $(1, 2)$, and $(2, 6)$, using as an initial estimate $c_1 \approx 1$, $c_2 \approx 1$.

We let $k_1 = 1$, $k_2 = 1$. Then:

$$f(x, k_1, k_2) = e^x$$

$$\frac{\partial f}{\partial c_1} = e^{c_2 x}, \quad \text{so} \quad \frac{\partial f(x, k_1, k_2)}{\partial c_1} = e^x$$

$$\frac{\partial f}{\partial c_2} = x c_1 e^{c_2 x}, \quad \text{so} \quad \frac{\partial f(x, k_1, k_2)}{\partial c_2} = x e^x$$

Hence the formula we desire to use for the first step is:

$$y = e^x + E_1 e^x + E_2 x e^x$$

In order to apply the method of Section 14.23, we combine the term e^x with y, giving:

$$y - e^x = E_1 e^x + E_2 x e^x$$

Now we can write the equations as:

$$\begin{pmatrix} e^0 & 0 \\ e^1 & e^1 \\ e^2 & 2e^2 \end{pmatrix} \begin{pmatrix} E_1 \\ E_2 \end{pmatrix} = \begin{pmatrix} 1 - e^0 \\ 2 - e^1 \\ 6 - e^2 \end{pmatrix}$$

or approximately:

$$\begin{pmatrix} 1 & 0 \\ 2.718 & 2.718 \\ 7.389 & 14.778 \end{pmatrix} \begin{pmatrix} E_1 \\ E_2 \end{pmatrix} = \begin{pmatrix} 0 \\ -.718 \\ -1.389 \end{pmatrix}$$

Upon multiplying by the transpose, we obtain:

$$62.987E_1 + 116.585E_2 = -12.216$$

$$116.585E_1 + 225.781E_2 = -22.479$$

$$E_1 = -.218, \quad E_2 = .0132$$

So that our next estimate is:

$$c_1 = .782, \quad c_2 = 1.0132$$

More careful calculation gives for this and succeeding steps:

Step	k_1	k_2	E_1	E_2
1	1	1	$-.218312$	.0131631
2	.781687	1.01316	$-.000921$	.0040536
3	.780766	1.01721	$-.000313$	.0002051
4	.780435	1.01742		

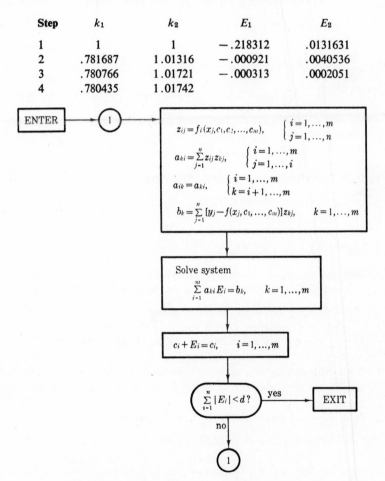

Figure 14–8: Least squares fit—nonlinear expressions

This solution differs slightly from the one obtained in Example 2 of Section 14.41. The difference is caused by the fact that the multiplication by y_i in Example 2 gave weighting that was only approximately, not exactly, correct.

The flow chart, Figure 14–8, describes the above iteration scheme. In this flow chart the functions f_1, f_2, etc. are defined by:

$$f_1(x, c_1, c_2, \ldots, c_m) = \frac{\partial f(x, c_1, c_2, \ldots, c_m)}{\partial c_1}$$

$$f_2(x, c_1, c_2, \ldots, c_m) = \frac{\partial f(x, c_1, c_2, \ldots, c_m)}{\partial c_2}$$

.

.

.

$$f_m(x, c_1, c_2, \ldots, c_m) = \frac{\partial f(x, c_1, c_2, \ldots, c_m)}{\partial c_m}$$

EXERCISE XXV

1. Perform the following least squares fits by hand:

   a. $y = c_1 + c_2 x$, points (0,1), (1,2), (2,4).
   b. $y = c_1 \sin x + c_2 \cos x$, points (0, 0), ($\pi/4$, 1), ($\pi/2$,1).
   c. $y = c_1 x + c_2 \ln x$, points (1,1), (2,2), (3,3).
   d. $y = c_1 + c_2 e^x$, points (0,2), (1,1), (2,0).

2. Draw a flow chart and write the program for making each of the following fits. Estimate the machine time to perform the calculation for 100 sets of data.

   a. Sixth degree polynomial, 10 points given.
   b. $y = c_1 + c_2 e^x + c_3 e^{2x} + c_4 e^{3x} + c_5 e^{4x}$, 8 points given.
   c. $y = c_1 + c_2 \cos x + c_3 \cos 2x + c_4 \cos 3x$, 20 points given.

3. Perform the following least squares fits by hand, giving equal weights to *relative* errors. Draw the curves and compute the errors at the given points.

   a. $y = \dfrac{c_1 e^{c_2 x}}{x^2}$, points (1,1000), (2,200), (3,100).
   b. $y = c_1 x^{c_2}$, points (1,2), (2,10), (3,20).

4. Perform the least squares fits of Problem 3, giving equal weights to *absolute* errors. Draw the curves and compute the errors at the given points.

5. Draw a flow chart and write the program for making each of the following fits, using the iteration method of Section 14.43.

   a. $y = c_1 e^{c_2 x} + c_3 e^{c_4 x}$,   10 points given.

   b. $y = c_1 \sin c_2 x + c_3 \sin c_4 x + c_5 \sin c_6 x$,   12 points given.

CHAPTER XV *Interpolation and Differentiation*

15.1 INTRODUCTION

We cannot claim to have covered the subject of digital computer use for mathematics through calculus without at least some coverage of the subjects of interpolation and differentiation. This coverage will be brief, compared to that usually given in books on numerical methods. The use of interpolation techniques is not as prevalent in digital computer calculations as in hand calculations, because of the already demonstrated capability of the computer to calculate quite complicated functions quickly. Computer methods for numerical differentiation find their main use in the solution of ordinary or partial differential equations, subjects which will not receive extensive coverage in this text.

It might seem unusual to combine the subjects of interpolation and differentiation in one chapter. As we proceed, however, it will become clear that in numerical work the two subjects are very closely related and do indeed belong as parts of the same discussion.

15.2 INTERPOLATION

The process of interpolation may be regarded as a special case of the general process of curve-fitting, discussed in the preceding chapter. A function, $y = f(x)$, is known to us only to the extent that we have some set of values (x_1, y_1), (x_2, y_2), ... , (x_m, y_m), and we wish to infer reasonable values of y for values of x intermediate between the given ones. The major difference between this problem and the general one of curve-fitting is that we are not interested in having the functional expression $f(x)$ have any particular form, or even having the same form for the entire range of values for x. For interpolation, then, we nearly always use polynomials for $f(x)$, since these are so easy to calculate. We may use different polynomials for different values of x. For example, we might use the first degree polynomial (straight line) passing through (x_1, y_1) and (x_2, y_2) to interpolate between the first two points, the

388

first degree polynomial passing through (x_2, y_2) and (x_3, y_3) to interpolate between the second and third points, and so forth. This is the ordinary method of linear interpolation commonly used in obtaining values between those tabulated in trigonometric or other tables. If more accurate interpolation were desired, it would be necessary to fit second, or third, or higher degree polynomials through the nearby points in order to obtain values intermediate between two points. The methods given in Chapter XIV are sufficient to allow us to do this without further ado. However, since we are now restricting ourselves to the case of polynomials, and particularly if we choose to let the given values of x_i be equally spaced, great simplifications occur which lead to formulae much easier to handle. These are the classical interpolation formulae of Newton, Stirling, Bessel, and others, found in standard texts on numerical analysis.

In Chapter VII we discussed methods of approximating functions by means of power series, and stated that such methods were ordinarily preferable to table look-up for finding values of a function in a computer. For functions whose formulae are extremely complicated in structure, or for functions which are only known at a set of points, a table of values can be stored in the memory, and a program written that will cause the machine to search through this table and then interpolate to obtain a value for the function at any point. Because of the amount of memory required to store a table of values, it is sometimes preferable to store a rather short table of somewhat widely spaced values and use a high order interpolation scheme, rather than store a long table of closely spaced values and use linear or other low order interpolation schemes.

15.21 Differences

As mentioned above, all the classic interpolation formulae involve passing a polynomial of degree n through $n + 1$ points and using points from this polynomial to represent the function of interest. For cases in which the values of x are equally spaced, the interpolation formulae are normally stated in terms of differences, so we will present them in this form.

If function $f(x)$ is known at a set of equally spaced values, spaced an amount h apart, the "differences" of $f(x)$ are defined as follows: Let the given values be:

$$y_1 = f(x_1)$$
$$y_2 = f(x_2) = f(x_1 + h)$$
$$y_3 = f(x_3) = f(x_1 + 2h)$$
$$y_4 = f(x_4) = f(x_1 + 3h)$$

The first difference of y_1 is defined to be:

$$\Delta y_1 = f(x_1 + h) - f(x_1) = y_2 - y_1$$

That of y_2 is:

$$\Delta y_2 = f(x_2 + h) - f(x_2) = y_3 - y_2$$

That of y_j is:

$$\Delta y_j = y_{j+1} - y_j \tag{15-1}$$

The second difference $\Delta^2 y_1$ is obtained by taking the first difference of Δy_1. Thus:

$$\Delta^2 y_1 = \Delta y_2 - \Delta y_1$$

and in like fashion:

$$\Delta^2 y_j = \Delta(\Delta y_j) = \Delta y_{j+1} - \Delta y_j$$

Higher order differences are defined in a similar manner:

$$\Delta^3 y_j = \Delta(\Delta^2 y_j) = \Delta^2 y_{j+1} - \Delta^2 y_j$$
$$\Delta^4 y_j = \Delta(\Delta^3 y_j) = \Delta^3 y_{j+1} - \Delta^3 y_j \tag{15-2}$$

$$\cdot$$
$$\cdot$$
$$\cdot$$

$$\Delta^k y_j = \Delta(\Delta^{k-1} y_j) = \Delta^{k-1} y_{j+1} - \Delta^{k-1} y_j$$

Table I demonstrates an easy format for taking differences by hand. In this table each difference is obtained by subtracting the two neighboring

TABLE I

x_1	y_1				
		Δy_1			
x_2	y_2		$\Delta^2 y_1$		
		Δy_2		$\Delta^3 y_1$	
x_3	y_3		$\Delta^2 y_2$		$\Delta^4 y_1$
		Δy_3		$\Delta^3 y_2$	
x_4	y_4		$\Delta^2 y_3$		
$\cdot$					
$\cdot$					
$\cdot$					
x_{m-3}	y_{m-3}				
		Δy_{m-3}			
x_{m-2}	y_{m-2}		$\Delta^2 y_{m-3}$		
		Δy_{m-2}		$\Delta^3 y_{m-3}$	
x_{m-1}	y_{m-1}		$\Delta^2 y_{m-2}$		
		Δy_{m-1}			
x_m	y_m				

differences in the next column to the left, taking in each case the lower value minus the upper.

Example 1. Write the difference table for $y = x^4$, where x takes on the integer values 0, 1, 2, ..., 6.

x	y	Δy	$\Delta^2 y$	$\Delta^3 y$	$\Delta^4 y$	$\Delta^5 y$
0	0					
		1				
1	1		14			
		15		36		
2	16		50		24	
		65		60		0
3	81		110		24	
		175		84		0
4	256		194		24	
		369		108		
5	625		302			
		671				
6	1296					

If the first entry in the table is denoted by (x_1, y_1), then, according to the definitions given above, each of the table entries has a unique designation, for example, $\Delta^2 y_1 = 14$, $\Delta^3 y_3 = 84$, etc.

Note that in the above table the fourth differences are constant and so the fifth and all higher differences are zero. This is because $y = x^4$ is a polynomial of fourth degree. It can be proved in general that, for a polynomial of nth degree, all nth differences are constant and all higher differences are zero. In this respect the differences are somewhat analogous to derivatives.

Note also that the successive differences are obtained by repeated subtractions, and that in accordance with the accuracy discussions in Chapter III, the relative error will have a tendency to grow as one proceeds to higher order differences. This fact is often used to assist in the detection of errors in tabulated values. A small and unnoticeable error in a tabulated value can produce a large and easily detectable discontinuity in a list of third or fourth differences. The high order differences are not to be trusted unless the table entries themselves are known to high accuracy.

15.22 Machine Construction of Difference Tables

In order to apply the classical interpolation formulas, it is frequently desirable to construct a table of differences and store it in the memory so that the differences need not be recalculated each time they are used. This can easily be done by repeated applications of equations (15-1) and (15-2).

The very simple flow chart in Figure 15–1 describes this operation, for constructing a table of up to nth order differences from a table having m stored values $y_1, y_2, \ldots, y_m$, corresponding to equally spaced values of x.

START

$\Delta y_j = y_{j+1} - y_j, \quad j = 1, \ldots, m-1$

$\Delta^k y_j = \Delta^{k-1} y_{j+1} - \Delta^{k-1} y_j, \quad j = 1, \ldots, m-k$

STOP

Figure 15–1: Formation of a difference table

A FORTRAN program for constructing such a difference table is quite straightforward. If we denote the quantity y_j by the FORTRAN variable Y(J) and the quantity $\Delta^k y_j$ by the FORTRAN variable DY(K,J), then the FORTRAN equivalents of the equations in the flow chart are:

DY(1,J) = Y(J + 1) − Y(J)
DY(K,J) = DY(K − 1,J + 1) − DY(K − 1,J)

In writing a program following the flow chart it is only necessary to use these statements in DO loops, with a DIMENSION statement which will set aside the required amount of storage for the table.

Example 1. Write a FORTRAN program that will input M values of y, where M may be as large as 1000, and construct a difference table for the first five differences.

A suitable program is:

```
      DIMENSION Y(1000),DY(5,1000)
      READ 100,M
      READ 101,Y(1)
      MM = M − 1
      DO 2 J = 1,MM
      READ 101,Y(J + 1)
    2 DY(1,J) = Y(J + 1) − Y(J)
      DO 3 K = 2,5
      L = M − K
      DO 3 J = 1,L
    3 DY(K,J) = DY(K − 1,J + 1) − DY(K − 1,J)
      STOP
  100 FORMAT(I4)
  101 FORMAT(E12.4)
      END
```

15.3 CLASSICAL INTERPOLATION FORMULAE

If a polynomial of degree n:

$$y = c_1 + c_2 x + c_3 x^2 + \cdots + c_{n+1} x^n$$

is to pass through $n+1$ given points, and if we substitute the points in this equation, we obtain $n+1$ equations in the $n+1$ unknowns $c_1, c_2, \ldots, c_{n+1}$. Once we solve these equations and determine these coefficients, the polynomial is completely determined. There are still different ways of writing the polynomial, however; the terms do not have to be written in ascending, distinct powers of x, but can be grouped into different factors or terms. For example, the polynomial:

$$y = -7 + 12x - 6x^2 + x^3$$

can be written as:

$$y = (x - 1) + (x - 1)(x - 2)(x - 3)$$

and it is still precisely the same polynomial, although the numbers which appear explicitly therein are different. The interpolation formulae write an nth degree polynomial in such a way that the differences as defined above are used directly, and the coefficients c_1, c_2, etc. never need be actually calculated. The different interpolation formulae essentially represent just different groupings of terms in the same basic polynomial.

15.31 Newton's Forward Interpolation Formula

An nth degree polynomial through the $n+1$ points (x_0, y_0), (x_1, y_1), $\ldots$, (x_n, y_n) where the values of x are equally spaced an amount h apart, can be written:

$$y = y_0 + \frac{\Delta y_0}{h}(x - x_0) + \frac{\Delta^2 y_0}{2h^2}(x - x_0)(x - x_1)$$

$$+ \frac{\Delta^3 y_0}{3! h^3}(x - x_0)(x - x_1)(x - x_2)$$

$$+ \cdots + \frac{\Delta^n y_0}{n! h^n}(x - x_0)(x - x_1)\cdots(x - x_{n-1}) \tag{15-3}$$

This is known as Newton's forward interpolation formula. If we let

$$u = (x - x_0)/h$$

then it can be written:

$$y = y_0 + \Delta y_0 u + \frac{\Delta^2 y_0}{2!} u(u-1) + \frac{\Delta^3 y_0}{3!} u(u-1)(u-2)$$

$$+ \cdots + \frac{\Delta^n y_0}{n!} u(u-1)(u-2) \cdots (u-n+1) \qquad \text{(15-4)}$$

Example 1.   Given the table of values:

x	1.0	1.1	1.2	1.3	1.4	1.5
y	2.0	2.1	2.3	2.7	3.5	4.7

Find the value of y at $x = 1.05$ using Newton's forward interpolation formula with $n = 4$.

The difference table, including up to fourth differences, is:

x	y	Δy	$\Delta^2 y$	$\Delta^3 y$	$\Delta^4 y$
1.0	2.0				
		.1			
1.1	2.1		.1		
		.2		.1	
1.2	2.3		.2		.1
		.4		.2	
1.3	2.7		.4		−.2
		.8		0	
1.4	3.5		.4		
		1.2			
1.5	4.7				

We have also:

$$h = .1, \qquad x_1 = 1.0, \qquad u = \frac{1.05 - 1.0}{.1} = .5$$

Hence by (15-4):

$$y = 2.0 + (.1)(.5) + \frac{(.1)}{2!}(.5)(-.5) + \frac{.1}{3!}(.5)(-.5)(-1.5)$$

$$+ \frac{.1}{4!}(.5)(-.5)(-1.5)(-2.5)$$

$$= 2.0 + .05 - .0125 + .00625 - .00390625$$

$$= 2.03984375$$

Remembering the discussions of accuracy in Chapter III, this calculation is of little value unless the values of x and y are known more accurately than is implied by the above table. If the value of y at $x = 1.0$ is only as good as is given in the table, then the number 2.0 represents a value whose absolute error is .05. Hence, the absolute error in y at $x = 1.05$ as determined above is at least .05, so the best that can be said for the answer is that $y = 2.04 \pm .05$. Linear interpolation would have given a result that was just as accurate. The higher order differences, which contributed to the less significant figures in the answer, can be used with confidence *only* if the original table entries were known with high accuracy. If the formula (15-3) is to be used on a computer, the calculation can be made more efficient by a better grouping of terms, as:

$$y = (((\cdots ((\Delta^n y_0/n!)(u - n + 1) + \Delta^{n-1} y_0/(n - 1)!)(u - n + 2)$$
$$+ \cdots + \Delta^3 y/3!)(u - 2) + \Delta^2 y_0/2!)(u - 1) + \Delta y_0)u + y_0 \qquad \text{(15-5)}$$

In this formula, each difference $\Delta^k y_0$ appears in the form $\Delta^k y_0/k!$. Let $\delta^k y_0 = \Delta^k y_0/k!$. If stored differences are to be used, the quantities $\delta^k y_0$ are more efficient for use than the quantities $\Delta^k y_0$. With these "adjusted differences," equation (15-5) becomes:

$$y = (((\ldots ((\delta^n y_0)(u - n + 1) + \delta^{n-1} y_0)(u - n + 2)$$
$$+ \cdots + \delta^3 y_0)(u - 2) + \delta^2 y_0)(u - 1) + \delta y_0)u + y_0 \qquad \text{(15-6)}$$

Example 2. Given M values of Y already stored, where $M \leq 1000$, for M equally spaced values of x beginning with XBEG and spaced DX apart, and a stored table of adjusted differences $DNY(K, J) = \delta^k y_j$, through third differences, write a FORTRAN subroutine that will perform third order interpolation using formula (15-6).

A suitable subroutine is:

```
       SUBROUTINE FNEWS3(Y,M,DNY,XBEG,DX,XINT,YINT)
       DIMENSION Y(1000),DNY(3,1000)
       MO=(XINT−XBEG+DX)/DX
   1 IF(MO)20,20,2
   2 IF(MO−M)3,3,20
   3 IF(M−3−MO)4,5,5
   4 MO=M−3
   5 FMO=MO−1
       XO=XBEG+FMO*DX
       U=(XINT−XO)/DX
       YINT=(((U−2.)*DNY(3,MO)+DNY(2,MO))*(U−1.)
      +DNY(1,MO))*U+Y(MO)
       RETURN
```

```
 20 PRINT 101
    STOP
101 FORMAT(31H OUT OF RANGE FOR INTERPOLATION)
    END
```

In this subroutine the machine first computes MO, the subscript that should correspond to the tabulated x value just before XINT, the value at which the interpolation is to be performed. Statements 1 and 2 then check to see if MO is less than 1 or greater than M, in which case the words "out of range for interpolation" are printed and the problem stopped. If MO is in range, statement 3 then checks to see if MO is greater than M − 3, for if it is, third differences will not exist in the difference table. In this case, M is set equal to M − 3, and then XO, the value of x at the tabulated value Y(MO) is computed, and equation (15-6) used to obtain YINT, the interpolated value of Y. In this subroutine, six multiplications or divisions are performed to find an interpolated value. In addition, 3M divisions must have been done to initially store the difference table; 3000 memory locations are required to store the difference table. Three subtractions and three divisions were saved by using the stored differences. If the subroutine is to be called at least M times in the problem, and if memory space is readily available, the stored differences are worth while. Otherwise, differences should be computed as needed.

It is possible to arrange equation (15-4) so that the contributions of the higher differences are determined recursively, and the process can be carried to any desired order and stopped. If the coefficient of $\Delta^k y_0$ in (15-4) is denoted by a_k, then a_k is seen to be given by:

$$a_k = a_{k-1}(u-k+1)/k$$

The flow chart in Figure 15–2 shows how the calculation can be done using this relation. The flow chart assumes that the differences $\Delta^k y_0$ and the

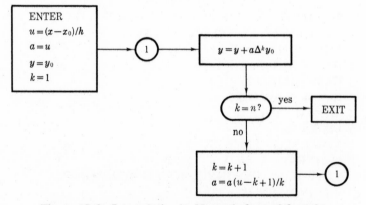

Figure 15–2: Interpolation by Newton's forward formula

values of x_0, h, and x are available and describes the computation of y by nth order interpolation.

Example 3. Given M values of y already stored, where $M \leq 1000$, for M equally spaced values of X beginning with XBEG and spaced DX apart, write a FORTRAN subroutine which will perform Nth order interpolation by Newton's forward formula where N is an input number to the subroutine.

A suitable program is:

```
      SUBROUTINE FNEW(Y,M,XBEG,DX,N,XINT,YINT)
      DIMENSION Y(1000),D(1000)
      MO=(XINT-XBEG+DX)/DX
      IF(M-N-1)21,21,1
    1 IF(MO)20,20,2
    2 IF(MO-M)3,3,20
    3 IF(M-MO-N)4,5,5
    4 MO=M-N
    5 FMO=MO-1
      XO=XBEG+FMO*DX
      U=(XINT-XO)/DX
      A=U
      YINT=Y(MO)
    6 DO 7 I=1,N
      J=MO+I-1
    7 D(I)=Y(J+1)-Y(J)
      IF(N-1)21,10,8
    8 DO 9 K=2,N
      DO 9 I=K,N
      L=N+K-I
    9 D(L)=D(L)-D(L-1)
   10 DO 11 K=1,N
      YINT=YINT+A*D(K)
      FK=K
   11 A=A*(U-FK+1.)/FK
      RETURN
   20 PRINT 101
      STOP
   21 PRINT 102
      STOP
  101 FORMAT(31H OUT OF RANGE FOR INTERPOLATION)
  102 FORMAT(45H ORDER OF INTERPOLATION
      INCORRECTLY SPECIFIED)
      END
```

In this subroutine statements 6 through 9 compute the differences needed, in a somewhat devious way to conserve storage. After these statements are completely executed, we have $D(1) = \Delta y_{mo}$, $D(2) = \Delta^2 y_{mo}$, etc., $D(K) = \Delta^k y_{mo}$. The reader may find it instructive to confirm this by following through that part of the program, say with $M = 500$ and $N = 3$. Statements 5 to 6 calculate the quantities in the first box of the flow chart, Figure 15–2, and statements 10 to 11 actually calculate the interpolated value of y in accordance with the flow chart.

15.32 Newton's Backward Interpolation Formula

The polynomial on the right side of (15-3) can be written:

$$y = y_n + \frac{\Delta y_{n-1}}{h}(x - x_n) + \frac{\Delta^2 y_{n-2}}{2! h^2}(x - x_n)(x - x_{n-1})$$

$$+ \cdots + \frac{\Delta^n y_0}{n! h^n}(x - x_n) \ldots (x - x_1) \tag{15-7}$$

In this form it is known as Newton's backward interpolation formula. If we let:

$$u = (x - x_n)/h$$

this formula takes the form:

$$y = y_n + \Delta y_{n-1} u + \frac{\Delta^2 y_{n-2}}{2!} u(u + 1) + \cdots + \frac{\Delta^n y_0}{n!} u(u + 1) \cdots (u + n - 1)$$

$$\tag{15-8}$$

Examples similar to those of the preceding section could be given for this formula, but will be omitted here. If the differences $\Delta^k y_j$, and the values x_n, h, and x are available, the flow chart, Figure 15–3, describes calculation of y by equation (15-8).

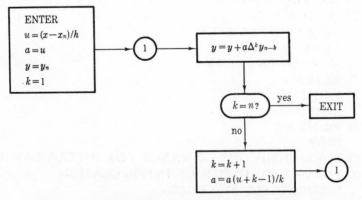

Figure 15–3: Interpolation by Newton's backward formula

15.33 Stirling's Interpolation Formula

This formula is a so-called central difference formula. It is written as a polynomial of degree $2n$, passing through the $2n + 1$ points (x_{-n}, y_{-n}), $(x_{-n+1}, y_{-n+1}), \ldots, (x_{-1}, y_{-1}), (x_0, y_0), (x_1, y_1), \ldots, (x_n, y_n)$. If we let:

$$u = (x - x_0)/h$$

it can be written:

$$y = y_0 + u\frac{\Delta y_{-1} + \Delta y_0}{2} + \frac{u^2}{2}\Delta^2 y_{-1}$$

$$+ \frac{u(u^2 - 1^2)}{3!}\frac{\Delta^3 y_{-2} + \Delta^3 y_{-1}}{2} + \frac{u^2(u^2 - 1^2)}{4!}\Delta^4 y_{-2} \qquad \text{(15-9)}$$

$$+ \cdots$$

$$+ \frac{u(u^2 - 1^2) \cdots [u^2 - (n-1)^2]}{(2n - 1)!}\frac{\Delta^{2n-1} y_{-n} + \Delta^{2n-1} y_{-n+1}}{2}$$

$$+ \frac{u^2(u^2 - 1^2) \cdots [u^2 - (n-1)^2]}{(2n)!}\Delta^{2n} y_{-n}$$

In this formula, each time n is increased by one, two new terms are added. The flow chart, Figure 15–4, shows how the formula can be used, assuming the values y_j, the differences $\Delta^k y_j$ and the values of x, x_0, and h are already stored.

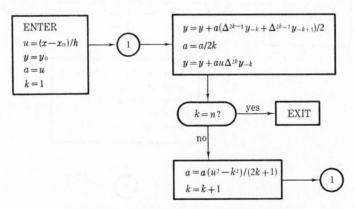

Figure 15–4: Interpolation by Stirling's formula

15.34 Bessel's Interpolation Formula

Bessel's formula is also a central difference formula, based on passing a polynomial of degree $2n + 1$ through $2n + 2$ points. In the notation of the preceding section, it is:

$$y = y_0 + u\Delta y_0$$

$$+ \frac{u(u - 1)}{2!} \frac{\Delta^2 y_{-1} + \Delta^2 y_0}{2} + \frac{(u - 1/2)u(u - 1)}{3!} \Delta^3 y_{-1}$$

$$+ \frac{u(u^2 - 1^2)(u - 2)}{4!} \frac{\Delta^4 y_{-2} + \Delta^4 y_{-1}}{2}$$

$$+ \frac{(u - 1/2)u(u^2 - 1^2)(u - 2)}{5!} \Delta^5 y_{-2} \qquad\qquad \textbf{(15-10)}$$

$$+ \cdots$$

$$+ \frac{u(u^2 - 1^2) \cdots [u^2 - (n - 1)^2](u - n)}{(2n)!} \frac{\Delta^{2n} y_{-n} + \Delta^{2n} y_{-n+1}}{2}$$

$$+ \frac{(u - 1/2)u(u^2 - 1^2) \cdots (u - n)}{(2n + 1)!} \Delta^{2n+1} y_{-n}$$

In this formula, as in Stirling's formula, each time n is increased by one, two terms are added to the expression. The flow chart, Figure 15-5, shows how the formula can be used, assuming the values y_j, the differences $\Delta^k y_j$, and the values of x, x_0, and h are already stored.

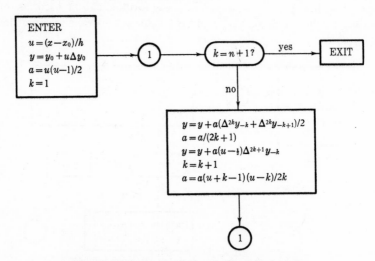

Figure 15–5: Interpolation by Bessel's formula

15.35 Lagrange's Interpolation Formula

This formula is the equation for an nth degree polynomial through $n + 1$ points (x_0, y_0), (x_1, y_1), $\ldots$, (x_n, y_n) which are not necessarily equally spaced.

It is:

$$y = \frac{(x - x_1)(x - x_2) \cdots (x - x_n)}{(x_0 - x_1)(x_0 - x_2) \cdots (x_0 - x_n)} y_0$$

$$+ \frac{(x - x_0)(x - x_2) \cdots (x - x_n)}{(x_1 - x_0)(x_1 - x_2) \cdots (x_1 - x_n)} y_1 \qquad \textbf{(15-11)}$$

$$+ \cdots$$

$$+ \frac{(x - x_0)(x - x_1) \cdots (x - x_{n-1})}{(x_n - x_0)(x_n - x_1) \cdots (x_n - x_{n-1})} y_n$$

It can be seen that this formula involves large numbers of multiplications and, hence, becomes quite slow if n is large. Since the other classical interpolation formulae as given in the preceding sections do not work for unequal intervals, this one is used, perhaps more often than it should be. Spline fits to be discussed in Section 15–4, offer advantages over Lagrange interpolation for unequally spaced intervals. Also, the formulae of the preceding sections can be adapted to unequal intervals by the use of so-called "divided differences," a process that will not be described here.

15.36   Remainder Terms

The above formulae represent ways of approximating a function by a polynomial of degree n (or of degree $2n$ or $2n + 1$ for the central difference formulae). In Chapter VII we discussed the method of approximating a function by a polynomial of degree n, using the Taylor Series. In that case we found that the difference between the given function and the polynomial could be expressed as a remainder term, which was then the error made when the polynomial was used to represent the function. Remainder terms exist for the above formulae also. They are:

For Newton's forward interpolation formula

$$R_n = \frac{f^{(n+1)}(\xi)}{(n+1)!} (x - x_0)(x - x_1) \cdots (x - x_n)$$

$$= \frac{h^{n+1} f^{(n+1)}(\xi)}{(n+1)!} u(u - 1) \cdots (u - n) \qquad \textbf{(15-12)}$$

where ξ is some value intermediate between x_0 and x_n.

For Newton's backward interpolation formula

$$R_n = \frac{h^{n+1} f^{(n+1)}(\xi)}{(n+1)!} u(u + 1)(u + 2) \cdots (u + n) \qquad \textbf{(15-13)}$$

For Stirling's formula

$$R_n = \frac{h^{2n+1} f^{(2n+1)}(\xi)}{(2n+1)!} u(u^2-1)(u^2-2^2) \cdots (u^2-n^n) \qquad \textbf{(15-14)}$$

For Bessel's formula

$$R_n = \frac{h^{2n+2} f^{(2n+2)}(\xi)}{(2n+2)!} u(u^2-1)(u^2-2^2) \cdots (u^2-n^2)(u-n-1) \qquad \textbf{(15-15)}$$

For Lagrange's formula

$$R_n = \frac{f^{(n+1)}(\xi)}{(n+1)!} (x-x_0)(x-x_1) \cdots (x-x_n) \qquad \textbf{(15-16)}$$

In these remainder terms, as in the Taylor remainder, our problem in estimating the remainder comes in estimating the derivative $f^{(n+1)}(\xi)$ (or $f^{(2n+1)}(\xi)$, or $f^{(2n+2)}(\xi)$) at the unknown point ξ. If we know the function f, we can make the estimate in the same manner as we did for the Taylor formula, by actually taking the $n+1$st derivative and then determining an upper limit on its value. If we do not know the function f, the best we can do is to assume that the $n+1$st derivative is approximately given by:

$$f^{(n+1)}(\xi) \approx \frac{\Delta^{n+1} y_0}{h^{n+1}}$$

or for the central difference formulae:

$$f^{(2n+1)}(\xi) \approx \frac{\Delta^{2n+1} y_{-n} + \Delta^{2n+1} y_{-n+1}}{2h^{2n+1}}$$

and:

$$f^{(2n+2)}(\xi) \approx \frac{\Delta^{2n+2} y_{-n-1} + \Delta^{2n+2} y_{-n}}{2h^{2n+1}}$$

If these estimates of the derivatives are substituted back in (15-12) to (15-15) and the results compared to the corresponding interpolation formulae, it is seen that the error as estimated in this fashion is just equal to the next term in the interpolation formula beyond those being used. It is possible to use this type of error estimate to choose the order of interpolation automatically. The flow chart, Figure 15–6, illustrates how this might be done for Striling's Formula. The flow chart assumes that the values y_j, the differences $\Delta^k y_j$, the values x, x_0, h, and a specified relative error E are available at the beginning of the calculation.

The flow chart, Figure 15–6, shows an automatic exit after $k = 5$, even if the specified accuracy has not been achieved. Some arrangment such as this

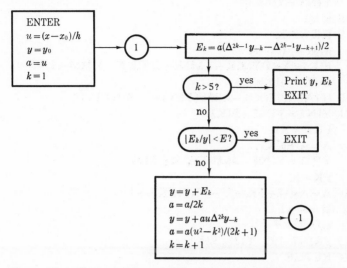

Figure 15–6: Interpolation by Stirling's formula with error control

is advisable. At this point differences up through the tenth difference have been used, and practical problems where the tabulated information is sufficiently accurate to warrant such high order interpolation are extremely rare.

Example 1. Given M values of Y already stored, where $M \le 100$, for M equally spaced values of X beginning with XBEG and spaced DX apart and difference tables up through 11th differences, write a FORTRAN subroutine that will do interpolation by Stirling's formula, using that order of interpolation which will make the relative error less than ERR.

A suitable program is:

```
      SUBROUTINE STIR(Y,M,DY,XBEG,DX,XINT,ERR,YINT)
      DIMENSION Y(100),DY(11,100),E(6)
      N=1
      MO=(XINT−XBEG+DX)/DX
    1 IF(MO)20,20,2
    2 IF(MO−M)3,3,20
    3 IF(MO−N)4,4,5
    4 MO=N+1
    5 IF(M−MO−N)6,7,7
    6 MO=M−N
```

```
  7 FMO=MO-1
    XO=XBEG+FMO*DX
    U=(XINT-XO)/DX
    A=U
    YINT=Y(MO)
  8 K=1
  9 KK=2*K
    MM=MO-K
    E(K)=A*(DY(KK-1,MM)+DY(KK-1,MM+1))/2.
    IF(K-5)10,10,13
 10 IF(ABSF(E(K))-ABSF(YINT*ERR))14,14,11
 11 YINT=YINT+E(K)
    FKK=KK
    A=A/FKK
    YINT=YINT+A*U*DY(KK,MM)
    FK=K
    A=A*(U+FK)*(U-FK)/(FKK+1.)
    K=K+1
    GO TO 9
 13 PRINT 101, YINT,E(K)
 14 RETURN
 20 PRINT 102
    STOP
101 FORMAT(33H DESIRED ACCURACY NOT ACHIEVED,
                     Y=,E12.4,4HERR=,E12.4)
102 FORMAT(31H OUT OF RANGE FOR INTERPOLATION)
    END
```

15.4 SPLINE FITS

A well-known way of interpolating by hand is to plot points and draw a smooth curve through these points using a draftsman's spline. The expert at drawing such curves can do so in such a way that not only the curve itself, but also its slope and its curvature, are continuous functions. Interpolation is done by merely reading points off the smooth curve thus generated. This type of interpolation is not at all difficult on a computer, and offers several advantages over the classical interpolation methods discussed above.

15.41 Derivation of the Equations

Let the given set of points be (x_1, y_1), (x_2, y_2), ... , (x_m, y_m), arranged in order of increasing values of x. We accomplish the spline fit by connecting each pair of adjacent points with a section of a third degree polynomial, matching up the sections so that the first and second derivatives are continuous at each point. Let $Z_1, Z_2, \ldots, Z_m$ be the values of the second derivative at the points. Then between points (x_k, y_k) and (x_{k+1}, y_{k+1}), the second derivative has the value:

$$y'' = Z_k \frac{x_{k+1} - x}{d_k} + Z_{k+1} \frac{x - x_k}{d_k} \tag{15-17}$$

where $d_k = x_{k+1} - x_k$.

Integrating, we obtain for the first derivative:

$$y' = -Z_k[(x_{k+1} - x)^2/2d_k] + Z_{k+1}[(x - x_k)^2/2d_k] + c_1 \tag{15-18}$$

where c_1 is a constant of integration. Integrating again, we obtain for the equation of the curve:

$$y = Z_k[(x_{k+1} - x)^3/6d_k] + Z_{k+1}[(x - x_k)^3/6d_k] + c_1 x + c_2 \tag{15-19}$$

where c_2 is a constant of integration. The constants c_1 and c_2 can be evaluated from the fact that the curve passes through (x_k, y_k) and (x_{k+1}, y_{k+1}). We have:

$$y_k = (Z_k d_k{}^2/6) + c_1 x_k + c_2$$

$$y_{k+1} = (Z_{k+1} d_k{}^2/6) + c_1 x_{k+1} + c_2$$

from which:

$$c_1 = [(y_{k+1} - y_k)/d_k] - [(Z_{k+1} - Z_k)d_k/6] \tag{15-20}$$

$$c_2 = [(y_k x_{k+1} - y_{k+1} x_k)/d_k] - [(Z_k x_{k+1} - Z_{k+1} x_k)d_k/6] \tag{15-21}$$

Substituting these values in (15-19), we have for the equation of the curve:

$$\begin{aligned} y = &[Z_k(x_{k+1} - x)^3/6d_k] + [Z_{k+1}(x - x_k)^3/6d_k] \\ &+ [(x_{k+1} - x)(y_k/d_k - Z_k d_k/6)] \\ &+ [(x - x_k)(y_{k+1}/d_k - Z_{k+1} d_k/6)] \end{aligned} \tag{15-22}$$

In this equation all quantities are known except Z_k and Z_{k+1}, the values of the second derivative at the end points of the interval.   One condition which will help determine these values is that the slope at (x_k, y_k) as determined from equation (15-18) above must be the same as that determined by the corresponding formula for the interval (x_{k-1}, y_{k-1}) to (x_k, y_k).   When the value of c_1 from (15-20) is used in (15-18) the equation becomes:

$$y' = -[Z_k(x_{k+1} - x)^2/2d_k] + [Z_{k+1}(x - x_k)^2/2d_k]$$
$$+ [(y_{k+1} - y_k)/d_k] - [(Z_{k+1} - Z_k)d_k/6] \tag{15-23}$$

The corresponding relation for the preceding interval is:

$$y' = -[Z_{k-1}(x_k - x)^2/2d_{k-1}] + [Z_k(x - x_{k-1})^2/2d_{k-1}]$$
$$+ [(y_k - y_{k-1})/d_{k-1}] - [(Z_k - Z_{k-1})d_{k-1}/6] \tag{15-24}$$

At the point (x_k, y_k), these relations give:

$$y'_k = (-Z_k d_k/2) + [(y_{k+1} - y_k)/d_k] - [(Z_{k+1} - Z_k)d_k/6] \tag{15-25}$$
$$= (Z_k d_{k-1}/2) + [(y_k - y_{k-1})/d_{k-1}] - [(Z_k - Z_{k-1})d_{k-1}/6]$$

or, collecting the unknowns Z_{k-1}, Z_k, and Z_{k+1} on one side of the equation:

$$Z_{k-1}(d_{k-1}/6) + Z_k[(d_{k-1} + d_k)/3] + Z_{k+1}(d_k/6)$$
$$= [(y_{k+1} - y_k)/d_k] - [(y_k - y_{k-1})/d_{k-1}] \tag{15-26}$$

We have an equation like this for each of the internal points, that is, $k = 2, 3,$ $\ldots, m-1$. There are $m-2$ equations in the m unknowns $Z_1, Z_2, \ldots, Z_m$. Two more conditions may be specified in order to determine these quantities completely. It is customary to place some additional condition on Z_1 and Z_m, the values of the second derivative at the end points. There are several reasonable choices for these values, and the particular choice will influence the shape of the fit, especially near the end points. We will demonstrate the fit for the use where the second derivative at each end is a linear extrapolation of the value at the two adjacent points. Stated another way, we will require the third derivative to be continuous at (x_2, y_2) and at (x_{m-1}, y_{m-1}). From equation (15-17) the third derivative is:

$$y''' = -Z_k/d_k + Z_{k+1}/d_k \tag{15-27}$$

Equating values for $k = 1$ and $k = 2$:

$$-Z_1/d_1 + Z_2/d_1 = -Z_2/d_2 + Z_3/d_2 \tag{15-28}$$

or:

$$-Z_1/d_1 + Z_2(1/d_1 + 1/d_2) - Z_3/d_2 = 0 \tag{15-29}$$

In like manner, equating values for $k = m - 2$ and $k = m - 1$:

$$-Z_{m-2}/d_{m-2} + Z_{m-1}/d_{m-2} = -Z_{m-1}/d_{m-1} + Z_m/d_{m-1}$$

or:

$$-Z_{m-2}/d_{m-2} + Z_{m-1}(1/d_{m-2} + 1/d_{m-1}) - Z_m/d_{m-1} = 0 \qquad \text{(15-30)}$$

Equations (15-29) and (15-30), along with equations (15-26), constitute m equations in m unknowns for the quantities $Z_1, Z_2, \ldots Z_m$. The equations are particularly simple, since only three of the unknowns appear in each. Once these equations are solved and the Z_k determined, equation (15-22) can be used directly for finding y for any value of x between x_1 and x_m.

15.42   Computer Use of the Spline Fit

Spline fit interpolation in the table of values $(x_1, y_1), (x_2, y_2), \ldots, (x_m, y_m)$ consists of determining which two points (x_k, y_k) and (x_{k+1}, y_{k+1}) the given value of x lies between and then finding y by the formula:

$$y = c_{1,k}(x_{k+1} - x)^3 + c_{2,k}(x - x_k)^3 + c_{3,k}(x_{k+1} - x) + c_{4,k}(x - x_k) \qquad \text{(15-31)}$$

where the constants $c_{1,k}, c_{2,k}, c_{3,k}, c_{4,k}$ have been previously computed and stored.   A flow chart for this operation is shown in Figure 15–7.

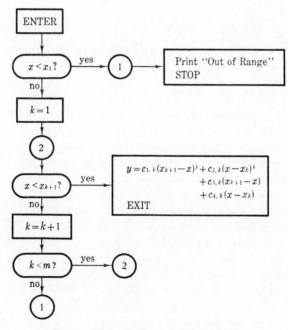

Figure 15–7: Spline fit interpolation

Example 1. Write a FORTRAN subroutine for spline fit interpolation in the table
of values (x_1, y_1) to x_m, y_m), where m may be as large as 100, where the constants
$C(1, k)$, $C(2, k)$, $C(3, k)$ and $C(4, k)$ are already computed and stored.

A suitable subroutine is:


```
      SUBROUTINE  SPLINE(X,Y,M,C,XINT,YINT)
      DIMENSION  X(100),Y(100),C(4,100)
      IF(XINT−X(1))7,1,2
  1   YINT=Y(1)
      RETURN
  2   K=1
  3   IF(XINT−X(K+1))6,4,5
  4   YINT=Y(K+1)
      RETURN
  5   K=K+1
      IF(M−K)7,7,3
  6   YINT=(X(K+1)−XINT)*(C(1,K)*(X(K+1)−XINT)**2
      +C(3,K))
      YINT=YINT+(XINT−X(K))*(C,(2,K)*(XINT−X(K))**
      2+C(4,K))
      RETURN
  7   PRINT 101
      STOP
101   FORMAT(31H OUT OF RANGE FOR INTERPOLATION)
      END
```


In the above subroutine, the location of XINT in the table is found by
comparing it with $X(K+1)$ for $K=1$, 2, etc., until a value $X(K+1)$ greater
than XINT is found.   If the values of XINT for which this subroutine is to
be used are spread uniformly through the table, an average of $M/2$ tests
will be required to find the proper place in the table.   A more efficient way
of performing this search can be used, a method analogous to the bisection
method of finding a root of an equation discussed in Section 10.3.   To use
this method, we would first compare XINT with $X(M/2)$.   If XINT is larger,
we would next compare with $X(3M/4)$, or if smaller, with $X(M/4)$, etc.   By
this process, the number of steps required to find the correct interval for
interpolation is about $\log_2(M)$.   For $M=100$, then, about 7 comparisons are
required, as opposed to an average of 50 for the program as shown.   For
larger tables, the effect becomes more dramatic.   The preparation of a flow
chart and program for the improved method is left as an exercise for the
reader.

15.43 Determination of Constants

In the preceding section it was assumed that the constants $c_{1,k}$, $c_{2,k}$, $c_{3,k}$, $c_{4,k}$ were available. These constants must be determined by solving equations (15-26), (15-29), and (15-30) for Z_1, Z_2, ... , Z_m, and then we have:

$$c_{1,k} = Z_k/6d_k \tag{15-32}$$

$$c_{2,k} = Z_{k+1}/6d_k \tag{15-33}$$

$$c_{3,k} = y_k/d_k - Z_k d_k/6 \tag{15-34}$$

$$c_{4,k} = y_{k+1}/d_k - Z_{k+1}d_k/6 \tag{15-35}$$

The equations for the Z_k are readily solved by an abbreviated version of the elimination method described in Chapter XII.

Let us make the definitions:

$$p_k = d_k/6, \qquad k = 1, \dots, m = 1$$

$$e_k = (y_k - y_{k-1})/d_{k-1}, \qquad k = 2, \dots, m$$

$$b_1 = 0$$

$$b_k = e_{k+1} - e_k, \qquad k = 2, \dots, m = 1$$

$$b_m = 0$$

Then we can write the system of equations (15-26), (15-29), and (15-30) in matrix form as:

$$AZ = b$$

where:

$$
A = \begin{pmatrix}
-1/d_1 & 1/d_1 + 1/d_2 & -1/d_2 & 0 & . & . & . & . & . & 0 & 0 \\
p_1 & 2(p_1 + p_2) & p_2 & 0 & . & . & . & . & . & 0 & 0 \\
0 & p_2 & 2(p_2 + p_3) & p_3 & . & . & . & . & . & 0 & 0 \\
0 & . & & & . & & & & & . & . \\
. & . & & . & & & & & . & & . \\
. & . & & . & & & & & . & . & . \\
0 & 0 & . & . & . & . & p_{m-2} & 2(p_{m-2} + p_{m-1}) & p_{m-1} \\
0 & 0 & . & . & . & . & -1/d_{m-2} & 1/d_{m-2} + 1/d_{m-1} & -1/d_{m-1}
\end{pmatrix}
$$

Making use of the special nature of the above matrix, the Z_i can be found and then the c_{ij} determined by using the flow chart shown in Figure 15–8.

START

    Input $x_k, y_k,$ $k = 1, \ldots, m$

$d_k = x_{k+1} - x_k$

$p_k = d_k/6$ $\left.\vphantom{\begin{matrix}a\\a\\a\end{matrix}}\right\}$ $k = 1, \ldots, m-1$

$e_k = (y_{k+1} - y_k)/d_k$

$b_k = e_k - e_{k-1},$ $k = 2, \ldots, m-1$

$a_{1,2} = -1 - d_1/d_2$

$a_{1,3} = d_1/d_2$

$a_{2,3} = p_2 - p_1 a_{1,3}$

$a_{2,2} = 2(p_1 + p_2) - p_1 a_{1,2}$

$a_{2,3} = a_{2,3}/a_{2,2}$

$b_2 = b_2/a_{2,2}$

$a_{k,k} = 2(p_{k-1} + p_k) - p_{k-1}a_{k-1,k}$

$b_k = b_k - p_{k-1}b_{k-1}$ $\left.\vphantom{\begin{matrix}a\\a\\a\\a\end{matrix}}\right\}$ $k = 3, \ldots, m-1$

$a_{k,k+1} = p_k/a_{k,k}$

$b_k = b_k/a_{k,k}$

$a_{m,m-1} = 1 + d_{m-2}/d_{m-1} + a_{m-2,m-1}$

$a_{m,m} = -d_{m-2}/d_{m-1} - a_{m,m-1}a_{m-1,m}$

$b_m = b_{m-2} - a_{m,m-1}b_{m-1}$

$z_m = b_m/a_{m,m}$

$z_k = b_k - a_{k,k+1}z_{k+1},$ $k = m-1, \ldots, 2$

$z_1 = -a_{1,2}z_2 - a_{1,3}z_3$

$c_{1,k} = z_k/6d_k$

$c_{2,k} = z_{k+1}/6d_k$ $\left.\vphantom{\begin{matrix}a\\a\\a\\a\end{matrix}}\right\}$ $k = 1, \ldots, m-1$

$c_{3,k} = y_k/d_k - z_k p_k$

$c_{4,k} = y_{k+1}/d_k - z_{k+1}p_k$

STOP

Figure 15–8: Determination of coefficients for spline fit

The following FORTRAN subroutine will accomplish the calculation for up to 100 points:

```
SUBROUTINE SPLICON(X,Y,M,C)
DIMENSION X(100),Y(100),D(100),P(100),E(100),C(4,100),
A(100,3),B(100),Z(100)
MM = M − 1
DO 2 K = 1,MM
D(K) = X(K + 1) − X(K)
P(K) = D(K)/6.
2 E(K) = (Y(K + 1) − Y(K))/D(K)
```

```
      DO 3 K=2,MM
   3  B(K)=E(K)-E(K-1)
      A(1,2)=-1.-D(1)/D(2)
      A(1,3)=D(1)/D(2)
      A(2,3)=P(2)-P(1)*A(1,3)
      A(2,2)=2.*(P(1)+P(2))-P(1)*A(1,2)
      A(2,3)=A(2,3)/A(2,2)
      B(2)=B(2)/A(2,2)
      DO 4 K=3,MM
      A(K,2)=2.*(P(K-1)+P(K))-P(K-1)*A(K-1,3)
      B(K)=B(K)-P(K-1)*B(K-1)
      A(K,3)=P(K)/A(K,2)
   4  B(K)=B(K)/A(K,2)
      Q=D(M-2)/D(M-1)
      A(M,1)=1.+Q+A(M-2,3)
      A(M,2)=-Q-A(M,1)*A(M-1,3)
      B(M)=B(M-2)-A(M,1)*B(M-1)
      Z(M)=B(M)/A(M,2)
      MN=M-2
      DO 6 I=1,MN
      K=M-I
   6  Z(K)=B(K)-A(K,3)*Z(K+1)
      Z(1)=-A(1,2)*Z(2)-A(1,3)*Z(3)
      DO 7 K=1,MM
      Q=1./(6.*D(K))
      C(1,K)=Z(K)*Q
      C(2,K)=Z(K+1)*Q
      C(3,K)=Y(K)/D(K)-Z(K)*P(K)
   7  C(4,K)=Y(K+1)/D(K)-Z(K+1)*P(K)
      RETURN
 101  FORMAT(2E12.4)
      END
```

15.5 NUMERICAL DIFFERENTIATION

When dealing with a function which is defined by some analytic expression, it is usually possible to find an analytic expression for its derivative by the methods of elementary calculus. If the function is extremely complicated, or if the function is known as a table of values, it may be necessary to resort to numerical differentiation. To perform numerical differentiation, we represent the function by one of the interpolation formulae and then differentiate the formula as many times as desired. For example, for Newton's forward interpolation formula we have:

$$\frac{dy}{dx} = \frac{dy}{du}\frac{du}{dx} = \frac{1}{h}\left\{\Delta y_0 + \frac{\Delta^2 y_0}{2!}\left[(u-1)+u\right]\right.$$

$$+ \frac{\Delta^3 y_0}{3!}\left[(u-1)(u-2)+(u)(u-2)+u(u-1)\right]+$$

$$\cdots + \frac{\Delta^n y_0}{n!}\left[(u-1)(u-2)\cdots(u-n+1)+u(u-2)\right.$$

$$\left.\cdots(u-n+1)+\cdots+u(u-1)\cdots(u-n+2)\right]\Big\}$$

$$\frac{dy^2}{dx^2} = \frac{1}{h^2}\left\{\Delta^2 y_0 + \frac{\Delta^3 y_0}{3!}\left[2(u-2)+2(u-1)+2u\right]+\right.$$

$$\cdots + \frac{\Delta^n y_0}{n!}\left[2(u-2)(u-3)\cdots(u-n+1)+2u(u-3)\right.$$

$$\left.\cdots(u-n+1)+\cdots+2u(u-1)\cdots(u-n+3)\right]\Big\}$$

etc. It is frequently of interest to have the value just at $x = x_0$, or $u = 0$. There we have:

$$(dy/dx)_{x_0} = (1/h)(\Delta y_0 - \Delta^2 y_0/2 + \Delta^3 y_0/3 + \cdots + (-1)^{n-1}\Delta^n y_0/n)$$

and:

$$(d^2 y/dx^2)_{x_0} = (1/h^2)\{\Delta^2 y_0 - \Delta^3 y_0 + \cdots$$

$$+ (-1)^n 2\Delta^n y_0 \times [1 + 1/2 + \cdots + 1/(n-1)]/n\}$$

Similar expressions can be developed for the other interpolation formulae. For the spline fit, the relations are simply:

$$dy/dx = -3c_{1,k}(x_{k+1} - x)^2 + 3c_{2,k}(x - x_k)^2 - c_{3,k} + c_{4,k}$$

$$d^2 y/dx^2 = 6c_{1,k}(x_{k+1} - x) + 6c_{2,k}(x - x_k)$$

Derivatives obtained from the interpolation formulae tend to be less accurate than function values themselves. Since accuracy is quite difficult to estimate, it will not be discussed here, but the reader is warned that it can be a serious problem.

15.51 Flow Charts

Direct differentiation of the classical interpolation formulae is somewhat messy because of the many products involved. It is easier to modify the flow charts for the classical interpolation formulae to give values of the derivatives. One merely differentiates all quantities in the flow chart which involve x. The flow charts given in Figures 15–9, 15–10, and 15–11 describe

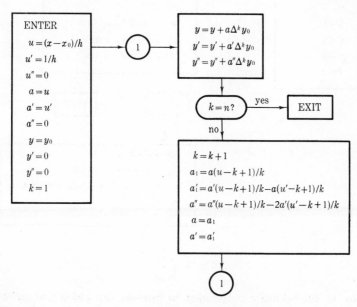

Figure 15–9: Newton's forward interpolation for function, first and second derivatives

the calculation of the function and its first two derivatives using the classical interpolation formulae. Prime denotes derivative by x.

EXERCISE XXVI

1. Given the table of values:

x	1	1.1	1.2	1.3	1.4	1.5	1.6	1.7	1.8	1.9	2.0
y	43.4	47.7	52.1	56.4	60.8	65.1	69.5	73.8	78.2	82.5	86.9

   a. Write a table of differences.
   b. Find the value at 1.05, using Newton's forward interpolation formula, $n = 3$.
   c. Find the value at 1.95, using Newton's backward interpolation formula, $n = 3$.
   d. Find the value at 1.55, using Stirling's formula, $n = 2$.
   e. Find the value at 1.55, using Bessel's formula, $n = 2$.

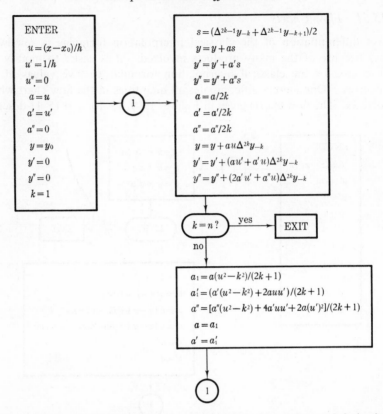

Figure 15–10: Stirling's interpolation for function, first and second derivatives

2. a. Write a FORTRAN program that will read in ten values of y, y_1, ... , y_{10}, an initial value x_1 and spacing h, then read x and call subroutine STIR of Section 15.36, and print y, for as many input values of x as may be given.
    b. Check your program and subroutine STIR by using $x_1 = 0$, $h = 1$, and ten points from the curve $y = x^2 - 5x$. Try ERR$= .1$, $.001$, $.0000001$.
    c. For $x = 1, 2, ... , 10$, a function is defined by the expression $y = \ln(x!)$. Use your program, with ERR $= .01$, to find y for $x = 1.5$ and $x = 7.5$.

3. a. Write a FORTRAN program that will read in ten pairs of values (x_1, y_1), ... , (x_{10}, y_{10}), call subroutine SPLICON of Section 15.43 to determine constants for a spline fit, then read x and call subroutine SPLINE of Section 15.42, and print y, for as many input values of x as may be available.
    b. Check your program by running Problem 2b, above. (You cannot specify the error, of course.)
    c. Use your program to perform Problem 2c.

4. Given M values of y already stored, where $M \leq 100$, for M equally spaced values of x beginning with XBEG and spaced DX apart, and difference tables

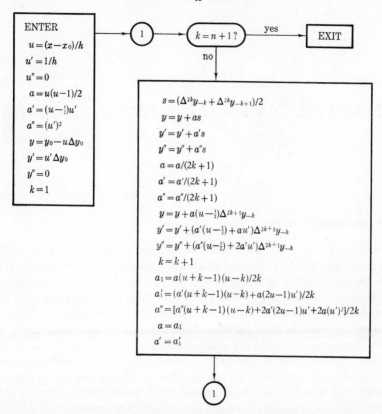

Figure 15–11: Bessel's interpolation for function, first and second derivatives.

through 11th differences, write a FORTRAN subroutine BESS that will do interpolation by Bessel's formula, using the order of interpolation that will make the relative error less than ERR. (See Example 1 of Section 15.36.)

5. Prepare a new flow chart and FORTRAN subroutine for the spline fit, based on the improved search method described in the last paragraph of Section 15.42.

CHAPTER XVI *Differential Equations*

16.1 INTRODUCTION

In problems in science and engineering, we are usually interested in studying the properties of some physical system and predicting its behavior. We do this by constructing a mathematical model of the physical system. We assign names to the things we can measure about the system and then represent them by symbols x, y, t, etc. The basic laws of physics tell us what relationships should exist between these quantities, and enable us to write down equations involving the mathematical symbols which represent them. If these equations can be solved, so that we can obtain numerical values for the various quantities, then we can say that we understand the mathematical model, and hopefully we have gained some useful information or insight concerning the behavior of the physical system it represents.

The physical laws which give us the equations quite frequently involve not only the quantities of interest, but also rates of change of these quantities. Mathematically these rates of change are represented as derivatives; the equations to be solved are called differential equations.

As is indicated by the generality of the above paragraphs, the field of differential equations is a broad one, having far-reaching applications in science and engineering. In this chapter we will give only a brief introduction to this important subject.

16.2 AN ELEMENTARY EXAMPLE

In a radioactive substance—say, radium—each atom is in an unstable condition, and sooner or later will cast off some of its excess energy as radiation. When it has done this it is no longer an atom of radium but has become an atom of something else. If we start out at a certain time with a given number of atoms of radium, can we predict how many atoms will be left at some later time? If the physicist takes a sample of the radioactive substance and places it in a detector which will signal when a radioactive decay

416

has occurred, he finds that the average number of decays per second is proportional to the amount of material present. This appears to be the basic law governing radioactive decay. In order to state this law in mathematical terms, let:

y = number of atoms of radium present in a sample

Since each decay signifies the disappearance of an atom of radium, the number of decays per second is:

$$-dy/dt$$

The above law then states that:

$$-dy/dt = \lambda y \tag{16-1}$$

where λ is a constant of proportionality determined experimentally.

Equation (16-1) is the differential equation that describes the problem. We would say that it is solved if given any particular time, t, we can determine the value of y.

We can write equation (16-1) as:

$$dy/y = -\lambda dt \tag{16-2}$$

and, integrating both sides we have:

$$\ln y = -\lambda t + c \tag{16-3}$$

where c is a constant of integration. Suppose that when we started, at time 0, there were exactly y_0 atoms. Substituting $y = y_0$ and $t = 0$ in (16-3), we find that:

$$\ln y_0 = c \tag{16-4}$$

which fixes the value of c. Substituting this back into (16-3):

$$\ln y = -\lambda t + \ln y_0 \tag{16-5}$$

or taking exponentials of both sides:

$$y = y_0 e^{-\lambda t}. \tag{16-6}$$

This equation represents the solution. Given any value of t, the corresponding value of y can be determined directly.

16.3 SYSTEMS OF LINEAR EQUATIONS WITH CONSTANT COEFFICIENTS

A very important class of differential equations is that in which there are several dependent variables, $y_1, y_2, \ldots, y_n$, and one independent variable, t, and the basic physical laws lead to the equations:

$$dy_1/dt = a_{11}y_1 + a_{12}y_2 + \cdots + a_{1n}y_n$$

$$dy_2/dt = a_{21}y_1 + a_{22}y_2 + \cdots + a_{2n}y_n \qquad \text{(16-7)}$$

.

.

.

$$dy_n/dt = a_{n1}y_1 + a_{n2}y_2 + \cdots + a_{nn}y_n$$

where the a_{ij} are constants.

Such a set of equations can be written for nearly any mechanical system of masses, springs, and shock absorbers, and its solution will give the motions of the masses as a function of time if they are given some initial motion. Such a set also can be written for an electrical circuit made up of resistors, capacitors, and inductors, and its solution will give the currents and voltages in the various parts of the circuit as a function of time for any set of initial currents or voltages. Such a system of equations also arises in the study of the stability of nearly any mechanical, electrical, chemical, or biological system. Because the equations can represent voltages in an electrical system, analogue computers are frequently used to solve equations of the above type. There are many occasions, however, when digital computer solutions are needed.

Higher order equations of the form:

$$a_1 \frac{d^n y}{dt^n} + a_2 \frac{d^{n-1} y}{dt^{n-1}} + \cdots + a_n y = 0$$

can also be written as a system of equations like (16-7) by letting:

$$y = y_1$$

$$y'_1 = y_2$$

$$\text{etc.}$$

$$\frac{d^{n-1} y}{dt^{n-1}} = y_n$$

Matrix notation can be used for the system of equations (16-7) if we define the derivative of a matrix to be the matrix made up of the derivatives of the individual elements, that is:

$$\frac{d}{dt}\begin{pmatrix} y_1 \\ y_2 \\ \cdot \\ \cdot \\ \cdot \\ y_n \end{pmatrix} = \begin{pmatrix} \dfrac{dy_1}{dt} \\[2mm] \dfrac{dy_2}{dt} \\[2mm] \cdot \\ \cdot \\ \cdot \\ \dfrac{dy_n}{dt} \end{pmatrix} \qquad \text{(16-8)}$$

Then if we let:

$$y = \begin{pmatrix} y_1 \\ y_2 \\ \cdot \\ \cdot \\ \cdot \\ y_n \end{pmatrix}, \qquad A = \begin{pmatrix} a_{11} & a_{12} & \cdots & a_{1n} \\ a_{21} & a_{22} & \cdots & a_{2n} \\ \cdot & & & \\ \cdot & & & \\ \cdot & & & \\ a_{n1} & a_{n2} & \cdots & a_{nn} \end{pmatrix} \qquad \text{(16-9)}$$

the system of equations (16-7) can be written:

$$dy/dt = Ay \qquad \text{(16-10)}$$

Because of the resemblance of equation (16-10) to equation (16-1) of Section 16.2, let us try a solution of the form:

$$y = \begin{pmatrix} c_1 e^{\lambda t} \\ c_2 e^{\lambda t} \\ \cdot \\ \cdot \\ \cdot \\ c_n e^{\lambda t} \end{pmatrix} = c e^{\lambda t} \qquad \text{where } c = \begin{pmatrix} c_1 \\ c_2 \\ \cdot \\ \cdot \\ \cdot \\ c_n \end{pmatrix} \qquad \text{(16-11)}$$

Then:

$$dy/dt = \lambda c e^{\lambda t} \tag{16-12}$$

and substituting in (16-10), we obtain:

$$\lambda c e^{\lambda t} = A c e^{\lambda t}$$

or

$$\lambda c = A c$$

or

$$(A - \lambda I)c = 0 \tag{16-13}$$

This is precisely the equation of Section 13.4 for determining the eigenvalues and eigenvectors of the matrix A. We found in Chapter XIII that there are n values of λ for which this system has a solution, and these are the eigenvalues of the matrix A. If these values are discrete, there is one eigenvector, u_i, corresponding to each eigenvalue λ_i. Thus we have found not one, but n different solutions:

$$u_1 e^{\lambda_1 t}, u_2 e^{\lambda_2 t}, \dots, u_n e^{\lambda_n t}$$

It can be proved that, for a system of linear differential equations such as (16-7), any linear combination of solutions is also a solution, so the most general solution we have found is:

$$y = k_1 u_1 e^{\lambda_1 t} + k_2 u_2 e^{\lambda_2 t} + \cdots + k_n u_n e^{\lambda_n t} \tag{16-14}$$

where $\lambda_1, \dots, \lambda_n$ are the eigenvalues of A, $u_1, \dots, u_n$ are the corresponding eigenvectors, and $k_1, \dots, k_n$ are arbitrary constants. Ordinarily in the physical problem we will have side conditions that determine the value of these constants. For example, we may know the values of $y_1, y_2, \dots, y_n$ for $t = 0$, that is, initial conditions for the problem of interest, and these will determine the k_i.

Example 1. Solve the system $y' = Ay$, where:

$$A = \begin{pmatrix} -1 & -2 & 2 \\ 3 & 4 & -2 \\ -1 & -1 & 3 \end{pmatrix}$$

subject to the initial condition:

$$y = \begin{pmatrix} 1 \\ 2 \\ 2 \end{pmatrix} \quad \text{when } t = 0$$

SOLUTION: The eigenvalues for A are obtained by setting:

$$\begin{vmatrix} -1 - \lambda & -2 & 2 \\ 3 & 4 - \lambda & -2 \\ -1 & -1 & 3 - \lambda \end{vmatrix} = 0$$

If we expand this determinant we obtain the characteristic equation:

$$-\lambda^3 + 6\lambda^2 - 11\lambda + 6 = 0$$

which has the roots:

$$\lambda_1 = 1, \qquad \lambda_2 = 2, \qquad \lambda_3 = 3$$

The eigenvector corresponding to λ_1 is obtained by setting:

$$(A - \lambda_1 I)c = 0$$

or

$$\begin{pmatrix} -2 & -2 & 2 \\ 3 & 3 & -2 \\ -1 & -1 & 2 \end{pmatrix} \begin{pmatrix} c_1 \\ c_2 \\ c_3 \end{pmatrix} = 0$$

This set of equations is satisfied if $c_1 = 1$, $c_2 = -1$, and $c_3 = 0$.   Thus an eigenvector corresponding to λ_1 is:

$$u_1 = \begin{pmatrix} 1 \\ -1 \\ 0 \end{pmatrix}$$

In like manner we can find that eigenvectors corresponding to λ_2 and λ_3 are:

$$\begin{pmatrix} 0 \\ 1 \\ 1 \end{pmatrix} \quad \text{and} \quad \begin{pmatrix} 1 \\ -1 \\ 1 \end{pmatrix}$$

Hence the general solution is:

$$y = \begin{pmatrix} 1 \\ -1 \\ 0 \end{pmatrix} k_1 e^t + \begin{pmatrix} 0 \\ 1 \\ 1 \end{pmatrix} k_2 e^{2t} + \begin{pmatrix} 1 \\ -1 \\ 1 \end{pmatrix} k_3 e^{3t}$$

This can be written:

$$y = \begin{pmatrix} 1 & 0 & 1 \\ -1 & 1 & -1 \\ 0 & 1 & 1 \end{pmatrix} \begin{pmatrix} k_1 e^t \\ k_2 e^{2t} \\ k_3 e^{3t} \end{pmatrix}$$

When $t = 0$, we have:

$$\begin{pmatrix} 1 \\ 2 \\ 2 \end{pmatrix} = \begin{pmatrix} 1 & 0 & 1 \\ -1 & 1 & -1 \\ 0 & 1 & 1 \end{pmatrix} \begin{pmatrix} k_1 \\ k_2 \\ k_3 \end{pmatrix}$$

so that:

$$k_1 = 2, \quad k_2 = 3, \quad k_3 = -1$$

and the solution is:

$$y = \begin{pmatrix} 1 & 0 & 1 \\ -1 & 1 & -1 \\ 0 & 1 & 1 \end{pmatrix} \begin{pmatrix} 2e^t \\ 3e^{2t} \\ -e^{3t} \end{pmatrix}$$

or

$$y_1 = 2e^t - e^{3t}$$

$$y_2 = -2e^t + 3e^{2t} + e^{3t}$$

$$y_3 = 3e^{2t} - e^{3t}$$

16.31   Linear Independence and Multiple Eigenvalues

In the above discussions it has been assumed that the eigenvalues λ_i are all discrete, that is, the characteristic equation has no multiple roots. In this case we obtain n different solutions of the form $u_i e^{\lambda_i t}$. These solutions are linearly independent, that is, no one solution is a linear combination of the other solutions. In Example 1 of Section 16.3, for instance, it is impossible to add terms containing e^{2t} and e^{3t} and obtain a term containing e^t. In the theory of differential equations, it is shown that a system of n first order differential equations has exactly n linearly independent solutions, so that the solution given by (16-14) is indeed the most general solution for the system.

If the characteristic equation has multiple roots, however, the above procedure may or may not give us n linearly independent solutions.

Example 1.   Find the general solution of:

$$\mathbf{y}' = \begin{pmatrix} 1 & 0 \\ 0 & 1 \end{pmatrix} \mathbf{y}$$

The eigenvalues are $\lambda_1 = 1$, $\lambda_2 = 1$, and the eigenvectors are solutions of the equations:

$$\begin{pmatrix} 0 & 0 \\ 0 & 0 \end{pmatrix} \begin{pmatrix} x_1 \\ x_2 \end{pmatrix} = \mathbf{0}$$

Since there are two unknowns and the rank of the coefficient matrix is zero, there are two linearly independent solutions. By inspection, these may be taken as:

$$\begin{pmatrix} 1 \\ 0 \end{pmatrix} \quad \text{and} \quad \begin{pmatrix} 0 \\ 1 \end{pmatrix}$$

With these two eigenvectors, we can write the general solution:

$$\mathbf{y} = k_1 \begin{pmatrix} 1 \\ 0 \end{pmatrix} e^t + k_2 \begin{pmatrix} 0 \\ 1 \end{pmatrix} e^t$$

Even though the functions e^t and e^t are not linearly independent, we still have two linearly independent solutions because there were two independent eigenvectors corresponding to the double eigenvalue. This does not happen in every case.

Example 2. Find the general solution of:

$$y' = \begin{pmatrix} 0 & 1 \\ -1 & 2 \end{pmatrix} y$$

To find the eigenvalues, we set:

$$\begin{vmatrix} -\lambda & 1 \\ -1 & 2 - \lambda \end{vmatrix} = 0$$

or

$$\lambda^2 - 2\lambda + 1 = 0$$

which has the solutions:

$$\lambda_1 = 1, \qquad \lambda_2 = 1$$

To find the eigenvector corresponding to λ_1, set:

$$\begin{pmatrix} -1 & 1 \\ -1 & 1 \end{pmatrix}\begin{pmatrix} x_1 \\ x_2 \end{pmatrix} = 0$$

These equations are satisfied if $x_1 = x_2 = 1$. Hence an eigenvector is:

$$\begin{pmatrix} 1 \\ 1 \end{pmatrix}$$

Clearly if we repeat the process with λ_2, we get nothing new, just the same thing over again. There must be another linearly independent solution, however, and some other method is needed to find it. One method is that known as variation of parameters. Since $y = u_1 e^t$ is a solution, we try making the substitution:

$$y = v(t)e^t, \qquad \text{where } v(t) = \begin{pmatrix} v_1(t) \\ v_2(t) \end{pmatrix}$$

is as yet unspecified. Then:

$$y' = v'e^t + ve^t$$

Substituting in the original equation:

$$v'e^t + ve^t = Ave^t$$

or

$$v' = (A - I)v = \begin{pmatrix} -1 & 1 \\ -1 & 1 \end{pmatrix} v$$

Now try:

$$v = \begin{pmatrix} 1 \\ 1 \end{pmatrix} t + \begin{pmatrix} h_1 \\ h_2 \end{pmatrix}$$

Then:

$$v' = \begin{pmatrix} 1 \\ 1 \end{pmatrix} = \begin{pmatrix} -1 & 1 \\ -1 & 1 \end{pmatrix} \left[\begin{pmatrix} 1 \\ 1 \end{pmatrix} t + \begin{pmatrix} h_1 \\ h_2 \end{pmatrix} \right]$$

Simplifying:

$$\begin{pmatrix} 1 \\ 1 \end{pmatrix} = \begin{pmatrix} 0 \\ 0 \end{pmatrix} t + \begin{pmatrix} -h_1 + h_2 \\ -h_1 + h_2 \end{pmatrix}$$

So the equation is satisfied if $h_1 = 0$ and $h_2 = 1$. Hence:

$$y = ve^t$$

is a solution if:

$$v = \begin{pmatrix} 1 \\ 1 \end{pmatrix} t + \begin{pmatrix} 0 \\ 1 \end{pmatrix} = \begin{pmatrix} t \\ t + 1 \end{pmatrix}$$

Hence two linearly independent solutions are:

$$y = \begin{pmatrix} 1 \\ 1 \end{pmatrix} e^t \quad \text{and} \quad y = \begin{pmatrix} t \\ t + 1 \end{pmatrix} e^t$$

and the general solution is:

$$y = \begin{pmatrix} 1 \\ 1 \end{pmatrix} k_1 e^t + \begin{pmatrix} t \\ t + 1 \end{pmatrix} k_2 e^t$$

The method used in Example 1 above can be generalized to apply to any case with multiple roots. Suppose λ_i is a root of multiplicity r for the equation:

$$y' = Ay \qquad \text{(16-15)}$$

and let q_1 be an eigenvector corresponding to λ_i. Making the substitution:

$$y = ve^{\lambda_i t}$$

we have:

$$y' = v'e^{\lambda_i t} + \lambda_i ve^{\lambda_i t} = Ave^{\lambda_i t}$$

$$\text{or}$$

$$v' + \lambda_i v = Av$$

$$\text{or}$$

$$v' = (A - \lambda_i I)v \qquad \text{(16-16)}$$

Now let:

$$v = q_1 t + q_2$$

Then equation (16-16) becomes:

$$q_1 = (A - \lambda_i I)q_1 t + (A - \lambda_i I)q_2$$

Since q_1 is an eigenvector corresponding to λ_i:

$$(A - \lambda_i I)q_1 = 0 \qquad \text{(16-17)}$$

and the equation becomes:

$$q_1 = (A - \lambda_i I)q_2 \qquad \text{(16-18)}$$

Hence the equation (16-16) is satisfied if we can choose a vector q_2 to satisfy (16-18). (Whether or not there is a solution depends, according to Theorem I of Section 13.32, on the rank of the matrix $A - \lambda_i I$ and the rank of the augmented matrix consisting of the elements of $A - \lambda_i I$ and one additional column consisting of the elements of q_1. If the system is inconsistent, then either all the linearly independent solutions corresponding to λ_i have already been found, or q_1 on the right hand side of (16-18) needs to be replaced by some other eigenvector or linear combination of eigenvectors corresponding to λ_i.) If we can solve (16-18), then, we have another solution to the differential equation:

$$y = (q_1 t + q_2)e^{\lambda_i t}$$

If λ_i is a root of multiplicity higher then two, let:

$$v(t) = q_1 t^2 + 2q_2 t + q_3$$

where q_1 and q_2 are the vectors determined above; when this is substituted into equation (16-16), we obtain:

$$2q_1 t + 2q_2 = (A - \lambda_i I)q_1 t^2 + (A - \lambda_i I)2q_2 t + (A - \lambda_i I)q_3$$

Using (16-17) and (16-18) in this relation, it simplifies to:

$$2q_2 = (A - \lambda_i I)q_3 \qquad\qquad \textbf{(16-19)}$$

and if we choose q_3 to satisfy this relation, we have another solution to the original equation:

$$y = (q_1 t^2 + 2q_2 t + q_3)e^{\lambda_i t}$$

Continuing in this manner, we can usually generate the other linearly independent solutions up to a number equal to the multiplicity of the root.

Example 3. Find the general solution of:

$$y' = \begin{pmatrix} 0 & 1 & 0 \\ 0 & 0 & 1 \\ -8 & -12 & -6 \end{pmatrix} y$$

To find the eigenvalues we set:

$$\begin{vmatrix} -\lambda & 1 & 0 \\ 0 & -\lambda & 1 \\ -8 & -12 & -6-\lambda \end{vmatrix} = 0$$

and obtain the characteristic equation:

$$-\lambda^3 - 6\lambda^2 - 12\lambda - 8 = 0$$

which has the roots:

$$\lambda_1 = -2, \qquad \lambda_2 = -2, \qquad \lambda_3 = -2$$

To find the eigenvector, we set:

$$\begin{pmatrix} 2 & 1 & 0 \\ 0 & 2 & 1 \\ -8 & -12 & -4 \end{pmatrix} \mathbf{q}_1 = \mathbf{0}$$

and find that this is satisfied by:

$$\mathbf{q}_1 = \begin{pmatrix} 1 \\ -2 \\ 4 \end{pmatrix}$$

and so one solution is:

$$\mathbf{y} = \begin{pmatrix} 1 \\ -2 \\ 4 \end{pmatrix} e^{-2t}$$

To find the vector $\mathbf{q}_2$, we set:

$$\begin{pmatrix} 2 & 1 & 0 \\ 0 & 2 & 1 \\ -8 & -12 & -4 \end{pmatrix} \mathbf{q}_2 = \begin{pmatrix} 1 \\ -2 \\ 4 \end{pmatrix}$$

This set of equations is satisfied by:

$$\mathbf{q}_2 = \begin{pmatrix} 1 \\ -1 \\ 0 \end{pmatrix}$$

and so another solution is:

$$\mathbf{y} = \begin{pmatrix} t + 1 \\ -2t - 1 \\ 4t \end{pmatrix} e^{-2t}$$

To find the vector q_3 we set:

$$\begin{pmatrix} 2 & 1 & 0 \\ 0 & 2 & 1 \\ -8 & -12 & -4 \end{pmatrix} q_3 = \begin{pmatrix} 2 \\ -2 \\ 0 \end{pmatrix}$$

This set of equations is satisfied by:

$$q_3 = \begin{pmatrix} 1 \\ 0 \\ -2 \end{pmatrix}$$

and so another solution is:

$$y = \begin{pmatrix} t^2 + 2t + 1 \\ -2t^2 - 2t \\ 4t^2 - 2 \end{pmatrix} e^{-2t}$$

and so the general solution can be written:

$$y = \begin{pmatrix} 1 \\ -2 \\ 4 \end{pmatrix} k_1 e^{-2t} + \begin{pmatrix} t + 1 \\ -2t - 1 \\ 4t \end{pmatrix} k_2 e^{-2t} + \begin{pmatrix} t^2 + 2t + 1 \\ -2t^2 - 2t \\ 4t^2 - 2 \end{pmatrix} k_3 e^{-2t}$$

16.32 Computer Methods

From the examples of the preceding sections it is clear that all the computer techniques need to solve systems of differential equations of the type illustrated above has already been given in Chapters XI, XII, and XIII. We must be able to find the eigenvalues and eigenvectors of a matrix, a subject covered in Section 13.4. Occasionally, in the case of multiple eigenvalues, we must solve a set of nonhomogeneous linear equations of the type:

$$(A - \lambda_i I)x = q_1$$

The method of Section 13.34 will suffice for this. It might be noted that the methods of Chapter XII do not work for this system, since:

$$\det (A - \lambda_i I) = 0$$

EXERCISE XXVII

1. Find the complete solution of the following sets of linear equations:

a.
$$y' = \begin{pmatrix} 2 & 2 \\ 4 & -3 \end{pmatrix} y$$

b.
$$y' = \begin{pmatrix} 1 & 1 & -3 \\ 0 & 2 & -3 \\ 0 & 0 & -1 \end{pmatrix} y$$

c.
$$y' = \begin{pmatrix} 1 & 0 & 0 \\ 0 & 2 & 2 \\ 0 & 4 & -3 \end{pmatrix} y$$

d.
$$y' = \begin{pmatrix} 0 & 1 & 0 \\ 0 & 0 & 1 \\ 1 & 0 & -3 \end{pmatrix} y$$

2. Write a FORTRAN program that will find the complete solution of a 2-by-2 system of homogeneous linear differential equations with constant coefficients.

3. A symmetric matrix is one whose corresponding elements across the main diagonal are equal, $a_{ij} = a_{ji}$. All the eigenvalues of a real symmetric matrix are real. Write a FORTRAN program, calling upon the subroutines of Chapters XI and XIII, that will find all linearly independent solutions of $y' = Ay$, for A a real symmetric matrix of order up to 20.

16.4 THE GENERAL FIRST ORDER EQUATION

So far the differential equations we have looked at have been amenable to analytic solution. The use of the computer for such equations has been as an aid in evaluating various constants involved in the solution. For most types of differential equations, however, an analytical solution cannot be obtained, and then the computer has the very different function of finding numerical values which trace out the solution. We consider this problem only for a first order equation in one dependent and one independent variable, which we may write:

$$dy/dx = f(x, y) \qquad\qquad \text{(16-20)}$$

If we consider x and y as coordinates of a point in an x, y plane, then this equation defines a slope at each point. The curve:

$$y = g(x) \qquad\qquad \text{(16-21)}$$

is said to be a solution of the differential equation if at every point on the curve its slope is equal to the slope defined by equation (16-20). Except under very unusual conditions, there is one and only one solution curve through each point in the (x, y) plane. In a physical problem we usually

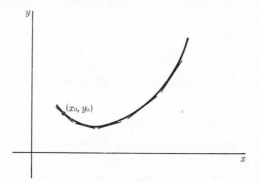

Figure 16-1

know one point of interest, and wish to trace the solution curve through that point. The situation is as shown in Figure 16-1. There is some point (x_0, y_0) at which we are to start, and some unknown solution curve through that point, whose slope at every point is given by (16-20).

The basic process we must follow to trace this solution curve is quite clear. Since the slope at each point tells us the direction the curve is going, we must start at the initial point, move in the direction of the slope as defined by equation (16-20) to a new point, find a new slope, and move again in a new direction to a next point, and so forth.

The fundamental difficulty with this process is also quite clear, and is shown in Figure 16-2. The slope changes from point to point along the curve with each infinitesimal change in position, while in a numerical process we must take finite, even if small, steps. Thus at the points we skip over in calculating,

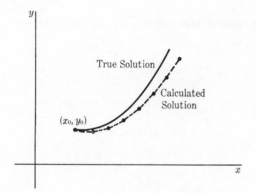

Figure 16-2

we will be using the wrong slope, and the solution we obtain may tend to wander away from the true solution.

The difference between the calculated solution and the true solution is called the error.   The amount of error that will occur depends on the method used to obtain new points on the calculated solution curve.   If the error grows at each step as we move away from the starting point, the method is said to be "unstable."   This is not a particularly fortunate choice of terminology, for, as we have seen earlier in the text, relative error rather than absolute error is frequently the best criterion in judging goodness of an approximation.

16.41   Methods of Numerical Solution

No one method of obtaining solutions for differential equations like equation (16-20) turns out to be the best in all cases.   There are many methods in use, each one representing a compromise among several competing considerations.   In each of these methods, information about the solution curve at one or more points is used to obtain an approximation to a new point on the solution curve.   First there is the problem of stability.   If the approximation used has a systematic bias, then the computed solution will wander away from the true solution.   Then there is the problem of step size.   If the approximation is a crude and simple one, it may be necessary to calculate points very close together, and consequently to make a prohibitively large number of calculations in extending the solution over the desired range of values of x.   If the step size is too small, roundoff error in making the calculation can become a dominant consideration.   On the other hand, if a more complex approximation method is used to allow larger steps or enhanced stability, the amount of calculation required at each point may become excessive.   Thus the whole subject is an involved one, and no attempt at exhaustive treatment will be made in this text.   Two representative methods are given in the following sections.

16.42   Runge-Kutta Method

In order to solve the equation:

$$y' = f(x, y)$$

starting at the point (x_0, y_0) we let:

$$x_1 = x_0 + h$$
$$x_2 = x_1 + h$$

etc.

$$x_n = x_{n-1} + h$$

and the corresponding y values on the calculated solution curve be y_1, y_2, ... , y_n. If we have calculated the points on the solution up to (x_n, y_n), we obtain the next point (x_{n+1}, y_{n+1}) by the following steps:

$$k_1 = hf(x_n, y_n) \tag{16-22}$$

$$k_2 = hf(x_n + h/2, y_n + k_1/2) \tag{16-23}$$

$$k_3 = hf(x_n + h/2, y_n + k_2/2) \tag{16-24}$$

$$k_4 = hf(x_n + h, y_n + k_3) \tag{16-25}$$

$$y_{n+1} = y_n + 1/6(k_1 + 2k_2 + 2k_3 + k_4) \tag{16-26}$$

Example 1. Calculate the first two steps of the solution of the equation:

$$dy/dx = x + y$$

starting from the point $x_0 = 0$, $y_0 = 1$, with $h = .2$.

SOLUTION: We have:

$$k_1 = .2(0 + 1) = .2$$
$$k_2 = .2(.1 + 1.1) = .24$$
$$k_3 = .2(.1 + 1.12) = .244$$
$$k_4 = .2(.2 + 1.244) = .2888$$
$$y_1 = 1 + 1/6(.2 + .48 + .488 + .2888) = 1.24280$$

For the next interval:

$$k_1 = .2(.2 + 1.24280) = .288560$$
$$k_2 = .2(.3 + (1.24280 + .14428)) = .337416$$
$$k_3 = .2(.3 + (1.24280 + .16871)) = .342302$$
$$k_4 = .2(.4 + (1.24280 + .34230)) = .397020$$
$$y_2 = 1.24280 + 1/6(.288560 + .674832 + .684604 + .397020) = 1.58364$$

Example 2. Calculate the first step of the solution of:

$$dy/dx = x + y$$

starting from the point $x_0 = 0$, $y_0 = 1$, with $h = .4$.

SOLUTION: We have:

$$k_1 = .4(0 + 1) = .4$$

$$k_2 = .4(.2 + 1.2) = .56$$

$$k_3 = .4(.2 + 1.28) = .592$$

$$k_4 = .4(.4 + 1.592) = .7968$$

$$y_1 = 1 + 1/6(.4 + 1.12 + 1.184 + .7968) = 1.58345$$

In the above two examples, we have presumably reached the same point on the solution curve, the first time by two smaller steps, the second time by one larger one.   The values obtained for y at $x = .4$ are seen to differ slightly.   For the above examples, an analytical solution can be found.   It is $y = 2e^x - x - 1$, which for $x = .4$ has the value $y = 1.58364$.   The error in the first case is below the level of accuracy to which the numbers were carried. The error in the second case was about $.00019$.   In the Runge-Kutta method, the error over an interval is proportional to h^4, so we would expect that reducing the step size by a factor of 2 should reduce this error by a factor of 16.

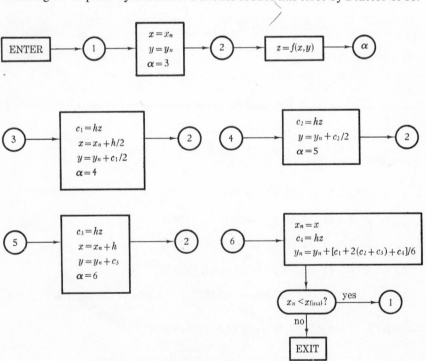

Figure 16–3: Integration by Runge-Kutta method

A flow chart for the Runge-Kutta method might appear as in Figure 16–3. This flow chart will take a starting set of values, (x_n, y_n), and compute new values, increasing x_n by an amount h each time, until the specified final value of x is reached. Normally the slowest part of the calculation is computing $f(x, y)$. For each point, the function $f(x, y)$ must be calculated four times, so the total execution time is determined by the size chosen for h and the time required for a computation of $f(x, y)$. If h is too large, the accuracy will be poor. If h is too small, the time requirement will be excessively large. A method for adjusting step sizes to retain sufficient accuracy without requiring excessive calculation time will be given below. The FORTRAN subroutine given below does the calculation following the flow chart in Figure 16–3. The floating point quantity D is used for the interval size.

x_0 y_0

```
      SUBROUTINE  RUNGKUT(XN,YN,D,XEND,YEND)
      GIVF(X,Y)=   (insert correct expression for f(x, y))
      DD=.5*D
    1 X=XN
      Y=YN
      J=1
    2 Z=GIVF(X,Y)
      GO  TO(3,4,5,6),J
    3 C1=D*Z
      X=XN+DD
      Y=YN+C1/2.
      J=2
      GO TO 2
    4 C2=D*Z
      Y=YN+C2/2.
      J=3
      GO TO 2
    5 C3=D*Z
      X=XN+D
      Y=YN+C3
      J=4
      GO TO 2
    6 XN=X
      C4=D*Z
      YN=YN+(C1+2.*(C2+C3)+C4)/6.
      IF(XN-XEND)1,7,7
    7 XEND=XN
      YEND=YN
      RETURN
      END
```

16.43   Step Size in the Runge-Kutta Method

It was mentioned earlier that the step size is important in determining running time and accuracy.   There is no a priori way of selecting in advance a proper step size, and it frequently happens that the step size should be adjusted during the calculation itself, using small steps in some regions and much larger ones in others.   Although it is somewhat expensive in machine time to do so, it is often advisable to have the machine do each interval with two different step sizes, as in Examples 1 and 2 above, and if the difference in results is intolerably large reduce the step size automatically, or if it is unnecessarily small, increase the step size automatically.   The flow chart, Figure 16–4, shows how this can be done.   The quantity E is the allowable relative error in *y* for each step assigned in advance.*   Boxes entered by connectors 1 through 5 are almost direct copies from the preceding flow chart, and the alterations are built around these.   In this flow chart, if the step size becomes too small, roundoff error may become dominant and the program go into an endless loop of reducing step size.   In order to prevent this, a stop has been put in at a step size arbitrarily chosen as .00000001.   The following is the corresponding FORTRAN subroutine.

```
      SUBROUTINE RKSTEP (XN,YN,ERR,XEND,YEND)
      GIVF(X,Y) =    (insert correct expression for f(x, y))
      D1 = .05
      D2 = .1
      ERG = .01*ERR
   11 D = D2
      K = 1
      X1 = XN
      Y1 = YN
    1 X = XN
      Y = YN
      J = 1
    2 Z = GIVF(X,Y)
      GO  TO(3,4,5,6),J
    3 C1 = D*Z
      X = XN + D/2.
      Y = YN + C1/2.
      J = 2
      GO TO 2
    4 C2 = D*Z
```

---

* It should be noted that control of the error at each step is *not* a guarantee of accuracy in the final solution.   Any error, however small, places one on a different solution curve, which may ultimately diverge widely from the desired solution.   Whether this will happen in a particular case depends on the stability properties of the differential equation involved, a subject beyond the scope of this book.

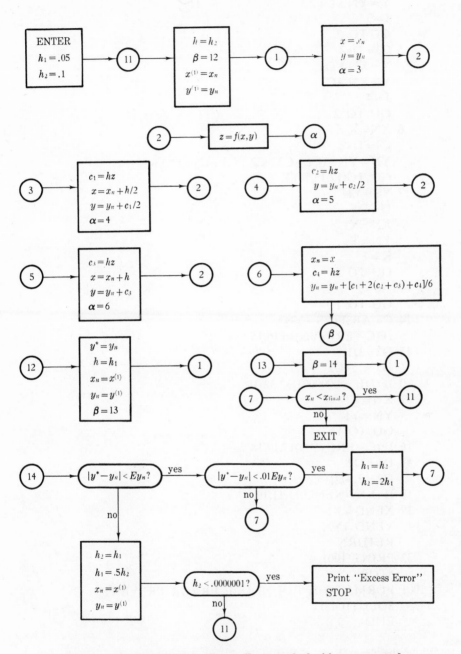

Figure 16–4: Integration by Runge-Kutta method with error control

```
          Y = YN + C2/2.
          J = 3
          GO TO 2
     5    C3 = D*Z
          X = XN + D
          Y = YN + C3
          J = 4
          GO TO 2
     6    XN = X
          C4 = D*Z
          YN = YN + (C1 + C2 + C2 + C3 + C3 + C4)/6.
          GO TO(12,13,14),K
    12    YS = YN
          D = D1
          XN = X1
          YN = Y1
          K = 2
          GO TO 1
    13    K = 3
          GO TO 1
    14    C = ABSF(YS - YN)
          IF(C - ERR*YN)16,16,15
    15    D2 = D1
          D1 = .5*D2
    30    IF(D1 - .0000001)32,32,31
    31    XN = X1
          YN = Y1
          GO TO 11
    16    IF(C - ERG*YN)17,17,18
    17    D1 = D2
          D2 = 2.*D1
    18    IF(XN - XEND)11,11,19
    19    XEND = XN
          YEND = YN
          RETURN
    32    PRINT 1001
          STOP
  1001    FORMAT(33H ROUNDOFF ERROR PREVENTS
          SOLUTION)
          END
```

While the flow chart in Figure 16–4 and the subroutine will ordinarily keep the step size adjusted to a proper value, it should be noted that they are not foolproof. Figure 16–5 shows a situation in which the method would be fooled. Both the small and the large step sizes are too large to detect the sudden change in the solution curve, and so the computed solution departs markedly from the true solution curve.

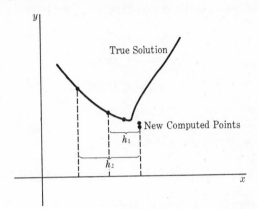

Figure 16–5

16.44 Milne's Method

Another method, which is typical of a large variety of so-called predictor-corrector methods, is that due to Milne. Here the value of y at a new point is predicted based on values at four preceding points by means of the formula:

$$y_{n+1} = y_{n-3} + (4/3)h(2y'_{n-2} - y'_{n-1} + 2y'_n) \qquad \textbf{(16-27)}$$

Then from this approximate value of y_{n+1}, an improved value is obtained by using the formula:

$$y_{n+1} = y_{n-1} + (1/3)h(y'_{n-1} + 4y'_n + y'_{n+1}) \qquad \textbf{(16-28)}$$

In order to start using this method, it is necessary that we already have the values of y at four consecutive values of x. These can be obtained by the Runge-Kutta method described in the preceding section, or by any of several other starting methods.

Example 1. Use the Milne method to extend the solution of:

$$y' = x + y$$

as obtained in Example 1 of Section 16.42, to $x = 1$.

From Example 1 of Section 16.42, we have the following points:

x	0	.2	.4
y	1	1.24280	1.58364

We have three points of the solution curve. In order to apply Milne's method we need one more. Applying Runge-Kutta once more, we obtain $x_3 = .6$, $y_3 = 2.04421$.

Since the differential equation says $y' = x + y$, we have:

$$y'_0 = 1$$
$$y'_1 = 1.44280$$
$$y'_2 = 1.98364$$
$$y'_3 = 2.64421$$

Thus the Milne predictor formula gives:

$$y_4 = 1 + (4/3)(.2)[2(1.44280) - 1.98364 + 2(2.64421)] = 2.65077$$

Hence the first approximation to y'_4 is:

$$y'_4 = .8 + 2.65077 = 3.45077$$

and the corrector formula gives:

$$y_4 = 1.58364 + (1/3)(.2)[1.98364 + 4(2.64421) + 3.45077] = 2.65106$$

For the next step, the predictor gives:

$$y_5 = 1.24280 + (4/3)(.2)[2(1.98364) - 2.64421 + 2(3.45106)] = 3.43586$$

The first approximation for y'_5 is:

$$y'_5 = 1. + 3.43586 = 4.43586$$

and the corrector formula gives:

$$y_5 = 2.04421 + (1/3)(.2)[2.64421 + 4(3.45106) + 4.43586] = 3.43630$$

The computations involved in Milne's method, once starting values have been obtained, can be described by a flow chart as shown in Figure 16–6.

The FORTRAN subroutine given below performs the calculation described by the flow chart. The four starting values for y and y' are presumed already available.

```
SUBROUTINE  MILNE(XO,Y,YP,D,XEND,YEND)
DIMENSION  Y(5),YP(5)
GIVF(X,Z)=    (insert correct expression for f(x, z))
```

```
      X=XO+3.*D
      A=1.3333333*D
      B=.33333333*D
   1  Y(5)=Y(1)+A*(YP(2)+YP(2)-YP(3)+YP(4)+YP(4))
      X=X+D
      J=1
   2  YP(5)=GIVF(X,Y(5))
      GO TO(3,4),J
   3  Y(5)=Y(3)+B*(YP(3)+YP(4)+YP(4)+YP(4)+YP(4)+YP(5))
      J=2
      GO TO 2
   4  IF(X-XEND)5,7,7
   5  DO 6 I=1,4
      Y(I)=Y(I+1)
   6  YP(I)=YP(I+1)
      GO TO 1
   7  XEND=X
      YEND=Y(5)
      RETURN
      END
```

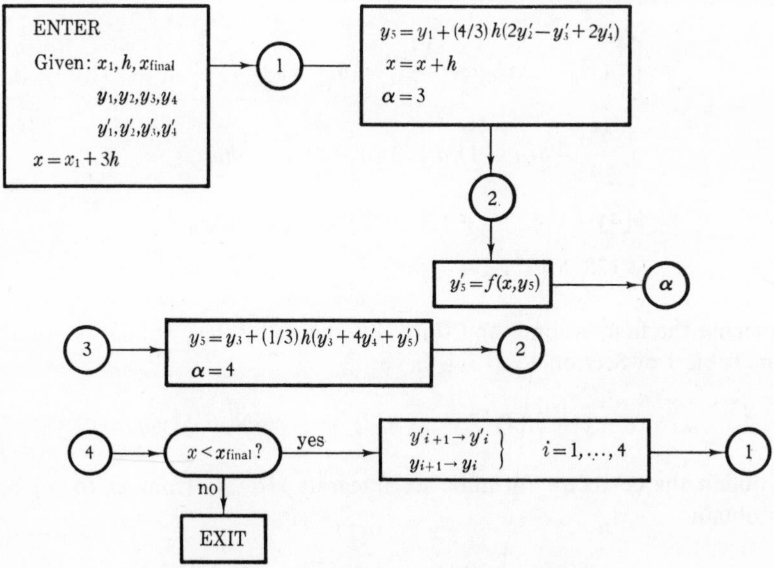

Figure 16–6: Integration by Milne's method

Since $f(x, y)$ is computed twice per step in Milne's method as opposed to four times per step in the Runge-Kutta method, the subroutine MILNE, above should ordinarily be about twice as fast as subroutine RUNGKUT given in Section 16.42.

16.45   Step Size in Milne's Method

When Milne's method (or any of many similar predictor-corrector methods) is used, there is an easy way of estimating the error per step.   Both the predictor and the corrector formula can be derived from Newton's interpolation formula, as follows:

Section 15.22 gives Newton's interpolation formula for a function $y(x)$. Now y' is also a function of x, so if we write Newton's interpolation formula for the function $y'(x)$, we have:

$$y' = y'_0 + \Delta y'_0 u + \frac{\Delta^2 y'_0}{2!} u(u - 1) + \frac{\Delta^3 y'_0}{3!} u(u - 1)(u - 2)$$

$$+ \frac{\Delta^4 y'_0}{4!} u(u - 1)(u - 2)(u - 3) + \cdots \tag{16-29}$$

In this formula, $u = (x - x_0)/h$, so $dx = h\, du$.   To obtain the predictor formula, we integrate the above from $x = x_0$ to $x = x_0 + 4h$ (or $u = 0$ to $u = 4$):

$$\int_{x_0}^{x_0 + 4h} y'dx = y(x_0 + 4h) - y(x_0) = y_4 - y_0$$

$$= \int_0^4 \left(y'_0 + \Delta y'_0 u + \frac{\Delta^2 y'_0}{2!} u(u - 1) + \frac{\Delta^3 y'_0}{3!} u(u - 1)(u - 2) \right.$$

$$\left. + \frac{\Delta^4 y'_0}{4!} u(u - 1)(u - 2)(u - 3) + \cdots \right) h\, du$$

$$= h[4y'_0 + 8\Delta y'_0 + (20/3)\Delta^2 y'_0 + (8/3)\Delta^3 y'_0$$

$$+ (28/90)\Delta^4 y'_0 + \cdots]$$

Replacing the first, second, and third differences by their values as obtained from Table I of Section 15.21, we have:

$$y_4 - y_0 = (4h/3)(2y'_1 - y'_2 + 2y'_3) + (28/90)h\Delta^4 y'_0 + \cdots$$

To obtain the corrector formula, we integrate (16–29) from x_0 to $x_0 + 2h$, and obtain:

$$y_2 - y_0 = h[2y'_0 + 2\Delta y'_0 + (1/3)\Delta^2 y'_0 - (1/90)\Delta^4 y'_0 + \cdots]$$

Again replacing the first, second, and third differences by their values as obtained from Table I of Section 15.21, we have:

$$y_2 - y_0 = (h/3)(y'_0 + 4y'_1 + y'_2) - (h/90)\Delta^4 y'_0 + \cdots$$

Since $x_0, x_1, \ldots, x_4$ may be any five consecutive values of x, the above formulae can be written in the general form given in Section 16.44. It is seen that the error in the value of y_{n+1} as determined by the predictor formula is about:

$$E_1 = (28/90)h\Delta^4 y'$$

and the error in y_{n+1} as determined from the corrector formula is about:

$$E_2 = -(1/90)h\Delta^4 y'$$

Let y be the true value at $x = x_{n+1}$, and y_{n+1}^* the value given by the predictor formula and y_{n+1} the value given by the corrector formula. Then:

$$y - y_{n+1}^* \approx E_1$$

and:

$$y - y_{n+1} \approx E_2$$

Subtracting the second of these relations from the first, we have:

$$y_{n+1} - y_{n+1}^* \approx E_1 - E_2 = -29 E_2$$

Hence the error in each step is approximately:

$$E \approx (1/29)(y_{n+1} - y_{n+1}^*) \tag{16-30}$$

Example 1. Determine the error in each step of Milne's rule for Example 1 of Section 16.44.

In that example, the step size was $h = .2$.
The predicted and corrected values for y_4 were:

$$y_4^* = 2.65077$$

$$y_4 = 2.65106$$

and the error is approximately:

$$E_4 \approx (1/29)(2.65106 - 2.65077) = .00001$$

The predicted and corrected values for y_5 were:

$$y_5^* = 3.43586$$

$$y_5 = 3.43630$$

and the error is approximately:

$$E_5 \approx (1/29)(3.43630 - 3.43586) = .00002$$

Since both y_{n+1}^* and y_{n+1} are determined in each step of the calculation, it is a trivial amount of work to determine the error at each step. Once the error has been determined, however, the problem of changing the step size is a little involved. To change step size at any point we must restart the solution at that point with four new starting values corresponding to the new step size. It is easiest to double or halve the step size, since in that way we can use values already available. To double the step size, we need *seven* values computed at the old step size. By dropping out three of these, we obtain four equally spaced values at the new step size. Three new values must then be computed before the step size can be doubled again. To halve the step size, it is necessary to interpolate values between some of those already available. For accuracy, it is wise to move back slightly from the point at which the step size became too large and to use a central interpolation formula for this purpose. Bessel's interpolation formula, Section 15.34, is frequently used for this purpose. It takes on a particularly simple form when used for the midpoint of an interval. Taking $u = 1/2$ and retaining terms only up to the fourth difference, we have:

$$y_{1/2} = y_0 + (1/2)\Delta y_0 - (1/16)(\Delta^2 y_{-1} + \Delta^2 y_0) + \cdots$$

Substituting the values of these differences as obtained from Section 15.21:

$$y_{1/2} = (1/2)(y_0 + y_1) - (1/16)(y_2 - y_1 - y_0 + y_{-1})$$

If the last accurate value of y we have obtained is y_n, then we may use this formula to obtain:

$$y_{n-3/2} = (1/2)(y_{n-2} + y_{n-1}) - (1/16)(y_n - y_{n-1} - y_{n-2} + y_{n-3})$$

and:

$$y_{n-5/2} = (1/2)(y_{n-3} + y_{n-2}) - (1/16)(y_{n-1} - y_{n-2} - y_{n-3} + y_{n-4})$$

In order to retain a set of seven values, so that the interval size can again be reduced if required, it is well to have the machine also compute:

$$y_{n-7/2} = (1/2)(y_{n-4} + y_{n-3}) - (1/16)(y_{n-2} - y_{n-3} - y_{n-4} + y_{n-5})$$

The derivatives may be interpolated in like manner, and then the solution restarted with the four values $y_{n-5/2}, y_{n-2}, y_{n-3/2}, y_{n-1}$.

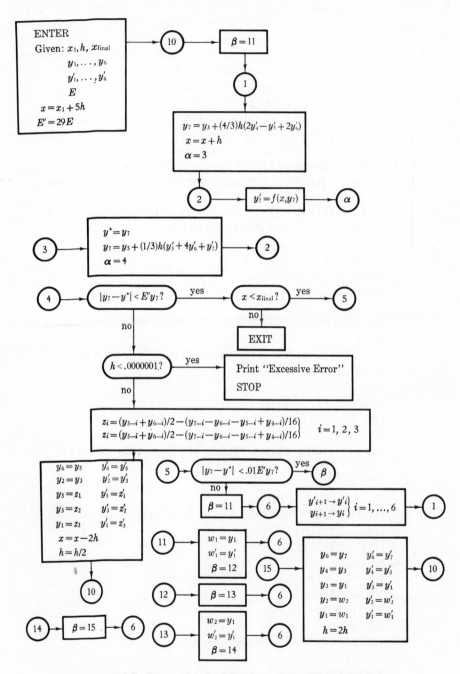

Figure 16–7: Integration by Milne's method with error control

The flow chart, Figure 16–7, shows a version of Milne's method in which the step size is automatically controlled so that the relative error in y for each step is less than some number E assigned in advance. As remarked in Section 16.43, control of the error for each individual step does *not* guarantee accuracy of the final result. A stop has been put in (after connector 5) to prevent an endless loop of reducing step size in the event that roundoff error becomes dominant. It is assumed that the flow chart is entered with *six* consecutive values of y and y' already available. In order to retain complete flexibility to reduce step size, the step size is never increased in this flow chart until the test entered by connector 5 succeeds five times in a row.

The FORTRAN subroutine MILSTEP given below will perform the calculation outlined in the flow chart. It requires six starting values of Y and YP.

```
    SUBROUTINE MILSTEP(XO,Y,YP,D,ERR,XEND,YEND)
    DIMENSION Y(7),YP(7),Q(3),QP(3)
    GIVF(X,Z)=   (insert correct expression for f(x, z))
    X=XO+5.*D
    ERP=29.*ERR
    ERG=.01*ERP
10  A=1.3333333*D
    B=.33333333*D
    K=1
 1  Y(7)=Y(3)+A*(YP(4)+YP(4)−YP(5)+YP(6)+YP(6))
    X=X+D
    J=1
 2  YP(7)=GIVF(X,Y(7))
    GO TO (3,4),J
 3  YS=Y(7)
    Y(7)=Y(5)+B*(YP(5)+YP(6)+YP(6)+YP(6)+YP6+YP(7))
    J=2
    GO TO 2
 4  C=ABSF(Y(7)−YS)
    IF(C−ERP*Y(7))20,20,21
20  IF(X−XEND)5,5,50
 5  IF(C−ERG*Y(7))7,7,30
30  K=1
 6  DO 31 I=1,6
    Y(I)=Y(I+1)
31  YP(I)=YP(I+1)
    GO TO 1
 7  GO TO (11,12,13,14,15),K
11  W1=Y(1)
    WP1=YP(1)
    K=2
```

```
   GO TO 6
12 K = 3
   GO TO 6
13 W2 = Y(1)
   WP2 = YP(1)
   K = 4
   GO TO 6
14 K = 5
   GO TO 6
15 Y(6) = Y(7)
   Y(4) = (3)
   Y(3) = Y(1)
   Y(2) = W2
   Y(1) = W1
   YP(6) = YP(7)
   YP(4) = YP(3)
   YP(3) = YP(1)
   YP(2) = WP2
   YP(1) = WP1
   D = D + D
   GO TO 10
21 IF(D − .00000001)40,40,41
40 PRINT 1001
   STOP
41 DO 42 I = 1,3
   Q(I) = .5*(Y(5−I) + Y(6−I)) − .0625*(Y(7−I) − Y(6−I)
   − Y(5−I) + Y(4−I))
42 QP(I) = .5*(YP(5−I) + YP(6−I)) − .0625*
   (YP(7−I) − YP(6−I) − YP(5−I) + YP(4−I))
   Y(6) = Y(5)
   Y(2) = Y(3)
   Y(5) = Q(1)
   Y(3) = Q(2)
   Y(1) = Q(3)
   YP(6) = YP(5)
   YP(2) = YP(3)
   YP(5) = QP(1)
   YP(3) = QP(2)
   YP(1) = QP(3)
   X = X − 2.*D
   D = .5*D
   GO TO 10
50 XEND = X
   YEND = Y(7)
```

```
          RETURN
    1001 FORMAT(33H ROUNDOFF ERROR PREVENTS
          SOLUTION)
          END
```

   This subroutine requires that six starting points be obtained by some
other method.   Subroutine RUNGKUT, given in Section 16.42, can be used
to obtain these values.   It is wise to use a small interval D for these starting
values, for accuracy, and let MILSTEP increase the interval later as it chooses.

   Because MILSTEP requires only two computations of $f(x, y)$ per step, as
opposed to twelve per step for subroutine RKSTEP given in Section 16.43,
it will ordinarily be on the order of six times as fast.

E X E R C I S E   X X V I I I

1. Using the Runge-Kutta method and a step size of .1, calculate four steps of
    the solution of:

    a. $y' = xy$, $y(0) = 1$.
    b. $y' = y + e^{-x}$, $y(0) = 2$.
    c. $y' = x + 2y$, $y(0) = .5$

2. Calculate the time required to solve the following equations from $x = 0$ to
    $x = 100$ by the Runge-Kutta method, using a step size of .1, on a fast machine.
    (Assume all operations except evaluating $f(x, y)$ are so fast they can be neglected.)

    a. $y' = ye^{xy} \sin x^2 + y^2$.
    b. $y' = x^2 + 3x^3 + \ln (x^2 + 4y^3)$.
    c. $y' = \sin xy + 4 \sin 2xy + 2 \sin 3xy + \sin 4xy + 5 \sin 5xy$.

3. Modify subroutine RUNGKUT of Section 16.42 to print out x, y, and y'.

    a. At each step.
    b. Every ten steps.
    c. Every time x has increased by .5.

4. Write a program that will solve the differential equation $y' = f(x, y)$ for values
    of x from 0 to 100, using subroutine RUNGKUT from Section 16.43 to start
    the calculation, and subroutine MILSTEP from Section 16.45 to complete the
    solution.   Have the values of x, y, and y' printed out once in each unit interval
    of x.

References

ALT, FRANZ L., *Electronic Digital Computers: Their Use in Science and Engineering,* New York: Academic Press, Inc., 1958.

ALT, FRANZ L., ed., *Advances in Computers,* Vol. I, New York: Academic Press, Inc., 1960.

BARTEE, THOMAS C., *Digital Computer Fundamentals,* New York: McGraw-Hill Book Company, Inc., 1960.

BOOTH, K. H. V., *Programming for an Automatic Digital Calculator,* New York: Academic Press, Inc., 1958.

FADDEEVA, V. N., *Computational Methods of Linear Algebra,* New York: Dover Publications, Inc., 1959.

GREENSPAN, D., *Theory and Solution of Ordinary Differential Equations,* New York: The Macmillan Company, 1960.

HAMMING, R. W., *Numerical Methods for Scientists and Engineers,* New York: McGraw-Hill Book Company, Inc., 1962.

HARRIS, L. DALE, *Numerical Methods Using FORTRAN,* Columbus, Ohio: Charles E. Merrill, 1964.

HARTREE, D. R., *Numerical Analysis,* Oxford: The Clarendon Press, 1952.

HASTINGS, C., *Approximations for Digital Computers,* Princeton, N.J.: Princeton University Press, 1955.

HERRIOT, J. G., *Methods of Mathematical Analysis and Computation,* New York: John Wiley & Sons, Inc., 1963.

HOLLINGDALE, S. H., *High Speed Computing Methods and Application,* New York: The Macmillan Company, 1959.

HOUSEHOLDER, A. S., *Principles of Numerical Analysis,* New York: McGraw-Hill Book Company, Inc., 1953.

JAMES, M. L., SMITH, G. M. and WOLFORD, J. C., *Analog and Digital Computer Methods in Engineering Analysis,* Scranton, Pa.: International Textbook Company, 1964.

KRYLOV, V. I., *Approximate Calculation of Integrals,* New York: The Macmillan Company, 1962.

KUNZ, KAISER S., *Numerical Analysis,* New York: McGraw-Hill Book Company, Inc., 1957.

LEDLEY, R. S., *Digital Computer and Control Engineering,* New York: McGraw-Hill Book Company, Inc., 1960.

MC CORMICK, JOHN M. and SALVIDORE, M. G., *Numerical Methods in FORTRAN,* Englewood Cliffs, N.J.: Prentice-Hall Inc., 1964.

MC CRACKEN, DANIEL D. and DORN, WILLIAM S., *Numerical Methods and FOR-TRAN Programming,* New York: John Wiley & Sons, Inc., 1964.

MEYERHOFF, A. J., ed., *Digital Applications of Magnetic Devices,* New York: John Wiley & Sons, Inc., 1960.

NIELSEN, KAJ L., *Methods in Numerical Analysis,* New York: The Macmillan Company, 1956.

PRAGER, WILLIAM, *Introduction to Basic FORTRAN Programming and Numerical Methods,* New York: Blaisdell Publishing Co., 1965.

RALSTON, A. and WILF, H. S., *Mathematical Methods for Digital Computers,* New York: John Wiley & Sons, Inc., 1960.

RICHARDS, R. K., *Digital Computer Components and Circuits,* Princeton, N.J.: D. Van Nostrand Company, Inc., 1957.

SANFORD, VERA, *A Short History of Mathematics,* New York: Houghton Mifflin Co., 1930.

SANGREN, WARD C., *Digital Computers and Nuclear Reactor Calculations,* New York: John Wiley & Sons, Inc., 1960.

SCARBOROUGH, J. B., *Numerical Mathematical Analysis,* 5th ed., Baltimore: The Johns Hopkins Press, 1962.

SMITH, CHARLES V. L., *Electronic Digital Computers,* New York: McGraw-Hill Book Company, Inc., 1959.

STANTON, RALPH G., *Numerical Methods for Science and Engineering,* Englewood Cliffs, N.J.: Prentice-Hall Inc., 1961.

STIBITZ, GEORGE R., and LARRIVEE, JULES A., *Mathematics and Computers,* New York: McGraw-Hill Book Company, Inc., 1957.

TODD, J., *Survey of Numerical Analysis,* New York: McGraw-Hill Book Company, Inc., 1962.

VON HANDEL, PAUL, ed., *Electronic Computers: Fundamentals, Systems, and Applications,* Englewood Cliffs, N.J.: Prentice-Hall Inc., 1961.

WENDROFF, BURTON, *Theoretical Numerical Analysis,* New York: Academic Press, Inc., 1966.

INDEX